McGraw-Hill Series in Health Science
Amos Christie, M.D., *Consulting Editor*

Mental Hygiene in Public Health

McGraw-Hill Series in Health Science
AMOS CHRISTIE, M.D., *Consulting Editor*

MENTAL HYGIENE IN
PUBLIC HEALTH

PAUL V. LEMKAU, M.D.

Professor of Public Health Administration
Division of Mental Hygiene
School of Hygiene and Public Health
The Johns Hopkins University

ON LEAVE AS
Director of Mental Health Services
New York City Community Mental Health Board

SECOND EDITION

The Blakiston Division
McGRAW-HILL BOOK COMPANY, INC.
New York   Toronto   London
1955

IN MEMORIAM

Adolf Meyer
and
Allen W. Freeman
whose teaching and inspiration
furthered the
integration of mental hygiene
and public health

Foreword

It would be difficult to find a more striking example of maturation that has gone on in the past few years in the mental hygiene field than is exemplified in the change between the first edition of this text in 1949 and the present edition. The intervening period has been most eventful. There has been an extraordinary development of public and private support for research in the mental health field; an acceptance by many public health workers of mental health as an important part of a balanced health program (witness the section of the World Health Organization devoted to mental health); a recognition of the important contributions of the social sciences to broader understanding of mental hygiene and preventive medicine in general; a crystallization of the concepts of the breadth of the preventive approach to medicine; the employment of the epidemiological method in studying mental health problems; a number of community mental health studies, and so on. Since Dr. Lemkau has been personally concerned with much of the history-making process, it is not surprising that he has most successfully incorporated it into the new edition of his book.

Dr. Lemkau as a pioneer in bringing together the fields of mental hygiene and public health has done an extraordinarily useful job. He has kept his clinical approach, simply transferring it from the individual patient in the hospital environment to the community. His attack on the problem has been an eminently practical one, even though he displays a thorough knowledge of the theoretical concepts involved.

Mental hygiene is a teamwork job and not a field for the psychiatrist alone. In pointing out that "mental hygiene depends primarily on the attitude-changing possibilities of communication between personnel of various degrees of training and the population, the needs of which are to be met" the basic problem is stated. Fortunately for public health workers this author points out that "there are things to do" in the mental hygiene field and tools with which to do them. These are what the public health man needs if he is to build a program that has possibilities of effective application.

Mental health extends into all the activities of health agencies whether they be official or voluntary. It involves the interpersonal relationships of the staff itself and extends into their far-flung activities with the public. Equally concerned are other agencies which serve the public, such as schools, churches, welfare and law enforcement agencies, and which do not have health as their major purpose. The problems of getting all diverse members of the team oriented so that they can understand each other's problems and work together in a coordinated way is something Dr. Lemkau understands thoroughly and which he is undertaking to do as executive head of the New York City Community Mental Health Board.

The plan of the book is a sound one and the execution thoroughly satisfactory.

It is difficult to conceive how changes as striking as those of the last six years can occur in the next period of this length. If they do, it is highly probable that Dr. Lemkau will have a large part in bringing them about and that, as an author, he will see that they are suitably documented and interpreted in a language which the nonspecialist can enjoy and applaud.

HUGH R. LEAVELL

Preface to Second Edition

Two divergent trends in science at its present stage of development place the mental hygienist in a dilemma. The first is a tendency toward specialization, in which highly specific techniques are used to solve highly selected problems. To do the most effective work along this line, the scientist chooses to confine the variables with which he deals to the smallest possible number, ruling out factors that may be granted as relevant and important, but that cannot be dealt with by the techniques in use. A scientist traveling this road must "put on blinders" so that he will not be distracted by interesting side events and paths that might divert him from his central effort.

The second trend involves recognition of the complex problems of the world of reality that can only be solved if attacked by all available investigative methods. This trend has led to the development of physical chemistry, astrophysics, social psychology, social anthropology and the like, including, of course, the professional fields dealing with the health and the illnesses of man. The need for a variety of scientific approaches is obvious, but the application of the concept presents many practical issues and, frequently, controversies. This is particularly true during the period of active development of new combinations of points of view and techniques. There is likely to be rivalry between disciplines attacking the same problem in its different aspects. Examples are the issue of defining the role of the public health nurse in relation to that of the social worker, and the contamination of the concept "public health" by the concept "socialized medicine," a confusion that gives rise to many serious problems for the health officer.

Where the health of the population is concerned, every piece of useful information, regardless of origin or techniques of collection, should be exploited to the fullest possible extent. The mental hygienist, particularly, becomes an arch-combiner of specialties for he must include in his purview not only the total person but also his environment, distant and close at hand, and including personalities that are effective in the environment. Specific facts about specific issues are to be used in mental hygiene whenever possible; but, at the same time, facts gained about reality situations, which can only be studied by the use of clinical methods that apply techniques gathered from many different specialities, must also be brought to bear in the solution of problems. The dilemma thus presented will be apparent many times in the development of this volume.

The writer who attempts a somewhat comprehensive book on the field of mental hygiene is constantly aware that he may cause harm by neglecting some area that is contributing or can contribute to the success of the field. If there are such failures, they are the author's responsibility, for no one who has been asked has failed to contribute to this book.

Four years as Chief of the Division of Mental Health of the Maryland State Health Department revealed the necessity for some of the major revisions that characterize this second edition of a book originally written before this experience. Furthermore, this volume is the result of many discussions in many different situations. First, students, anxious because they must shortly face responsibility in the field, tend to ask penetrating and very practical questions in searching for answers from the body of accumulated experience. Institutes such as the one in Berkeley, California, in 1948, attended by health officers and other personnel, and work with committees such as those of the National Institute of Mental Health, where the administrative detail of the National Mental Health Act was worked out, have contributed a wealth of experiences, more than could be completely absorbed. To all these should be added extensive work with state, local, and national voluntary mental health associations, and with many lay groups whose questions and suggestions have been incorporated into the subject matter of this text.

Formal and informal discussions with fellow faculty members in the School of Hygiene and Public Health have made possible the clarification of many concepts and principles and have had great influence upon the content of the book. Perhaps the most influential persons have been Dr. Benjamin Pasamanick and Dr. Marcia Cooper, of the Division of Mental Hygiene. Both have read and criticized much of the manuscript and Dr. Cooper supplied the information to bring the case illustrations up to date. To them the author expresses his gratitude and indebtedness.

Both Dr. Adolf Meyer and Dr. A. W. Freeman have died since the publication of the first edition. These two physicians were very different personalities; their works represent examples of the widely different kinds of material that must be incorporated into a functional mental hygiene. To have had the opportunity to learn from them, indeed to work with them, was a rare privilege.

Finally, appreciation must be expressed to Mrs. Carol Van Vranken and Mrs. Gwen Peterson, the loyal secretaries who translated the longhand into typed draft and the draft into a presentable manuscript.

PAUL V. LEMKAU

Contents

Part One

THE PLACE OF MENTAL HYGIENE
IN PUBLIC HEALTH

CHAPTER ONE

The Field of Mental Hygiene

"The proper study of mankind is man." Since the beginning of recorded history, everyone has attempted to understand why he did as he did. At the same time everyone works at the even harder job of understanding his neighbors. When their behavior is within the ordinarily tolerated range it is fascinating, to be sure, but the riddles of persons whose actions are unusual, whose ways of thinking are odd, or whose moods are inappropriate are even more arresting. It has been only five or six generations since some hospitals in the United States charged admission for the public to look at the insane and hear them speak. The emotionally charged statements the patients made and the behavior they showed were of interest to the public, in all probability, not only because these were odd, but also because the "normal" people could identify ideas and moods of their own in the patients. The same idea is present in many volunteers who enter mental hospitals today, though they go to aid the patients and not to indulge curiosity. The working of the personality in health and disease is indeed an arresting interest for all.

THE PERSONALITY

Symbols and Their Meanings. The human being is a vastly complicated animal, far more complicated than any other. This is largely because he can use symbols. When he wishes to speak of "something that will hurt you and has orange-colored masses flying above material which gives off red light" he can condense and symbolize it all—and a great deal more—in the word "fire." He can also speak in symbols of things that have no material existence. When he wishes to say, "I think slowly, weep often, have no appetite, feel decreased sex interest, and am blunted in my love for my family," he needs to say no more than that he is "depressed."

The meaning of "fire" and "depressed" for the listener will depend on

3

where and how he has heard and used them before. "Fire" to the combustion engineer will have a highly technical meaning as well as the everyday one; it may lead him into reveries about the structure of high-pressure boilers, or it may bring to mind that his little girl burned her foot on the radiator that morning. To the dull person "fire" may mean nothing more than the word alone, but it might also engender a spasm of fear because of a past danger-laden encounter with this hotness that is not fully understood. To the chronically hilarious person, "depression" will mean something he has never felt, cannot understand, and has little sympathy for. To a psychiatrist "depression" would raise immediate questions about diagnosis and prognosis. If he were inclined to the history of his subject, names and biographies of men long dead might enter his reverie. The reaction depends upon the sort of person involved and what the previous experience of the person has been.

Person and Personality. Strictly speaking, every human being is unique. To talk about groups of people and their characteristics is not really correct, since in any group each person is different from every other one. Any attempt at grouping is a violation of the idea of individuality. Nevertheless, generalizations must be made if man is to be understood and if his problems are to be studied by any sort of comparative method.

The escape from the dilemma has been found by objectifying the individual somewhat and talking about personalities rather than persons. "Personality" means everything that the person is and does and the impressions he makes on other human beings. It is the person as an object that can be studied, first from this aspect, then from that. Personality can be partitioned into various traits, which can be compared with traits in other personalities, whereas if the person were dealt with directly his individuality would be lost and there would no longer be a subject for discussion. No doubt this distinction will seem academic to some, but the concept of personality has proved a useful tool in studying the behavior of persons.

The Building of Personality. The personality at any moment is the result of two types of influence: (1) the constitution of the individual; (2) the experience he has passed through since his genetic future was sealed at the moment of conception. All our human capacities are dependent upon genetic factors. Constitutional factors at the core of the personality determine the timetable which dominates the flow of events throughout the lifetime of the individual. Thus the constitution determines when the child will walk, when the girl will become the woman capable of reproduction, when she will cease to be able to reproduce. It will determine, within limits, the strength of the person and when he must retire from competition at the various levels of activity. The very size of the person is determined genetically to a considerable extent. Size frequently makes a vast difference in the evaluation the world makes of a person. Basketball has put a special premium on very tall men, but height has always been a social and economic asset.[1]

While these timing and size determinations are largely of constitutional origin, variations are introduced by experiences encountered. For several generations the men in the United States have been growing taller and heavier.[2] As for timing of life events, it has been shown that girls now undergo the menarche about 6 months earlier than did their mothers.[3] Such changes in a generation are unthinkable on a genetic basis; hereditary changes come far more slowly.

Personality traits, too, are to some extent of constitutional origin. They are difficult to measure, however, and are probably even more subject to environmental modification. It will be the burden of most this volume to discover what modifications of personality are possible and what agents are effective in the process. The constitutional core of the person, based on his heredity, and its amalgamation with experience of living so that together these form a personality or personality structure, are depicted analogically in Fig. 1. The central concept of personality formation is that the life and times of the individual contribute in its building and subsequent structure.

The diagram shows that the individual personality is built upon a hereditary base that contributes both assets and liabilities. These capacities, which come into being at conception, may or may not become functional in the new personality, depending on factors in the environment. The diagram also illustrates that the constitutional core functions throughout life, being the largest factor both in setting the schedule for development to maturity and in determining the rate of catabolic changes in the later years. The opportunity for the environment to become functional is present as soon as conception takes place. Thereafter the individual's growth depends upon multiple factors acting together; e.g., during intrauterine life rubella may change the constitutional capacity to develop a sound body to such an extent that a grossly deformed child may result.

Just as there may be faults in the hereditary base on which the personality rests, so there may be poorly integrated experiences that weaken the total structure as it continues building through the lifetime of the individual. Such an experience as emotional neglect in infancy may

[1] See References at end of chapter.

permanently reduce the constitutional capacity to grow, so that the infant loses the ability to develop structural or psychological functions he might otherwise have enjoyed.

Personality Breakdown and Mental Illness. The diagram also furnishes a convenient way to visualize the way stress of any sort may lead to breakdown of the personality. If the constitutional core is weak, or if many life experiences have been poorly integrated, or if—as is always the case when breakdown occurs—both are something less than the maximum, the personality structure will break more easily.

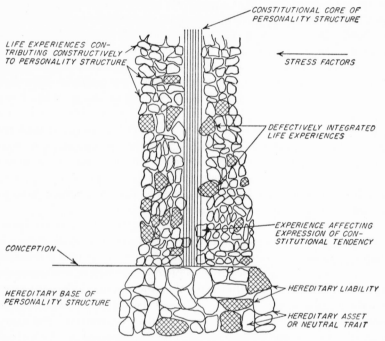

Fig. 1. Diagram of personality structure.

Environmental stress and inherent strength of personality are directly related. The greater the stress, the greater the inherent strength must be to protect from actual disease. If the life stresses are not overly great, overly concentrated, or of too long duration, or if they are cushioned by emotional support or the skilled technique of another person in some way, the personality may develop successfully even though its inherent strength may not be great. Conversely, if the stress is too great, too concentrated, or extends over too long a time, no personality will have inherent strength enough to withstand it. The result will be a reactive behavior disorder that may amount to disease. The classic example is that of the combat soldier, and the picture has been clarified greatly by recent military experience in World War II and in Korea.

To protect the structure from breakdown under stress, the structure itself may be modified through psychiatric treatment or may be protected from the stress. Protection may be supplied either by relieving the stress directly, as by giving financial relief when the stress comes from poverty, or by interposing another personality to help absorb the force of the stress if it be psychological. Such interposition is dependent upon interviewing technique to a considerable extent, i.e., upon the ability of two personalities to face stress in a way that is helpful to the personality suffering it.

Convenient as this diagram is, it should always be remembered that it is an analogy, not a picture of personality as it actually exists. It has many faults. Perhaps the most important is that it is a static picture whereas personality development is dynamic, realigning the remembered past in terms of new experiences constantly being added.

The inherent strength of personality is not static, although it is generally agreed that it has a large genetic element that is not subject to change. If each experience is well assimilated, the end result will be a sound, strengthened personality structure. If it is poorly assimilated, it may give rise to a weak spot in the structure, which remains to give trouble if stress bears upon it in the future. Thus the strength of a personality at any time depends not only upon the inborn element, but upon past experience and reaction to past experience as well. The concept is that mental diseases are the result of an imbalance in the relationship between the stress and the constitution as modified by the past experience of the individual. It is well to point out that the meaning of the word "constitution" varies greatly as used by different workers. Some believe the inborn elements are all-important; others place much more emphasis on the weak spots left sensitive by incomplete or imperfect integration of past experience.

The "constitutional strength" is modified by the past experiences of the individual. In some cases this modification is clearly on the basis of organic change, e.g., when the brain is damaged during intrauterine life or when later it is damaged by birth injury, disease, or nutritional deprivation. Other risks to the organic base of the personality include trauma, toxins, and infections. Such factors reduce the capacity of the organic structure of the individual to withstand the stresses inevitably encountered in the course of a lifetime.

When the human personality structure "breaks down" into disease it can do so in a relatively small number of ways. Disease patterns are seen over and over again, and no entirely new types of reaction have been described for many years, though more exact classification and re-classification goes on constantly. It is somewhat reassuring that the limits of human reactive possibilities are probably now known to a very large degree, even though it is recognized that classifications do change as development of the medical specialty studying such reactions—psychiatry—continues to progress. The Appendix gives a short description of the larger groupings of psychiatric illnesses now recognized.

THE TREATMENT OF MENTAL DISORDER

This idea of the interplay of personality structure and stress factors leads to the basic concepts of treatment. Indeed, the usefulness of the hypothesis in treatment is one of the main reasons for its value. Stresses on the personality can be modified and, with greater difficulty, the personality structure can be changed by the reconstruction of past experiences not properly assimilated at the time of their occurrence. These modifications allow the personality to recover its equilibrium. Another postulate has been introduced, namely, that the human personality tends to recover from mental disease when the etiological agents have been removed.

The functioning of the human being, the person, includes all levels of action from the relatively simple chemical and physical reactions taking place in the body cells to the tensions and manners of an intellectual conversation. The conversation, for example, is the result of the functioning of the association and motor areas of the brain, which is the result of the interaction in series of the neurons of various cortical layers. These are dependent upon the physicochemical properties of cells and on certain combinations of elements in the cell walls, the cytoplasm, and the nuclei. These combinations are the result of the ability of those cells to assimilate certain materials brought through the blood stream, which gets them through the action of enzymes in the digestive tract. The host of unknowns involved in the integration levels leading to what we like to call the highest level, human interrelationship, is obvious.[4] The unknowns at the top level are the greater because of the innumerable unknowns upon which they are dependent. The self-healing of the unencumbered personality postulated above is, of course, possible only when none of these levels has been irrevocably damaged as a result of stress.

All mental patients do not recover. Some conditions are static, and some grow worse with the passage of time, even though external stresses appear to be successfully modified and the personality structure is shored up in every possible way. Half the hospital beds of the country are occupied by psychiatric patients, and half of these are chronic cases who will be in hospitals for many years. Suppose, for instance, that the stress consisted of a severe head injury, resulting in the death of cells at the cortical level. Such cells cannot be regenerated, though recent work indicates that there may be hope for more complete restoration of function after healing.[5] Function dependent on destroyed cells is henceforth impossible, although intact areas may take over some of their functions. The result is a permanently injured patient.

The situation becomes more difficult if the stress does not directly affect an organ and destroy it. Let us grant for the moment that emotional stress can cause hyperthyroidism. In some cases, removal of the stress might cause the thyroid gland to return to normal configuration and function, but there might also be cases where the hyperthyroid state would persist after all the stress had been adjusted. In such a case some other treatment than psychiatric would be necessary to restore the proper functioning of the personality. Or take the combat soldier who returns from the front shaking and crying, jumping at every slightest noise, unable to sleep, vomiting all food, and haunted by his horrible experiences. Sleep, induced if necessary by sedation, results shortly in the restoration of much of his emotional control. The crying stops, and he can talk more freely of many of his experiences. Appetite comes back gradually, and tremor diminishes. Much later the startle reaction wanes, until only certain explosive noises make him jump. Restlessness and difficulty in concentration may persist an even longer period before the patient is entirely well. The combat soldier may be supposed to have a pretty good constitution; his personality structure was comparatively sound when he began the stress that ended in his illness. Yet when the stress was removed, he did not recover "all at once," but gradually. The functions of the highest integrative levels—in the example used here, the ability to concentrate and to proceed calmly in living—are the last to return completely.

A concept of chronic mental disease may now be presented. In spite of relief of causative stress, the person may fail to recover because some factor fails to heal itself enough to allow a return to an equilibrium of health. This failure may be due to actual loss of tissue, as in the brain-injury case; to continued organic malfunction, as in the thyroid overactivity; or to the failure to achieve successful integration of psychological experiences, as in the "battle fatigue." The attempt to return people to efficient living after they have sustained injury at any level that results in mental disease is the medical field of psychiatry, the healing of mentally diseased people.

There have been many conflicting schools of thought in psychiatry concerning the etiological concepts presented above. One basic type of thinking is that all psychiatric illness is primarily due to anatomical or physiological disease. The second holds that mental illnesses find their primary cause in life experience in terms of psychological stress. The real issue here is around the word "primary." The "organicist" believes that the pathology comes before the behavior disorder and is the sole cause of it. The "psychogeneticist" tends rather to believe that the organic dysfunction is the result of overstimulation or understimulation of certain physiological processes due to the pressure upon the nervous and endocrine systems as a result of emotional conflicts. This is an oversimplified statement; to complete it would require discussion of timing of conflict and stimuli and many other issues which complicate the problem. There are few workers now who hold that the "mind" is independent of the body and that "mental" disease can exist without bodily involvement and vice versa. Most completely accept the idea that the human being is a unit and that all his functions are integrated when he "behaves," whether this behavior consists of cancer or a delusion.

Furthermore, psychiatrists use whatever treatment is appropriate to the case. If the brain has been damaged, this may be reeducation to bring into function undamaged areas to replace functionally those that have been destroyed. This is probably what is done in the retraining of persons who have lost their power of speech through damage to the originally developed speech centers of the brain. Detoxification is the treatment of choice in acute alcoholism or lead poisoning. Mental illnesses due to brain tumor are cured through the removal of the tumor and correction of the secondary effects of the expanding lesion. Mental illness due to nutritional deprivation is cured by furnishing the required substances. Destruction of the invader cures mental illnesses due to processes of infection if they are arrested before the brain tissue has been damaged.

The shock treatments, by the use of insulin, deprivation of oxygen, or electrically or chemically induced convulsions, are empiric treatments at the present time. Undoubtedly they have a profound effect on the body in some way that stimulates it to readjust to stress in a less pathological way; but, equally undoubtedly, they also act psychologically. In any case, the psychiatrist uses such treatments when they promise relief to the patient. In occasional cases another as yet largely empiric treatment, lobotomy, may be used to interrupt neural connections so that the suffering of the patient is relieved to some extent.

The psychiatrist will also deal with social, family, and individual psychological stresses. The need may be simply to help the patient adjust to an immediate, easily recognizable stress that has precipitated the personality breakdown—perhaps a frustration at work or a failure to deal with marital or child-parent relationships satisfactorily. The problem may find its cause farther back, so that adjustment to inadequate assimilation of long-past experience will have to be made. Such treatment may require a great deal of time and profound emotional experiences by the patients before recovery takes place.

THE PREVENTION OF MENTAL ILLNESSES

The etiology of mental disease that has been outlined obviously offers an opportunity to promote mental health. Experiences are constantly being built into the personality structure. The way they are built in or assimilated may be subject to modification. It is known from investigations of people already ill that their past experiences, both social and personal, have influenced their ability to withstand stress. In some cases their retrospective attitudes toward these experiences can be modified in a helpful way so that recovery occurs. Since poorly assimilated past experiences appear to be factors in the causation of illnesses, it may logically be inferred that the way experiences are assimilated as they occur is important in determining the resistance to future stress.

Obviously, it is desirable that structure be spared excessive strains. All preventive medicine has as its aim the avoidance of stress on the person at some level of his functioning. This may be protection from invasion of the body by a specific bacterium, but it may also include promoting health through good nutrition, which may involve giving subsidies with which to purchase food. Housing is of interest to preventive medicine in the sense that poor ventilation or inadequate heat places stresses on the bodily and mental functioning of the person that deplete his general health. The unique objective of mental hygiene as a part of preventive medicine is to ensure that the personality structure is as sound as its genetically determined base permits. The aim of programs for the promotion of mental health is to influence the process of assimilating or integrating experiences to the end that the personality structure will better withstand stress.[6]

In this process of assimilation, experiences must be absorbed by a constitution many elements of which are fixed genetically. These fixed elements influence the operation of the assimilative process. Suppose, for instance, that there is a genetically determined feeble-mindedness. This will mean that experience can be absorbed only at a slow rate and to a limited extent. The mother of such a child must be cautioned to start toilet training rather late in order not to push him beyond his constitutionally determined rate of learning. Not only rate of learning but also content of experience must be considered. A person whose constitution includes a genetically determined brown skin will absorb experiences concerning the place of the Negro in American society in quite a different way from the person with a genetically determined "white" skin.

The Relation of Stress to Constitution. Experience is constantly affecting the personality structure. In so far as the person assimilates his experiences comfortably and continues a "normal" growth pattern, we may assume that the balance between stress and constitution is satisfactory. The rate of learning in a special class for mentally deficient children may be a satisfactory experience for the feeble-minded child, while the rate of learning expected in an ordinary class would represent an intolerable stress for him. The experience of discovering that certain job opportunities are closed to Negroes may be a simple experience for the white youth, but for the Negro it may be a stress of great magnitude. Thus any given impact may constitute a satisfactory experience or a stress depending upon the genetic and the experience-determined make-up of the individual.

The Promotion of Mental Health. The prevention of mental illness may be done along two general lines: (1) the protection of the brain from damage and the promotion of good general health; (2) efforts aimed at the healthy assimilation of life experiences into the personality structure of the individual as these experiences are occurring. This second line is identical with the promotion of mental health. Together these lines of attack are the subject matter of mental hygiene as the term is used in this book. The first concept is familiar in the field of public health and will be discussed but little in this volume. The second is not so well recognized and will be discussed in more detail.[7]

Other Definitions of Mental Hygiene. The definition just given is more specific than is generally used. Historically, the mental hygiene movement has included concern for the care of all types and grades of mental disease and defect as well as the promotion of mental health and the prevention of the mental illnesses. The attack has expanded from the treatment of the severely ill to the treatment of early disease, and finally to the application of methods to ensure the proper assimilation of experiences as they occur. All these levels of attack are included in the term "mental hygiene" as it is commonly used. The most modern emphasis, however, is on preventive methods directed toward the population at large and toward the early treatment of problems. Early treatment of course, means the detection of discomforts as early in their course as possible, the assumption being that the defects in structure and the stress elements will at that time be more amenable to adjustment.

The field of mental hygiene and some of its relations to psychiatry and medicine in general are shown in Fig. 2. Psychiatry is primarily concerned with curative medicine and with the care of chronic patients for whom methods of cure are not yet available, but it is also concerned with the early treatment of ill persons so that more serious disturbance will not occur. Mental hygiene concerns itself with the prevention of mental illnesses, the promotion of mental health, and, together with psychiatry, with early treatment to arrest behavior disorder in its early stages.[8]

The Prevention of Brain Damage. Mental hygiene has its closest connection with general medicine and public health in its interest in the protection of the central nervous system from damage by the factors outlined in Fig. 2. This is the most simple and familiar type of prevention. This approach has led to the marked reduction of general paresis of the insane,[9] for example, and may lead, through improved obstetrical practices, improved nutrition, accident prevention, etc., to reduction in incurable cases of mental deficiency.[10,11] Control of infectious diseases has already tremendously reduced the occurrence of the mental illness delirium, and may reduce congenital malformations as new methods are discovered in immunization against such diseases as rubella. Nutritional knowledge has already reduced the incidence of pellagrous psychosis. Further work may reduce prematurity with its added risk of brain injury during the birth process. Most of these areas are not generally recognized as being of great mental hygiene concern, but much success has been gained through attention to the prevention of central-nervous-system damage. There remain many challenging problems for solution through research by specialists interested in preventing behavior disorders.

Prophylaxis in the Psychogenic Disorders. The unique field for mental hygiene, however, lies in the prevention of psychogenic, psychological experience-determined, behavior disorders. As shown in Fig. 2, efforts here may be divided into two types: (1) preparation of the personality to meet general and not immediately predictable stress; (2) preparation for acute and immediately predictable stress. The second area, being less complex, will be discussed first.

There are critical points in every human being's existence which are known to be more or less stressful. The prime example is military service for the male, in the course of which he is likely to be uprooted from his family, social, and cultural foundations and precipitated into an all-

FIG. 2. THE FIELD OF MENTAL HYGIENE.

Preventive area (mental hygiene)
"Primary prevention" *

Therapeutic area (psychiatry)
"Secondary prevention" *

Organic area

Protection of nervous tissue

1. Prenatal injury
2. Birth injury
3. Trauma
4. Infection
5. Toxins
6. Malnutrition

Psychogenic area

Preparation for unpredictable stress (promotion of mental health) †

1. Parent education †
   a. Education for parenthood (schools and other groups)
   b. Physical-emotional development (anticipatory guidance)
   c. Family-life education (maturation of the family)
   d. Group living in larger groups
2. Teacher and community leader education
   a. Physical-emotional development
   b. Individual variation
   c. Counseling methods
   d. Group dynamics and methods
   e. Large group living
3. Public education
   a. Range of human variation
   b. Sources of human behavior
   c. Group living
   d. Eugenics
   e. Character of mental illness
   f. Treatment of mental illness
   g. Needs in the field and ways of meeting them
4. Social security provisions

Preparation for acute predictable stress

1. Military mental hygiene
2. Educational counseling
3. Vocational counseling
4. Preparation for childbirth
5. Preparation for retirement
6. Social case work

Counseling and case work (symptoms of disorganization of behavior are apparent)

1. Social case work, including financial relief
2. Marital counseling
3. Probation work

Outpatient treatment

1. For children
2. For adults (epidemiological leads)

Hospital treatment

1. General hospital
2. Psychiatric hospital

Rehabilitative Efforts

* See Reference 9 in this chapter.
† "Education" as used here includes all methods and media as appropriate: group discussion, radio, etc.

male, authoritative, regimented milieu. Adaptation to such a milieu is known to constitute a stress, and it has been demonstrated that preparation for the stress at this juncture may protect from illness and from asocial behavior.[12] There can also be preparation for the predictable stress of combat conditions. Many other predictable situations are discussed in the book, together with some of the ways the preparation may be or is being carried out.

The preparation for the less predictable stresses likely to occur during a lifetime lies primarily in promoting the sound growth and development of the individual so that there will be the least possible number of unresolved conflicts to weaken personality structure and, equally important, maximal development of those faculties by which conflicts are resolved. In general, this may be said to come about through the development of the capacity to relate effectively to other human beings and to be able to make a successful adaptation to a social and cultural situation. By "adaptation" is not meant an absence of spontaneity on the part of the individual, a way of adjusting smoothly into any situation. It means rather that the individual is able to find a niche in his culture that gives him some satisfaction and a measure of success, a sense of progress, and a sense of status, whether this be leadership or followership.

SUMMARY

The personality is the product of accumulated experience and attitudes acting together with a unique constitution, to give rise to a more or less integrated personality structure. Depending on how well experience is integrated into this structure and on the inherent strength of the constitution, the personality is strong and can withstand stress, or is weak and succumbs easily, the person slipping into maladjustment or mental illness. The aim of mental hygiene is to do everything possible to ensure that experiences are satisfying and are properly integrated as they occur, so that the personality structure can stand strong through the recurrent stresses and strains of living, successfully integrating these experiences also as they are encountered.

REFERENCES

1. Jones, H. E.: "Physical Ability as a Factor in Social Adjustment," *J. Educ. Research* 40 (1946).
2. Dublin, L. I.: *The Facts of Life from Birth to Death*, The Macmillan Company, New York, 1951.
3. Gould, H. N., and M. R. Gould: "Age of First Menstruation in Mothers and Daughters," *J.A.M.A.* 98:1349–1352 (1932).

4. Meyer, Adolf: "Objective Psychology or Psychobiology," *J.A.M.A.* **65**:860–863 (1915).
5. Windle, W. F., C. D. Clemente, D. Scott, Jr., and W. W. Chambers: "Structural and Functional Regeneration in the Central Nervous System," *Arch. Neurol. & Psychiat.* **67**:553–554 (1952).
6. Lemkau, P. V., B. Pasamanick, and M. Cooper: "The Implications of the Psychogenetic Hypothesis for Mental Hygiene," *Am. J. Psychiat.* **110**:436–442 (1953).
7. Lemkau, P. V.: "Toward Mental Health: Areas That Promise Progress," *Ment. Hyg.* **36**:179–209 (1952).
8. Lemkau, P. V.: "The Field of Mental Hygiene," abstract in *Internat. M. News* **8** (1954). To be published in *Japan J. Pub. Health.*
9. Gruenberg, E.: "The Prevention of Mental Disease," in "Mental Health in the United States," *Ann. Am. Acad. Polit. & Social Sc.* **286** (1953).
10. Lilienfeld, A. M., and B. Pasamanick: "The Association of Maternal and Fetal Factors with the Development of Epilepsy. I. Abnormalities in the Prenatal and Paranatal Periods," *J.A.M.A.* **155**:719–724 (1954).
11. Anderson, George W.: "Obstetrical Factors in Cerebral Palsy," *J. Pediat.* **40**:340–375 (1952).
12. Cohen, R. R.: "Mental Hygiene for the Trainee; Method for Fortifying the Army's Manpower," *Am. J. Psychiat.* **100**:62–71 (1943).

CHAPTER TWO

Mental Hygiene as a Public Health Responsibility

THE INDIVIDUAL AND PUBLIC HEALTH

Mental hygiene had its origin in psychiatry and began, therefore, as a concern about the treatment of individual patients. It is only in the last few decades that psychiatry has furnished the theoretical basis for the interest in the building of the personality structure.[1] Mental hygiene could not develop programs for the promotion of mental health in populations until this theoretical basis was available; consequently, preventive programs directed toward whole populations are recent developments.

Public health has had somewhat the opposite development. It began with concern about factors that affect the health of groups rather than individuals, and at present is being forced to take individual health and individual treatment more into consideration. The history of public health begins when man began to live together in groups. Its earliest concerns dealt with drainage, building codes, the cleanliness of food, and the disposition of waste. Epidemic disease rather than individual illness has been its prime interest.[2]

Early public health theories were as little scientific as early psychiatric ones. The conception of pestilence as a punishment by the gods, or as being caused by the stink of filth is in the same category as the belief in the "sacred disease" and in demon possession of the psychiatry of an earlier day. With the discovery of vaccination against smallpox a new and modern scientific era appeared. The bacteriologic and immunologic advances of the later nineteenth and early twentieth centuries made techniques available for the protection of society from many contagious and epidemic diseases. Industrial hazards, the importance of which was indicated by simple observation and later confirmed by statistical studies, were early included in the field of public health.

Disease is always a greater problem in the low-income classes. Con-

17

tagious diseases particularly have always been a greater threat in the crowded, poorly ventilated homes of the poor. For this reason there has always been a close relationship between public health and social-welfare agencies. Psychiatry also has had a long history of association with such agencies, for psychiatric illnesses are frequently chronic and the long-term care needed has been available only through charitable or tax-supported agencies for by far the larger part of the population. At the present time, more than 95 per cent of all psychiatric patients in the United States are under care in public hospitals, supported completely or in part through taxes. Governments for centuries have provided some medical care for the indigent. This has usually been a function of the public health agency, either voluntary or tax-supported. The furnishing of medical care has meant that public health has always had some concern for the care of the individual patient during its history, even though its primary mission has been the prevention of epidemic and contagious diseases. During the latter half of the nineteenth century and until fairly recently, the treatment aspect of public health was somewhat eclipsed in the successive conquering of one epidemic disease after another. The remarkable extension of life expectancy completely justifies the relative neglect of individual care by public health agencies during this period.

The control of epidemic illnesses has brought reduction in general death rates, primarily through saving the lives of infants and young children. The persons saved are living only a little longer than did their forebears, but there are more of them "exposed to risk" of long life. A larger proportion remain in the population to be attacked by the various illnesses that become significant causes of death after the age of 40 or 50. The age distribution of the population is changing rapidly as general public health measures against infectious illnesses become effective in ever-enlarging areas over the world.[3]

Diseases that attack older people are very different from infectious diseases. Heart disease, cancer, diabetes and its complications, and arteriosclerosis have risen to places of greater importance as causes of death. In such diseases as these death comes, generally, at the end of a long period of illness and, frequently, of disability. The attention of public health is shifting to the diseases of this group. For the most part, problems in these diseases are those of the individual sick person. Etiology is relatively unknown in many instances, and prevention at present is largely "secondary prevention" (Fig. 2), i.e., early treatment to lower morbidity and delay death. Generally, the aim has to be melioration of an existing condition rather than actual prevention. Faced with the problem of the prevention and cure of this type of condition, public health has been forced into a revival of the individual-treatment aspects of the maintenance of the public health.

The object of medical care in this group of diseases is not primarily to prevent death but to delay it and to keep the ill individual productive as long as possible. The aim becomes not only to add years to life but to maintain life during the added years. Medical knowledge now available allows no attack on most of this group of diseases which can be applied in the same way to the whole of a population. The ill people must be considered as a succession of individual cases, each with its own specific regimen of treatment. This is a very different problem from that presented by a population of infants practically every one of whom can be immunized by identical procedures with very little attention paid to differences between individuals.

Another trend has been operating to bring the individual into focus in public health—the tendency for governments to place the responsibility for medical care of citizens on their public health agencies. The medical care of the indigent has always been a governmental responsibility. The trend appears to be that not only the indigent but perhaps a far larger part of the population will, in the future, look to some sort of a public health agency for treatment in time of sickness. How far this trend shall go is, of course, as much a political as a health question.

HOSPITALIZATION AND PUBLIC HEALTH

Like medical care, hospitalization has not in the past been a primary responsibility of public health in many countries. It is, after all, a problem of the individual, not of the group, except in the case of contagious diseases. On the other hand, a new concept has appeared, that the public health agency should be responsible for any problem of health in the community that is too big or too expensive to be managed by the individual or by nongovernmental groups. Under this definition, the public health agency may well deal in any type of medical treatment in or out of hospital, rich or poor, infectious disease or psychiatric disability, depending upon the definition of the terms "too expensive" and "big." Mustard summarizes these concepts in his definition of a public health responsibility: [4]

> A health problem becomes a public health responsibility if or when it is of such a character or extent as to be amenable to solution only through systematized social action. Its relative importance varies with the hazard to the population exposed. This hazard may be qualitative, in terms of disability or death; quantitative, in terms of proportion of the population affected; it may be actual or potential.

Mental illnesses are responsible for filling almost half the available hospital beds and produce a greater volume of long-term morbidity than any other group of illnesses.[5] As it faced the problem of chronic disease, public health discovered that mental illnesses were terribly chronic; almost half the patients hospitalized remained in hospital for more than a year. While admission rates for psychiatric hospitals are only one one-hundredth as large as for all other types of hospitals, the population in these hospitals, in the United States and many Western European countries, is nearly as great as for the general hospitals.[6] This could only mean that, by present methods of treatment, hospitalized psychiatric illnesses must be considered 100 times as chronic as those illnesses for which treatment could be obtained in the nonpsychiatric hospitals.

Psychiatric hospitalization has for many centuries been recognized as a public responsibility, certainly falling within the definition quoted. In most countries it has been assigned to the public health agency, but in the United States, mostly for historical reasons discussed later, it has been the responsibility of a separate agency of government. This was a public health agency, to be sure, but one which attended mostly to problems of the health of a succession of sick individuals rather than to the health of the population from which they came. As psychiatry has made its advances in knowledge and theory regarding prevention of disease, the agency responsible for the care of psychiatrically ill individuals has, in many instances, become concerned about the mental health of the whole population. This enlarged concept has brought the public health department and the agency of government operating psychiatric hospitals to a point of cooperation described more fully in Chap. 6.

PUBLIC HEALTH ORGANIZATION

Public health, in order to deal with group health problems, has developed in two general directions. The first of these is the increase of scientific information about disease by laboratory study and epidemiologic research. This field has received much attention and has been presented in various literary forms. The second development has less of the adventurous element and gets less public acclaim. This is the building up of an administrative organization to make knowledge functional in the community. It is one thing to know that diphtheria can be controlled in a population if it is immunized, but quite another to get all the people immunized. The latter demands an organization to reach every individual in the community. Public health has done this administrative job well. It has developed successful techniques, so that the agencies now, in general, command great respect.

As a result, there is a tendency to load public health agencies with new functions and responsibilities. Some fear that this may take place too rapidly and with too diffuse aims, so that administrative efficiency may be endangered. There is a legitimate basis for alarm that the addition of cancer programs, geriatric programs, programs for the hospitalization of the chronically ill, and programs for medical care—and for mental hygiene—may dilute public health efforts and so overload administration that it will lose its effectiveness where it is now successful. Personnel is already burdened, techniques in these newer fields are not settled, and evaluation of the effect of programs in them is extremely difficult. The fact remains, however, that these newly recognized problems are, in varying degree, public health responsibilities and that the trials they impose on public health administration will have to be worked through to the best solutions within the range of possibility.

PROGRAMMING AND ITS REQUIREMENTS

In general, a public health agency cannot deal with a public health responsibility until medical research and its resultant knowledge make it possible to construct a program which is applicable to the population to be served. Sometimes when the threat to health is immediate and severe, efforts will be made even though it is recognized that there is little scientific basis for them. Bonfires were built in the streets to control cholera before it was discovered that purification of the water supply would prevent it. When no specific methods for the control of poliomyelitis were known, public assemblages were prohibited and swimming pools were closed. It is only fairly recently that medical knowledge of personality structure has been sufficient to act as a base for a program of mental hygiene that could be applied to a population.

To reach the population requires a relatively large number of trained people. This limits the kinds of techniques that can be used in programs in two ways: (1) the cost must not be too high; (2) the techniques must not be too difficult. Freeman [7] has made the point that a technique that can be mastered by only a few hundred persons is of little value in public health. If the technique is medical, it must be within the capacity of the average physician; if it is an engineering technique, the ordinary sanitary engineer must be able to use it; if it is a nursing service, the nurse of average training and intelligence must be able to include it in her armamentarium.

In addition to the assembling of personnel of varied professional backgrounds, the public health agency faces the problem of making it possible for them to work as a team toward a common objective. This aspect of administration is receiving increasing attention as programs extend further and further into the life of the community. It is not enough that the health officer knows his job and can present it to the public. Each member of his staff must also be familiar with the goals of the department and, even though devoted to his particular specialty, must be able to interpret it in terms of the larger goal to be achieved. One of the aims of this volume is to inform public health teams of certain additional responsibilities falling upon them in the promotion of mental health. Existing personnel are also faced with adjusting to new types of professional persons entering the health team. The philosophies and aims of these new team members are also included in this volume so that they may be integrated as smoothly and efficiently as possible.

THE RELATION WITH MENTAL HYGIENE

Mental hygiene, developing from a primary interest in the sick patient to an interest in the promotion of mental health in the general population, soon discovered the field of public health. On the other hand, public health, as soon as it included the noninfectious diseases within its realm, promptly found that the mental diseases had to be considered very seriously. They produced a very large proportion of all morbidity and constituted so large a problem that governmental agencies were invariably needed to provide necessary care. At present each field regards the other as pregnant with possibilities, but the relationship is still often found to be immature—and perhaps idealistic, like so many human reactions of immaturity.

There appear to be three main reasons why the two medical disciplines have stayed rather distant from each other for so long a time.

Mental Hygiene as Science. The first of these is the general suspicion on the part of scientific men that mental hygiene is not a science at all but a form of art that cannot be studied by straightforward, sharply defined methods. Although in some cases this objection is a rationalization of the fear of mental disease, having its origin in the old demonology, there is some truth in it and it must be answered. The answer involves the nature of facts. Adolf Meyer handled the problem by stating that "a fact is anything that makes a difference," [8] anything that effects a change. This definition clears away a great deal of troublesome verbiage regarding mensurability and leaves science unbound as regards its possible fields of interest and study. For example, when a child has whooping cough he is likely to get more attention from the people in the household than when he is not coughing, retching, and otherwise ill. In the process of resuming his usual position in the family upon recovery from the infection, he may have temper tantrums, both because he objects to the withdrawal of the former disproportionate sympathy and attention and because he is trying to recover it. These temper tantrums are as much within the realm of scientific study as are the immunologic reactions secondary to the recovery from the invasion of the body by the bacillus of pertussis. Yet the method of observation of the facts concerned is very different in the two cases. The immunologic reaction, occurring at a level of integration comprehensible in terms of chemical reactions, is determined with laboratory tools and away from the patient, whose only contribution to the procedure is a blood sample. The temper tantrum, however, may not be observable by the person required to evaluate it, since in our culture such reactions tend to be concealed as private family matters. Also, the child's resentment is not toward the investigator usually, but toward someone much closer, usually the parent. The parent is not likely spontaneously to bring the matter up; the subject of emotional reactions following the illness will probably have to be opened by the investigator. The child will not be amenable to direct questioning, partly because he recognizes nothing unusual in his reaction—he has no "insight"—but also because language may not be sufficiently developed. The parent will, then, become the informant. His account may be as accurate as he can make it, but it will be biased by his language habits, by his attitudes toward display of emotion and particularly of rage, and by whatever shame or discomfort he may feel because he fails to achieve control over the child. The evaluation of the severity or even the presence or absence of tantrums will have to be on the basis of the prejudiced account of a biased witness. But the difficulty of the evaluation does not change the essential character of the fact or relieve the scientist from taking it into consideration.

In studying the facts of mental hygiene one is bound by some trying limitations. The only animal suitable for the critical experiments in the field is man himself. No other animal shows all the functions with which the experiment must deal, or has the capacity to indicate the results. These results are of such a nature that words must be used to express them. The use of words itself represents a whole field of scientific endeavor, semantics,[9] some of the problems of which have been discussed in Chap. 1.

Furthermore, experiments in mental hygiene may require the observation of a generation or more before conclusions may be reached. The techniques of observation of human reactions are not yet stabilized enough to set up long-term experiments in mental hygiene. An example of this was seen a few years ago when it was decided to test the hypothesis that persons developing certain types of mental illnesses have personality characteristics which are related to the later development of the disease. The city in which the study was to be done had been served by two busy psychiatric out-patient departments for many years. These clinics were frequently used to evaluate children for social agencies in connection with the decision to place them in foster care, and at times of other radical changes in their lives. The child was, then, not examined because of personal difficulties, but rather because of social situations related to him. Such examinations, it was expected, would give the data on personality traits and characteristics which could be related to the psychosis which developed later but was unforeseen at the original examination. The results of the study were entirely negative.[10] The trouble was that the old clinic records were inadequate to answer the question "What kind of personality did this person have before this illness?" The necessary material had not been recorded, simply because it had not been recognized as having any predictive or research value. Mental hygiene experiments require years of study with methods that are and can remain standard. Methodology in the evaluation of personality is still changing so rapidly that standardization of methods for long-term experiments is extremely difficult.[11] There is, however, research in mental hygiene now under way in which observations of individuals are made over a significant period of time so that the effective factors can be singled out for evaluation. In such experiments an attempt is made to relate the data on the infancy of the child, for example, to what the child is at the preschool level and, eventually, to his personality configuration as an adult.

Finally, an experiment is always of greatest value if variables can be controlled and the experiment repeated. This is never the case with man as the experimental animal unless the experiment is short, and even then preexperimental variables cannot be controlled. In other words, mental hygiene is in the position of having to observe and interpret human living. To use another of Adolf Meyer's concise phrases, the "experiment of nature" [12] is the experiment that has to be used, the attempt being to interpret the action of variables rather than to control them. Although all these considerations make the study of the problems of mental hygiene difficult and frequently make mensuration impossible, they do not eliminate the field from the consideration of scientists concerned with knowledge of mankind and his illnesses.

Mental Hygiene as a Public Health Program. Public health is the branch of medicine that puts knowledge about the prevention of disease to work in the population. Mental hygiene has not been able to put knowledge forward for use in the population until relatively recently; such knowledge simply did not exist. Psychiatrists had no program to offer so long as they concerned themselves almost exclusively with people so sick they had to be hospitalized. The first idea useful in populations was that of early treatment in order to arrest the development of more serious illness. There is still room for a great deal of experimental work in this field, but there are now available a few techniques that can be offered to public health as standardized enough to be multiplied. We can begin to conceive that the need might be filled. The approach to genuine prophylaxis outlined in Chap. 1, is still more recent, and only a few standardized ways of working are now available. Even these few are of relatively recent origin. It is not remarkable that public health has, at times, regarded mental hygiene as howling for recognition in relation to the care of populations but having nothing more than a tremendous problem to offer. This situation has now changed somewhat; there are things to do, and public health shows more willingness to accept its responsibility for the mental health of populations now that it encounters more than frustrating, answerless statistics in the field.

Public Health and Psychiatric Hospitalization. The final difficulty standing in the way of building mental hygiene into the structure of public health is the fact that mental hygiene, using the term in its broadest meaning, has been and must be so deeply concerned with the hospitalization of the mentally ill. Psychiatric hospitals are very old, older than modern public health agencies, and very large.

In the state of Maryland, the health department operates chronic-disease and tuberculosis hospitals.* In 1952, citizens were furnished 515,929 days of hospitalization under these programs.[13] In the same year, the state mental hospitals, operated by the State Department of Mental Hygiene, furnished 3,531,375 hospital days of care.[14] It should also be noted that the mental-hospital program has been growing at a rate only a little faster than that of the increase of the general population, while the chronic-disease program is a new one showing extremely rapid expansion. The budget for all the various public health programs, including the hospitalization, the program of sanitation, hospital inspection, medical care for the indigent and medically indigent, crippled children, an epilepsy program, a mental hygiene program, a program

---

* Tuberculosis hospitals became the responsibility of the health department in 1947, and chronic-disease hospitalization in 1948. The state health department is responsible for the subsidy of private hospitals for the care of indigent patients but is not responsible for the administration of these beds.

for the study of alcoholism, a venereal-disease program, vital-statistics record keeping, and all other activities of the health department was $11,551,754. Psychiatric hospitalization and the follow-up of discharged patients cost $10,086,331. These figures exclude the capital investment in real estate and buildings, which is much greater for the state psychiatric hospital system.

When the public health administrator thinks of mental hygiene, the financial and administrative burden of one hospital bed to each 200 of the population stands before him. There is reasonable fear that the health department would be swallowed up and lose its identity if it linked forces with the tremendous and old, although in most places badly neglected, governmental agency dealing with the hospitalization of psychiatric patients. This fear, plus an overconsciousness of too little training in psychiatry, is responsible for the introductory clause the mental hygienist hears so often in talking with health officers, "Of course, I don't know anything about your field. . . ." The problem is much the same as it would be if the general hospitals in a state were suddenly taken over by government and the health department given the order to run them.

The psychiatric hospital was once the only mental hygiene agency known. There is now knowledge and theory available to extend beyond the hospital, to early treatment and to prophylactic efforts directed toward the protection of the total population and to the promotion of mental health. As public health has seen these opportunities more clearly, it has included them as public health responsibilities more completely—though avoiding responsibility for the hospitalization in the field, in the United States at least.

Psychiatrists are not always cordial to the concept that mental hygiene is a public health responsibility, at least in the sense that the specialized public health agency has any direct responsibility in the field.[15] There are those who feel that since, as a rule, the state psychiatric hospitals have the large pool of trained psychiatrists under their jurisdiction, it is reasonable for the hospitals to be responsible for all mental hygiene work in the state as well. Some psychiatrists, however, have pointed out that mental hygiene and psychiatric therapeutics are not the same. Furthermore, they draw a distinction between therapeutic skill and the job of administration and public education required to bring these services to a population. In the past, the psychiatric hospital has been isolated from the community, including the medical community. The psychiatrist is neither trained nor experienced in dealing with the local problems of administration and does not usually have the skills of the trained health officer in organizing communities for action as regards health matters. The state psychiatric hospital system usually has no local organization constantly on duty to carry out its program, while the health department has as a basic aim a health officer and a staff available to provide knowledge of local conditions.

There are as yet no data available to indicate the correct solution to this problem. Experiments are being carried on with all types of administrative patterns. In many countries, however, such administrative and educational programs are in process of development and are matters of great concern both to psychiatrists and to public health leaders. The psychiatrists are anxious that the care of psychiatric patients reach the highest possible level of excellence and that the promotion of mental health be carried out through scientifically sound procedures. The public health leaders are anxious to establish a service to populations that will meet all the needs of the personality, from protection against organic illness to protection against the stultifying effects of emotional neglect of infants.

MENTAL HYGIENE PROGRAMMING

In Chap. 1, the contributions which classic public health practice has made to the prevention of the psychiatric illnesses were briefly discussed. The administrative machinery that has made possible these accomplishments is in existence and operating. What methods does public health have already in operation that can be used in an attack on "psychogenic" mental illness, and what means are available to increase the mental health of the community? It has already been pointed out that public health agencies have developed an administrative pattern for putting ideas into effect in populations through the use of teams of different types of personnel, each specialized, though all working toward a common aim.

Contact with the Public. The methods of meeting the public at the local level are well developed and are functioning. They may be divided into two types, personal contact and various nonpersonal methods, although the two are usually combined. The personal contact is effected by health department personnel and through "key people" in the community. The health-department personnel in contact with the public are the health officer and his clinical and technical assistants, the public health nurse, and the education staff of the department.

The public health officer is a physician particularly trained to deal with disease and promote health on a community-wide level. Knowledge of health promotion and the prevention of disease is of no value unless it is put into practice among the people, and the health officer is trained to get this job done. This involves the use of legal power in the enforcement of ordinances, rules, and laws, but more frequently it is accomplished by teaching and persuasion, the induction of a state of mind in the public which makes it want to carry out the scientifically demonstrated and recommended practices. Public health then has two distinct phases: the knowledge of the practices which are desirable, and the knowledge of how to get practices established. The first is largely a matter of medical generalizations and specifics learned in clinical practice and from the laboratory. The second is a matter of influencing attitudes involving the area of the social sciences, anthropology, sociology, and particularly psychology, psychiatry, and in so far as it can be separated from them, mental hygiene. The recognition that the technique of changing attitudes is an essential part of public health has become more and more important as the degenerative and conflict-induced illnesses have come to the fore, a change that coincided with the conquering of the infectious diseases. Immunization, water supply, and sewage control can, to some extent at least, operate on the base of authority and law. Restriction of individual activity, consistent use of insulin, recurrent examination for carcinoma, the building of sound personality structures, are matters that can be achieved only through attitude-changing techniques. These, therefore, form an increasingly important part of the armamentarium of the well-trained official. Unfortunately, these techniques are still too much in the area of the art of public health rather than its science. It is confidently hoped that expansion of research will follow the expanding recognition of the problem and that the natural laws in this area will become as useful in public health practices as the natural laws governing the growth and spread of pathogenic microorganisms.[16]

The techniques by which the health officer organizes the community for health action are adequately discussed in the texts on public health administration.[17,18,19] They include the community lay health council, the use of particular "key people" individually or in groups, the use of voluntary health associations concerned with particular diseases—mental diseases, cancer, poliomyelitis, and the like. They include interesting the public at various levels, e.g., the local community to help provide housing for the clinic or an office for the nurse or a salary for some service persons. The county health department must convince the citizenry, the political powers, and the board of health, usually politically appointed, to gain its ends of better protection of the people from disease and for the promotion of health. The state and national movements are not dissimilar in design. The essence of public health at all levels is the building of the understanding of influential persons as to what it is about and why. The skill displayed in this administrative area will determine the success or failure of its projects.

One of the key groups in bringing the public to willingness to act healthfully is the medical practitioners. In this day when the medical profession in some countries reacts so violently to "socialized medicine" (which is too often identified directly with organized public health) the medical profession is tremendously important. The practitioner must not only be convinced that the health department's program is sound and as little competitive as possible; he must also be induced to teach health practices. Physicians are frequently part-time employees of the health department, and it may be assumed that they carry the teaching into their own practices when they are not working as members of the department. This is but a small part of the work of the health department which is accomplished through the physicians. No public health program can be successful unless backed by the local physicians; any such program can be completely sabotaged by them if they choose to act against it. Any new program is therefore presented first to the leaders of the profession and to the medical society for approval before it is launched. With varying degrees of enthusiasm and with more or less direct personal persuasion, the physician then helps the program along by his influence over his patients and their families. He becomes an extension of the health department in this sense.

The development of public health nursing has put a powerful tool into the hands of public health officials in the area of influencing the incidence of illnesses involving attitudes as a part of their etiology.[20,21,22,23] The contact between the nurse and her patient or client has been extensively studied. Methods for making this contact more effective educationally are constantly being devised, and research on what attitudes are available for manipulation by the nurse is also being given much thought. Educational methods directed toward the profession are under constant experimentation and study, even though evaluation is recognized as being extremely difficult in this area.

It is recognized that cultural factors operate to influence personality development profoundly, both through the function of the family in transmitting the culture from generation to generation, and in the child's later, and perhaps equally influential, contacts outside the family. Public health interest in the large cultural influences on attitude formation and fixation has shown astonishing expansion in recent years. The leadership of the American Public Health Association in setting standards for housing, with special attention to housing of the aged, is an evidence of this. Similarly, the great attention being paid to the techniques and arts of community organization is a recognition of the community's influence in the development and stabilization of attitudes that affect health.

The health department has a special relationship with the school system. In general, schools accept a limited responsibility for the health of the pupils.[24] In the discharge of this responsibility the school looks to the health department for methods and practices and, frequently, for personnel and service. As a part of the child's education, good health practices are taught. The weight of the influence of classroom education and the influential personalities of teachers may thus become agencies by which the health department meets the public.

The health department also persuades the public to use good health practices through the community's leaders. Clergymen fit into the public health department's methods of meeting the public need and have some specific advantages of approach for mental hygiene. Club leaders of both adult and children's groups may also be effective in the teaching of good health practices. Voluntary groups specially organized to meet some specific health problem, such as the National Foundation for Infantile Paralysis, the National Tuberculosis Association, Mental Health Associations, and the Red Cross may also be parts of the total health effort of the community. The whole of the health effort is of concern to the public health department; working relationships with such organizations are or should be maintained. The necessarily close relationship of the health department with private and public welfare organizations has already been mentioned and is of the greatest educational significance.

Aside from the personal contacts with the public and contacts through organizations not a part of the health department, there are the establishments of the health department itself for caring for the health of the citizenry. Maternal and child health clinics afford an opportunity for influencing people in a setting of the greatest willingness to change for the benefit of the child. Venereal-disease clinics are centers for disseminating information about those diseases. Consultation services in the various specialties of medicine provided to local physicians serve to raise the level of practice and to stimulate the public to expect more from the physicians. Tuberculosis case-finding campaigns bring information to the public, as do the various more or less routine immunization procedures. Mental health clinics not only serve psychiatrically disturbed children and adults, but also act as educational influences in the community.

The educational function of the public health department has become of such great importance that specialists have been developed to work primarily in that field. Although education as a part of personal contact and service remains the most effective approach, reading material, posters, films, etc., are also of great importance and deserve the study and planning now going forward to make them actually reach and educate the public.

All these contacts with the public, with varying degrees of effectiveness in various health departments, have become the functional tools of health work, reaching the public with service and education. Mental hygiene has a place in all health problems, since all are charged with an emotional aura that must be dealt with if the patient is to progress to the highest level of health. In these medical contacts, mental hygiene programs have the opportunity to try to gain respect for and promote knowledge of the distinctly human rather than only the mechanistic functions of the human being. The human aspects are by no means entirely neglected at present; if that were the case, probably no program would work at all. However, this part of programs can probably be improved and extended by mental hygiene knowledge and practice. Certainly the scientific study of this aspect is an exciting prospect, little developed as yet.

Evaluation. One of the most urgent problems of mental hygiene and psychiatry is that of evaluating the effect of efforts in any direction. Public health as a scientific discipline has given much attention to this problem, developing the specialties of biostatistics and epidemiology with the primary purpose of building the structure of scientific logic and method whereby cause and effect may be evaluated in the health field. As these specialties have developed they have become capable of dealing with more and more complicated cause-and-effect relationships, taking into consideration constantly larger numbers of variables of circumstances and time. There is real basis for hope that the scientific logic and methods already developed can contribute to the evaluation of the effect of attitude-changing on health. There is also basis for hope that, as more specialists in the mental health field learn of the methods and their opportunities, these specialists will be asked more frequently to test their mettle on the difficult evaluation problems in the field of mental health and mental illness and the changes taking place in these fields. Thus far, the methods have proved useful practically exclusively in the process of describing the incidence and prevalence of mental ill-health of various types and, to a lesser extent, its distribution in populations.* Extremely few studies deal in change of incidence,[25] and even fewer attempt to relate the changes to possible causes by statistical means. Although there are great difficulties in the problem, there appears to be no basic reason why the methods of

* These data are summarized in the Appendix.

epidemiology cannot be applied more fully in mental hygiene. When this is done, we shall be in a position better to measure the extent of problems and to evaluate the effect of work. To hope for any complete realization of this state in the near future would be foolish. Yet it is an end much to be desired and worthy of research effort.[26]

SUMMARY

Public health has developed until its field includes all ill-health in the population so severe or so widespread that management at other than governmental level is economically and sociologically unsound or impossible; it also includes the promotion of health. Mental hygiene has grown so that its aims include the prevention of mental illnesses through the promotion of mental health, by the direct prevention of some mental illnesses, and through the early treatment of cases. As the diseases producing mortality in the younger age groups came under control, public health encountered the group of illnesses where prevention of morbidity rather than mortality must be the goal. Mental illnesses thus became a major concern in public health thinking. These illnesses for the most part are dependent upon men's attitudes rather than upon man's position as a competitor for survival against other organisms.

Public health methods include administrative techniques for getting health knowledge to work in populations. Included also are methods for reaching and influencing the thinking and action of populations. Methods for evaluating the results of doing these tasks and for comparing results of various methods in accomplishing them are also available, though not yet well enough developed to deal with problems of evaluation in health education or mental hygiene to any satisfactory extent.

This organization, this personnel, and these methods offer great opportunities to put mental hygiene to work in a scientific and effective way for the improvement of the mental health of populations.

REFERENCES

1. Lemkau, P. V., B. Pasamanick, and M. Cooper: "The Implications of the Psychogenetic Hypothesis for Mental Hygiene," *Am. J. Psychiat.* 110:436–442 (1953).
2. Maxcy, K. F.: Rosenau's *Preventive Medicine and Hygiene,* 7th ed., Appleton-Century-Crofts, Inc., New York, 1951.
3. Leavell, H. R., and E. G. Clark: *Textbook of Preventive Medicine,* McGraw-Hill Book Company, Inc., New York, 1953.
4. Mustard, H.: *An Introduction to Public Health,* 2d ed., The Macmillan Company, New York, 1944.
5. Perrott, G. St. J., L. M. Smith, M. Y. Pennell, and M. E. Altenderfer: *Care*

of the Long-term Patient, Table 6, U.S. Public Health Service, Publication 344, Government Printing Office, Washington, D.C., 1954.

6. Ewing, O. R.: *The Nation's Health, A Ten Year Program; A Report to the President,* Government Printing Office, Washington, D.C., 1948.
7. Freeman, A. W.: Class lectures, School of Hygiene and Public Health, The Johns Hopkins University, Baltimore, Md., unpublished.
8. Meyer, Adolf: "Leading Concepts of Psychobiology (Ergasiology) and of Psychiatry (Ergasiatry)," in *The Collected Papers of Adolf Meyer,* vol. III, "Medical Teaching," p. 228, Johns Hopkins Press, Baltimore, 1951.
9. Walpole, H. R.: *Semantics; The Nature of Words and Their Meanings,* W. W. Norton & Company, Inc., New York, 1941.
10. Stevenson, P. H.: "Early Psychiatric Contact with Individuals Later Becoming Psychotic," D.P.H. thesis, School of Hygiene and Public Health, The Johns Hopkins University, Baltimore, Md., 1941, unpublished.
11. Macy, I. G.: *Nutrition and Chemical Growth in Childhood,* vol. I, "Evaluation," chap. I, Charles C Thomas, Publisher, Springfield, Ill., 1942.
12. Meyer, Ref. 8, p. 94.
13. Riley, R. H. (Director, State of Maryland Department of Health): Personal communication, 1954.
14. Perkins, C. T. (Commissioner, State of Maryland Department of Mental Hygiene): Personal communication, 1954.
15. Editorial Comment, "Shotgun Wedding," *Psychiatric Quart.* **24**:391–394 (1950).
16. Leavell, H. R.: "Contributions of the Social Sciences to the Solution of Health Problems," *New England J. Med.* **247**:885–897 (1952).
17. Maxcy, Ref. 2.
18. Smillie, W. G.: *Preventive Medicine and Public Health,* The Macmillan Company, New York, 1946.
19. Leavell and Clark, Ref. 3.
20. Lemkau, P. V.: "What Can the Public Health Nurse Do in Mental Hygiene?" *Pub. Health Nursing* **40**:299–303 (1948).
21. Cooper, M. M.: "The Relationship of Mental Hygiene to Growth and Development," *Pub. Health Nursing* **43**:248–251 (1951).
22. Zimmerman, K. A.: "The Public Health Nurse and the Emotions of Pregnancy," *Pub. Health Nursing* **39**:63–67 (1947).
23. Lemkau, P. V., and J. Freund: "Training Personnel for Rural Child Psychiatry," *Proceedings of the Fourth International Congress on Mental Health,* Mexico City, December, 1951," p. 101–112, Columbia University Press, New York, 1952.
24. Health Education Council: *Suggested School Health Policies: A Charter for School Health,* 2d ed., The Council, New York, 1946.
25. Goldhammer, H., and A. Marshall: *Psychosis and Civilization,* Free Press, Glencoe, Ill., 1953.
26. *Epidemiology of Mental Disorder,* papers presented at a round table at the 1949 annual conference of the Milbank Memorial Fund, Nov. 16–17, 1949, Milbank Memorial Fund, New York, 1950.

CHAPTER THREE

Techniques in Mental Hygiene: Leadership Personnel

As has already been made clear, mental hygiene has evolved largely from psychiatric practice and theory. For programs in public health, whether these be in the hands of official public health agencies or under other auspices, dependence for clinical service and leadership in preventive programs must still rest to a very large extent upon specialists in this field. The psychiatrist, particularly when he operates outside hospitals, rarely works alone; usually he has assistants specially trained to work with him. The ancillary or auxiliary professions, as they are called, are primarily clinical psychology and psychiatric social work, though the mental health nurse consultant is becoming recognized in this area, especially in the health department setting. These professionally trained persons operate as a team, each member accepting particular tasks in diagnosis and treatment and all planning their operations in conferences together.

THE TOOLS OF MENTAL HYGIENE PROGRAMS

The tools available for use in mental hygiene are almost entirely nonmechanical. There are few items in mental hygiene program budgets aside from payment of personnel. Mental hygiene cannot use such things as syringes and laboratory apparatus in its work, and iron and terra cotta pipes do not embarrass its programs by their cost. This, of course, does not mean that the mental hygienist has no stake in programs for the control of epidemic disease. For example, the control of syphilis is of the greatest concern to him, since through it paresis can also be controlled. But other people are particularly trained and equipped to do this kind of mental hygiene. What is left to the psychiatrist at present is the task of attempting to prevent psychogenic mental illnesses, those arising out of persistent and severe conflict within the individual. He is also concerned with illnesses related to social deprivations that may bring long-term stress upon personalities. He recognizes that such situations as extreme poverty or lack of space, equipment, and personnel to offer recreation to certain classes of the population lead in some instances to severe personality warping that may amount to mental illness. But the budget items for welfare and recreation are not included in the mental health program. Like communicable-disease control, these functions have great value in addition to their preventive effect as regards the mental illnesses, and this work is done by others, though frequently with the active support and sometimes at the instigation of the psychiatrist. With regard to such situations the psychiatrist may be in the position of the epidemiologist, seeing through his clinic work where the lack in such resources is most actively producing cases of behavior disorder.[1]

The principal and basic objective of mental hygiene work is to modify attitudes and unhealthy behavior secondary to unhealthy attitudes. Attitude changing, a special and peculiarly intensive type of educational process, is done mostly through more or less intimate contact of personalities. One of them feels, or can be lead to recognize, some need; the other has some special training or background that can offer help to fill the need.

PROFESSIONAL PERSONNEL

Eventually, perhaps there will be so great a dissemination of mental hygiene teaching that specialists will not be needed, though this seems unlikely in any foreseeable future. The prime tools of mental hygiene are specially trained professional persons. In order that public health personnel may more clearly grasp what sort of people will be found available for mental hygiene work, the various professions will be described.

The Psychiatrist. A psychiatrist is first a physician, a medical graduate who has had at least one year's experience as an intern in a general hospital. Studies have shown that many in the general public do not know that the specialist in psychiatry does hold a medical degree and is licensed as a physician.[2] Following the general internship, the physician enters upon specialty training in or under the auspices of a psychiatric hospital that has been approved for training in the specialty— in the United States, by the American Medical Association. Typically, specialist training takes 3 or more years. Formerly all this time could be spent in a mental hospital, but recently the qualifying board in the United States has advised that the training period shall include at least 6 months' supervised work in an outpatient setting.[3]

During the training period the resident has the opportunity to diagnose and treat all varieties of mental illnesses. Usually the patients he sees are so ill that hospitalization is required, though with more training taking place in outpatient services less severely ill patients are now more often included in the resident's experience. In addition to clinical experience, the residency also includes academic instruction in psychology, psychopathology, and the social sciences—more or less, depending upon the training center. Until very recently little has been taught about the growth and development and behavior of the normal personality; the accent has been upon the identification and treatment of the abnormal, and little concern has been given to the population from which the patient comes. The most influential centers are now training psychiatrists in this basic public health area, but such training will not have been within the experience of very many psychiatrists who have been specialists for any length of time.[4]

Psychiatric hospitals are generally rather isolated from population and medical centers. The country is supposed to be a healthier place than the city for mentally ill people, just as it has been supposed to be for tuberculosis patients. In addition, many mentally ill patients are not physically impaired, and for centuries it has been assumed that farm work had a particularly therapeutic value for them. Also, psychiatric hospitalization is a severe drain on the public purse, so that the farms surrounding most mental hospitals were and still are used to reduce the cost of feeding the patients in the hospital. Furthermore, the specialty has not been too cordially looked upon by medicine generally during the era of laboratory advances of the last hundred years; psychiatric illnesses are frequently very chronic and tend to remind physicians that there are still many unknowns to be learned. For all these reasons the psychiatrist is not likely to be able to learn a great deal about the population's mental hygiene problems. Until very recently he has had little opportunity and little stimulation to see and study mental hygiene needs of the community and the ways of meeting them.

After he has completed his residency, the psychiatrist in the United States practices for an additional 2 years and is then ready to be examined by a specialty board. If he passes, he is granted recognition by his colleagues as a certified specialist. At the present time the American Psychiatric Association has approximately 8,000 members (a very high percentage of practicing psychiatrists) and about 4,000 of these have been certified as specialists in psychiatry or in both psychiatry and neurology.

In his training the psychiatrist learns to use most of the known forms of treatment. The most important of these is probably psychotherapy, a process of multiple interviews centering on those events of the patient's life history that appear to have left persistent and destructive conflict in their wake. He is also trained to some extent in hospital (particularly ward) management, since it is recognized that the quality of morale in nurses and attendants in contact with patients is an extremely important factor in therapy. He is trained to administer the shock therapies, insulin and electroshock, among others, and to select those cases likely to profit by their administration. There is training concerning the brain operations which are occasionally useful in the control of symptoms in some types of cases, though the operations themselves are usually carried out by neurosurgeons.

Psychoanalysis is a specialty within a specialty and requires additional training in a psychoanalytic institute. This additional training goes on concomitantly with the practice of psychiatry. In addition there are certain academic courses in psychopathology and psychoanalytic therapy, both dominated very strongly by freudian theory or by that of Freud's followers of various grades of deviation from their founder. The psychiatrist wishing to qualify as a psychoanalyst must undergo a personal analysis, lasting rarely less than one year, of no less than three hourly sessions per week and frequently a longer period of more frequent sessions. He must then psychoanalyze several patients under supervision. The institute then certifies him as psychoanalyst, and he is considered qualified to practice this specialized type of therapy.[5]

Child psychiatry is another specialty within psychiatry which requires special training, replacing part of that already outlined or in addition to it. Such specialists usually work in a clinic under a qualified child psychiatrist for several years. As in other areas of psychiatric postgraduate education, there is some doubt about how much, if any, training in child psychiatry the ordinary psychiatrist should have. There is also doubt as to whether there is justification for considering this field as a subspecialty in the sense that the psychoanalysts have insisted on complete segregation from the general educational system in that specialty.[6]

The basic training necessary to qualify for examination by the American Board of Psychiatry and Neurology may be considered the aim of all but the most independent-minded physicians practicing psychiatry at the present time. It is probably not too unfair to judge the competence of psychiatrists by their progress in the training leading to Board qualification. However, many good psychiatrists are not interested in being judged competent by their fellows and refuse to subject themselves to these rather rigid patterns of training. It is fair to point out also that the objective of certification is relatively recent and that it has become far more important since certain large employers of psychiatrists in the United States have offered considerable salary differentials in favor of certified candidates.

The statements above regarding the training and experience of psychiatrists are generally true for the United States and, with some variation, for Canada and the United Kingdom. In continental Europe, psychiatrists are frequently trained and eventually certified through universities, according to various types of procedure depending upon the country. In other areas, medical specialization has not progressed so far and strict qualifications are not laid down.

Mental hygiene programs are difficult to evaluate. They cannot be gauged by such simple tests as the percentage of the population immunized against one or another specific disease. In most cases the only insurance the administrator has that his program of mental hygiene is as effective as it can be made with the knowledge now available is through the selection of a competent leader for his program. This leader usually must be selected on the basis of his training along the lines indicated above and, of course, on the usual personal and health qualifications. It should be apparent that most psychiatrists will not be equipped immediately to understand the objectives of public health and, generally speaking, will have little knowledge of the variety of clinical, epidemiological, preventive, and vital statistical services that health departments offer. This is likely to be true almost everywhere, though with some notable exceptions. The Minister of Health of Yugoslavia, for example, was for a time a psychiatrist, and the Director General of the World Health Organization from 1947 to 1953 was also a psychiatrist.

While the psychiatrist is likely to have little public health training, it must also be recognized that public health personnel is likely to be equally inadequately trained in psychiatry and mental hygiene. Just as psychiatric training is including more and more instruction and experience in community issues, so public health training is tending to include more useful material about interpersonal relationships in general and specific material about psychiatric problems and their management and control.[7] It would be unrealistic, however, at the present moment not to recognize the gulf to be crossed before the two types of specialists can work together profitably. Good will and a deep conviction of opportunity to be exploited for increasing the public health are necessary for the rapid development and smooth function of programs of mental hygiene under public health auspices.

The Clinical Psychologist. A psychologist is a college graduate with a varying amount of postgraduate training. The profession is aiming at having all its members practicing in the field hold Ph.D. degrees. This requires 4 years of postgraduate training, 3 of which are usually in residence in a university and one in a clinical setting, usually a psychiatric hospital or outpatient clinic, where the candidate works under supervision. He is accomplished in the use of a variety of tests of mental function and capacity including aptitude tests, intelligence tests, and the projective techniques. He is also trained to some extent in psychotherapy. In general, the psychologist's education gives considerable attention to research methods and design. In many places the evaluation and research aims of the psychiatric clinic are considered the psychologist's responsibility in large degree. Many psychologists now in practice have not received such complete training; usually these hold a master's degree in this field which is granted after 1 to 2 years of postgraduate education. In general, it may be said that the psychologist with the Ph.D. degree will consider himself sophisticated in the research area. He will expect to select and administer such tests as may be necessary to answer questions about the intellectual level and certain personality traits in the subject and to administer some types of psychological treatment.[8]

The issue of psychologists' doing treatment is a matter of considerable controversy at the present time. In general, the medical profession tends to be jealous of its treatment prerogatives and to resist any other profession sharing this responsibility except under fairly rigid supervision. Psychologists point out, on the other hand, that their training in personality function is more intense than that of many physicians, even psychiatrists, and that therefore they may well be competent to do psychotherapy. The national professional association of psychologists in the United States upholds the position of medical supervision for psychologists doing psychotherapy, but individual members of the profession frequently carry on quite independent therapeutic practice in most states. Historically, psychologists were originally assigned certain rather specific and restricted treatment problems that included considerable retraining therapy rather than general psychotherapy. They worked with reading disabilities, speech disorders, the retraining of aphasic patients, etc. Gradually, however, the full range of psychotherapy has come to be included in the aims of training for the profession. Evolution of the field is still going forward, not without considerable friction here and there, and the present situation is far from stable.[9]

Clinical psychologists are not in such short supply as psychiatrists, and their salaries are lower. Frequently a psychiatrist cannot be found who can or will work for the small salary provided in public budgets for the director of clinical services in mental health programs. Furthermore, a psychologist may be well trained in evaluating and meeting community needs. It may therefore be concluded that a psychologist should be accepted to administer the program. Under this arrangement, he would have the responsibility for preparing the community to make optimal use of such clinic facilities as might be available, recruiting clinicians, and performing the duties of the administrator of the program. He would also be responsible for such in-service training programs as might be contemplated for personnel of the health department and for meeting the demands of the public for educational material, talks, discussions, etc. Such a proposition can appear very attractive and in some cases it has worked fairly well. However, there are risks involved in having a nonmedical person ultimately responsible for treatment services. Furthermore, it is much more difficult for a nonmedical administrator to work with medical health officers. Some of the reasons for this may lie in prejudice and lack of appreciation of the professional training of the psychologist, but the fact remains that it is difficult for nonphysicians to lead physicians in new and relatively unfamiliar directions.

Many of the same considerations apply if any nonmedical persons are assigned as directors of clinics. Even if the psychiatrist doing the clinic work is a part-time employee and the other personnel full-time, as occasionally is the case, it is almost always wisest to keep leadership and authority in medical hands if possible. One of the great dangers in psychiatric work is that the personnel will be prejudiced in favor of one narrow concept of etiology or treatment. The medical background and the experience and training of the psychiatrist make him somewhat less likely to fall into this sort of trap than the psychologist, with his more narrow training.

These suggestions are not accepted by all. In selecting a leader for the mental hygiene program, however, the conclusion presented here is that the margin of safety lies in medical—psychiatric—leadership; similarly, that treatment by psychologists should not be done under health-department auspices except under medical supervision that is more than nominal. In public education the psychologist may be entirely competent to operate fairly independently.

The Psychiatric Social Worker. Psychiatric social work is a specialty within the field of general social work. It requires about the same length of training as does medical social work, with which the public health administrator may be more familiar. Over most of the country, psychiatric social workers are in very short supply.[10] The demand for their services has tended to raise salaries for them above rates for personnel of training of equal length and intensity in other specialties of social work and in nursing. This produces problems in setting merit-system requirements and in fixing salaries in some official agencies.

Psychiatric-social-work training leads to the master's degree and requires 2 years of education beyond the baccalaureate level. A considerable proportion of one of these years is spent in a field placement in a psychiatric hospital or, perhaps more usually at present, in outpatient clinic settings. Courses in psychology, anthropology, and sociology are usually included, as well as specific training in case taking and recording. Much attention is given to the intricacies of interpersonal relationships within the family and in other group settings. The interview, both as an investigative and as a therapeutic tool, is perhaps the principal concern of psychiatric-social-work training. Most of the schools of social work teaching this specialty tend to teach psychoanalytic psychopathology and psychology, though this is by no means universally true.[11]

This specialty developed as an extension of the staff of the psychiatric hospital into the community from which the patient comes, and into the home of the patient. The psychiatric social worker was originally a field worker used to collect pertinent information concerning the situations surrounding the onset and progress of the illness, so that it would be available to the treating psychiatrist. The value of the information-collecting interviews proved to be much greater than that of the information gathered, however. The worker was found to be able to change attitudes on the part of families so that they were better able to assist in the patient's therapy and better able to plan for his return to home and community when his condition improved.[12] One result of this finding has been an increasing use of psychiatric social workers in "family-care" programs in which certain patients hitherto regarded as permanently hospitalized are able to be placed in their own or in foster families. These programs relieve the community of the greater expense of hospital care but, more importantly, they make possible the successful rehabilitation of a considerable number of patients.[13]

With the development of the child-guidance clinic, psychiatric social work took on a different orientation. When the patient is a child, information concerning him is much more important than when an adult is under treatment, since the child is not able to communicate his difficulties directly in many instances. It was early discovered that psychiatric symptoms in children are often reflections of family disorganization or of psychopathological reactions of one or both parents. Therapy practiced with the child is likely to be ineffective unless the parents are also intimately involved in the treatment procedure. Traditionally, the psychiatric social worker is assigned the task of treating the parents. It is interesting to speculate why the nonmedically trained person should have therapeutic responsibility for dealing with what most agree is the etiology of the child's difficulty while the psychiatrist treats the symptom, the child. There seems to be no real reason for this time-honored method of operation, and its wisdom is being questioned in an increasing number of clinics. Nevertheless it is at present the most common pattern.[14]

Therapeutic work done by psychiatric social workers, unlike that done by psychologists, is rarely questioned, possibly because the work is not usually directly with the patient himself but with the family. Another factor is that the psychiatric social worker has shown less tendency to set up as an independent therapist. The whole training in this profession is toward working as a member of a team under the leadership of a psychiatrist. Supervision of less experienced workers by more experienced ones is a matter of considerable importance in training and in continuing professional work in agencies employing more than a very few workers. This profession has made, along with nursing, contributions to the practice and theory of the supervisory relationship which many other professions, including psychiatry, have used extensively in the design of training programs. Perhaps because of these traditions the administrator has little problem with overaggressive workers in this field requesting larger responsibilities than he feels they are able to carry. The opposite difficulty is perhaps less uncommon; the psychiatric social worker may have been so much supervised and so exactly trained in a specific pattern of working that he is not free to adapt his skills easily to new sorts of situations. The administrator may find psychiatric social workers timorous in the face of working alone in isolated areas where the profession had been previously unknown and where the team relationship is very different from that in a full-time urban clinic with a wide range of social services. Perhaps the differences in the relationship of medicine to psychiatric social workers and psychologists also has something to do with the fact that psychologists are more frequently males while social workers are typically females.

For reasons similar to those discussed earlier in relation to psychologists, there may be the temptation to appoint a psychiatric social worker as director of mental health programs. In general, the same objections hold. Some psychiatric social workers receive specific training in group discussion and education techniques and are particularly suited for this sort of mental health educational programs. Some have talent in administration. But there remain the problems inherent in nonmedical leadership for programs designed as prevention for disease, whatever its kind, and the practical problem of effective rapport in medical programming when one of the planners is nonmedical and is, furthermore, recognized as acting as a substitute for a medical man.

The Mental Health Nurse Consultant. Specialist consultants in public health nursing are recognized as important in the development of new programs involving the daily work of staff public health nurses. Usually such consultants are not to be regarded as having a separate place in nursing divisions for very extended periods of time. Rather, they will function for a period of years until the new program and its objectives and techniques become integral parts of the generalized nursing procedures of the department. The specialist consultant then would become a generalized consultant—a role she does not, of course, completely abandon even while acting in the specialist consultant capacity. To fill this need in the present period of rapid expansion of mental hygiene interest and application in health departments, specialization in mental hygiene has been developed for public health nurses. The rather cumbersome title "mental health nurse consultant" is usually assigned the position.[15]

This specialist is a nurse with training as a public health nurse beyond that received in nursing school. She has a baccalaureate degree and in addition is experienced in staff nursing and in nursing supervision. The academic requirements to reach this level of education usually include at least one year beyond the R.N. certification. The specialist training in most schools and universities offering such education requires an additional 18 months' work, about half of it in residence at the educational center, the other half in field work under its general supervision. The courses now supplying this training show a healthy variation in programs offered. Some offer considerable training in basic public health sciences, some in nursing education, some in social sciences and in the techniques and philosophy of social work. Some stress the inclusion of material in hospital psychiatric nursing more than others. In all courses, however, there is in common stress on psychodynamics, growth and development of the personality, and on community organization for dealing with mental health problems. There is also in common a field placement, frequently involving two types of experience. The first of these is the functioning of a well-organized outpatient psychiatric clinic including children in its case load. Here the student is usually under psychiatric-social-work supervision. The second placement is in a health department and includes observation of and participation in the work of a practicing mental health consultant.[16]

This nurse specialist is a new type of personnel, the first graduate having completed the course about 1948. The exact limits of her field of effective work are not yet clearly worked out. The first descriptions of the work of such nurses in the field were presented at the 1953 meeting of the American Public Health Association, though more or less predictive statements appeared earlier.[17] The consultants now employed appear to act in varied capacities. Primarily they are consultants to other staff members on problem cases. They may help in making the decision as to whether referral to psychiatric clinics or other social agency is required. They help design patterns whereby cases may be handled by the staff nurse whose knowledge and techniques may be sharpened so that this is possible. In some cases, the consultant carries responsibility for in-service education. In this capacity she may orient new nurses toward the mental hygiene objectives of programs as they enter the department. She may teach in local health departments or districts about to get psychiatric clinical service on how best to use it, what information about cases referred will be most useful to the clinicians, problems of record keeping and forwarding, scheduling appointments, and such matters. She aids in preparing the nurses to teach the community to use its psychiatric resources more efficiently. Conversely, she may work with the clinical group, teaching nursing and health department interests and activities so that it may learn to make itself most useful to the particular community it is designed to serve.

In relation to her colleagues in the administrative chain, she may be a member of a team to prepare a manual on nursing in catastrophe, or prepare material for inclusion in a manual on the care of various types of crippled children, the care of prenatal patients, etc. Personnel selection and maintenance problems are other fields in which her advice may be sought. In short, she represents mental hygiene in the planning and operation of nursing services, in both centrally and peripherally functioning departments.

The question as to whether the nurse consultant should have responsibility for patient care in the outpatient setting remains unsettled. Some feel the ordinary clinic team of psychiatrist, psychologist, and psychiatric social worker should be expanded to include a specially trained public health nurse. Others feel that the consultant can be more effective if she works with the staff nurses seeing cases than if she carries a case load of her own. This is an area of active experimentation at present, and the interpretation of the experiments is far from clear.[18] If a preference were to be risked, however, it would be that the consultant nurse not be directly involved with cases under therapy. A possible exception might be where she feels she cannot maintain her work satisfactions and expertness unless she has some supervised clinical responsibility. This should be limited to a definitely part-time activity and should not be any major part of the mental hygiene program of the health department. The nurse consultant should remain primarily identified as a public health nurse, not a member of a specialized clinical service. To do otherwise loses the opportunity for her to influence the wide range of programs and policies of the health department. As has been indicated, not all interested in the development of the nurse mental health consultant agree with these tentative conclusions.

It is clear from the discussion thus far that the consultant is considered as operating at an administrative level above that of the local public health unit. If the local units were counties, the consultant or consultants would be at the state level; if a city with health districts, at the city rather than the district level. This, of course, will obviously depend upon the size of the local unit and the amount of administrative autonomy it is allowed. It must be noted that the position of mental health nurse consultant has as yet been established in only a small number of administrative units. It is recommended that more such positions be established so that the effectiveness of these consultants can be more generally apparent.

The nurse trained as a nurse consultant in mental hygiene is agreed to be more valuable as a generalized consultant or as a nurse supervisor than one without this special training. A number of them are functioning under these titles by preference, but some also because training has outstripped the number of positions open to them, a matter of administrative balance that needs correction.

THE CLINICAL TEAM CONCEPT

Development of psychiatric outpatient clinics in the last thirty-five years has been marked by the identification of the team of psychiatrist, psychologist, and psychiatric social worker as the clinical service unit.[19] In general, personnel from these three professions trained in the last ten years will have had some education and experience with the team relationships. If placed in a community, they will be able to offer sound diagnostic and therapeutic service—granting of course, the usual variation in personality that must be considered in all personnel selection. Many team members individually may also have some grasp of mental health opportunities and needs in the community, but the team has developed very few techniques for meeting these needs as a teamwork job. These functions are more likely to be carried by individual members. The extension of the team beyond clinical service to include public education is being attempted in many areas, but little progress has been made either in practice or in research in this area. The health administrator will be wise not to expect a mental health team, as a team, to respond to these needs, at least not until all the members have become educated by familiarity with the community and with the other services offered by the health department. The clinical team developed as a clinical service; to extend beyond this will require further development.

Because this team has within itself sufficient personnel to satisfy the needs of most of its members for professional and social contact, it has less drive to identify itself with the rest of the department of health than would otherwise be the case. For this and other reasons, there are frequent complaints that the team actively excludes the health department personnel. One factor tending toward isolation is the very frequent insistence on confidentiality of records. A locked file from which the staff nurse and the health officer himself are excluded is a definite deterrent to communication between the health department and its mental hygiene team. Psychiatric records containing highly personal and intimate detail cannot be left open for all to peruse. To put informative abstracts in the family case folder is a duplication of effort to some extent, and the writing of an expurgated version is not likely to be a challenge to the workers concerned. It is hoped that some day the important medical facts in cases, whether they concern the patient's adultery or his tuberculin reactions, may be equally noninflammatory. Meanwhile, communication will have to be maintained by verbal transmission of necessary information and the recording of abstracts.

This same issue is a bothersome one in regard to case conferences. Does one vary the content of the history if the staff nurse is present, or is the full record discussed? How much does one say if the child-patient's schoolteacher or principal is present? Does the family physician, if he responds to his invitation to attend, get all the history? Or does he get just part of it, which may be insufficient to meet his need to understand what goes on and thus possibly leave him frustrated and unwilling to come to conferences again? Is there any difference in the amount of information given to a social worker and that shared with a nurse? Do secretaries who type records gossip about the material they have seen? If so, are all records to be kept in script, which all too frequently is illegible and difficult to summarize?

In general, experience shows very few instances in which psychiatric case material has "leaked" to the detriment of the health department. Recorded information loses much of its gossipy character once it has been written. The impression—and hope—is that the danger of sharing records with health department and other responsible professional personnel has been exaggerated. In any locality, however, the decisions will have to be made jointly by the health officer and the clinic team.

The three-profession team is not a *sine qua non* of outpatient psychiatric service, though it is probably the optimal arrangement at present. The position taken here is that the psychiatrist is essential and that direct psychiatric services of therapeutic intent should not be undertaken without this member of the team. Beyond this there is much reasonable variation to be experimented with. While it is, perhaps, a little uneconomical, therapeutic efforts of the psychiatric social worker can be carried by the psychiatrist or the psychologist, the latter under supervision, and the investigative part of her work by a public health nurse, who may also be useful in carrying out the therapeutic plans. The psychometric function of the psychologist can be taken by the psychiatrist where necessary, or by the psychiatric social worker, with, of course, the training and efficiency of the tester being taken into consideration in evaluating the results. His therapeutic functions can be divided betwen the psychiatrist and social worker, or assigned to specialists such as speech or reading instructors in the school system, where psychometricians may also be found. Variation from the standard pattern is likely to make the clinic ineligible for membership in the American Association of Psychiatric Clinics for Children,[20] but this is rarely important to a group operating locally unless it includes the definitive training of specialists among its aims. The standard clinic team, developed independently of public health departments and primarily in urban settings, need not be presumed to be the only or necessarily the best organization to deliver services in a rural local health department. But it is a standard, and deviations from it should be approached experimentally and after careful consideration of resources in relation to the needs to be met.

SUMMARY

Mental hygiene depends primarily on the attitude-changing possibilities of communication between personnel of various degrees of training and the population the needs of which are to be met. Specialized personnel available are psychiatrists, psychologists, psychiatric social workers, and mental health nurse consultants. The first three of these are trained to work together as a team in diagnostic and therapeutic efforts. In some cases the nurse is added to the team, but more generally she acts as a consultant within the health department and as liaison agent between it and the clinical service. Excluding the nurse, these persons are usually uninformed about the extent and complexity of health departments and about the functions of its personnel, just as the health department personnel is not cognizant of the detail of psychiatric work. An initial period of orientation, duing which some frictions will develop, is to be expected. Isolation of the psychiatric clinic team happens easily and is to be avoided by making case discussion as complete as possible and capitalizing on all persons in health department and the community who are able to contribute to the understanding and therapy of cases. The complete team is not necessary for all clinic services, though medical leadership is considered essential. The psychiatric clinical team has no techniques for community services directed at all the population; it serves this need largely through the education of key professional persons in the community. Individual team members may have value in programs of broad community education or preventive programs.

REFERENCES

1. Stevenson, G. S.: "Dynamic Considerations in Community Functions," *Ment. Hyg.* 34:531–546 (1950).
2. Redlich, F. C.: "What the Citizen Knows about Psychiatry," *Ment. Hyg.* 34:64–79 (1950).
3. *Information for Applicants, Rules and Regulations,* The American Board of Psychiatry and Neurology, Inc., 102 Second Avenue, S.W., Rochester, Minn., 1953.
4. Whitehorn, J. C. (ed.): *The Psychiatrist: His Training and Development,* American Psychiatric Association, Washington, D.C., 1953.
5. Ebaugh, F. G., and C. A. Rymer: *Psychiatry in Medical Education,* p. 380–382, The Commonwealth Fund, New York, 1942.
6. Whitehorn, Ref. 4, chap. 7, pp. 101–113.
7. *Conference on Training in Public Health Mental Health, June 2–3, 1952* (mimeographed), The Harvard School of Public Health, Boston, 1952.
8. "Training in Clinical Psychology," *Transactions of the First Conference, May 27–28, 1947,* The Josiah Macy, Jr., Foundation, New York, 1947.
9. The Committee on Clinical Psychology: *The Relation of Clinical Psychology to Psychiatry,* Group for the Advancement of Psychiatry, Report 14, Topeka, Kans., July, 1949.
10. Whitehorn, Ref. 4, p. 155.
11. "Education for Psychiatric Social Work," *Proceedings of the Dartmouth Conference,* American Association of Psychiatric Social Workers, New York, June, 1950.

12. Meyer, Adolf: "Historical Sketch and Outlook of Psychiatric Social Work," *Hosp. Social Serv.* 5:221–225 (1922).

13. DeWitt, H.: "The Function of the Social Worker in the Total Treatment Program in a State Hospital," *Am. J. Psychiat.* 105:298–304 (1948).

14. Witmer, H. L.: *Psychiatric Interviews with Children,* The Commonwealth Fund, New York, 1946.

15. *Report of Conference on Mental Hygiene Education for Public Health Nurses, November* 14–18, 1949, National Organization for Public Health Nursing, New York, 1949.

16. National League of Nursing Education: *Descriptive Criteria for Evaluation of Advanced Programs of Study in Psychiatric Nursing and Mental Hygiene,"* The League, New York, 1949.

17. Boone, Dorothy: "Mental Health Nursing Consultation," paper read at the 81st annual meeting of the American Public Health Association, New York, 1953, to be published.

18. Henderson, Adele L.: "Activities of a Mental Health Nurse," *Pub. Health Rep.* 65:331–336 (1950).

19. Greenberg, H. A.: *Child Psychiatry in the Community,* G. P. Putnam's Sons, New York, 1950.

20. *History, Purposes and Organization of the American Association of Psychiatric Clinics for Children,* The Association, 1790 Broadway, New York (no date available).

CHAPTER FOUR

Techniques in Mental Hygiene: Methods

Perhaps the main tool to be used in mental hygiene programs is people of various skills, from the highly specialized psychiatric treatment team to the confident and comfortable community figure—the corner druggist, the midwife, the executive with a reputation for having his office door open. Leadership will usually have to be recruited from the groups described in Chap. 3. In this chapter the kinds of things this personnel and others may be expected to do, exclusive of their clinical duties as diagnosticians and therapists, will be discussed. The techniques and methods described here will not be the stock-in-trade of every psychiatrist, psychologist, and social worker, though a constantly increasing number of these professionals are gaining such skills in training or through experience.

All the techniques to be described require considerable skill, and for many no small amount of natural aptitude and talent as well. No one person is able to handle all of them with equal perfection, and many will be found deficient in one or another. There are those who can write effectively but who speak poorly; training will improve their effectiveness as speakers, but these will probably lag behind the talented person who seems to speak with little effort and with great effect. One who can lecture to large audiences with confidence may find himself mute and ill at ease in the more intimate setting of the small discussion group that meets repeatedly. Some are able to do radio work well but fail when they must face a live audience.

METHODS FOR CHANGING ATTITUDES

In mental hygiene work involving larger numbers of people, there is a dilemma concerning the leader of a group. Should he be expert in the content of his field, what shall be taught, so that he will never or rarely be caught "off base"? Or should he be highly skilled in the technical procedures of group leadership and dynamics, perhaps being inadequately prepared concerning the material under discussion? Obviously, the ideal is to have both the knowledge and the skill to get it across, but this is rather hard to find in a single person.

In recent years there has been a tendency to feel that group leadership is a skill that can be exercised independent of the subject matter to be discussed. If a group leader is clever enough with his techniques, he can draw out of the group before him or from resource persons the knowledge necessary to solve the problems posed and need not know anything more than the bare essentials about the field himself. There is no question that it is occasionally possible to bring together a group of highly trained scientists from various fields, put with them a leader from still a different scientific field, and obtain thereby a high production of new ideas for research. It is doubtful that such a group could successfully be led, however, by someone who was not well grounded in some scientific field and had enough general knowledge to know what was going on scientifically as well as in terms of interchanges, emotional or otherwise, between the persons of the group.

This is, of course, an essential problem in health education and, in spite of the success of that specialty in public health, cannot yet be said to be settled. There is always the problem as to whether the limited time available for training should be given more to the "what" or to the "how" of health education, and the answer is always a compromise. Some schools are unwilling to make any compromise in the direction of sacrificing time from gaining knowledge to learning how to transmit it to others and thus train no health educators at all. No school goes all out for education in methods of teaching only, though critics occasionally accuse some of doing so.

Moreover, there is a danger that method will be confused with content and tend actually to replace it. This is not likely to be the case when the subject matter is tuberculosis or nutrition, but it does happen in mental hygiene. Here it is easy to assume that if the audience "talks" some mental health promotion has been accomplished. This is not always the case; it depends upon what is discussed and with what intensity of feeling and sense of identification the discussion goes forward. Satisfaction in the fact that a method makes it possible for people to talk together may lead to a false conclusion that it is good for the group as well as good method. This may reflect inadequate clarification of the goal of the meeting in terms of content and attitude changing. The person attempting to use the various techniques in the field of mental hygiene should be clear as to the objective to be reached, and methods should be selected on the basis of the aim and the content to be taught; method or technique is always subservient to content and aim.[1]

THE AIMS OF MENTAL HEALTH EDUCATION

In general education, the primary aim is to impart a particular body of information to a person or persons. It is generally recognized that it is much easier to accomplish this if the person wants to learn the subject matter and if it is presented in an interesting fashion. To this extent his emotional involvement is sought, his intellectual curiosity aroused. The attitude toward the subject matter is a help toward the primary objective of learning it, not a goal in itself.

In mental hygiene teaching the content is frequently secondary, the attitude primary. While it is a fine thing for parents to know that there is a period of negativism in normal child development, it is much more important that they reach an attitude of appreciation that this "no-saying" period is a step toward adult consciousness of individuality and toward the ability to make decisions. The content—the fact of the predictability of the period of negativism—is perhaps less important than the parents' appreciation that the child has a developing personality for which they have some responsibility.

In mental hygiene work with students at any level, postgraduate or picked at random from the general population, attitude change will always accompany and be an integral part of the teaching of content material. The aim will always be to teach more than fact; it will also be to mold attitude so that the facts learned can be useful to the person learning them. Blocks standing in the way of change of attitude must be removed so that changes in behavior can occur. It is frequently a matter of ethical judgment to decide when there is sufficient scientific evidence to justify an effort to change behavior.

IN-SERVICE EDUCATION

A public health department is an industry. It is a peculiar industry in that its "profits" are not in money but in lives saved and discomfort due to disease avoided through preventive measures or alleviated through treatment and through the promotion of health. Like most industries, however, the public health agency employs many different types of personnel, professional and otherwise, in the production of better health for the community.[2]

The product of the health department is obtained partly by impersonal means. People are not very highly emotionally involved with dams and pipes once good water is supplied them. Once sewers are in, they become more or less impersonal projects that someone has administrative responsibility for, but little more. Sewers and public water supplies infrequently involve direct contact between health department personnel and the individuals who use such services. Perhaps it is because of this that few health departments are called upon to administer these services any longer and have little responsibility for them other than routinely checking their efficiency.

By far the larger part of public health activity involves influencing people's actions rather directly. This extends from inducing the restaurant owner to keep his place of business sanitary to persuading a mother to have her child immunized. Tasks of this sort inevitably involve a personal relationship with the individuals served. Such relationships depend on the attitudes of the personnel involved. The activity may be on an authoritarian basis. It may be done with the lackadaisical attitude of getting a job done, or with superficial enthusiasm based on hoping to get approval from the supervisor. On the other hand, there may be a healthy attitude of appreciation for the total goal of the health department, appreciation of the opportunities and limitations of the persons to be served, and a genuine aim of winning their cooperation.

The persons who carry out the services of the health department that involve meeting the public will probably reflect the patterns of relationship within the department. They will treat the person needing service somewhat as they are treated by their immediate supervisors. The supervisor will carry down the sort of handling he receives from his superior. It is this, of course, that makes it so important that the ultimate leader, usually the health officer, be acquainted with personnel management as well as other technical matters. Where the producing agent must produce new and different behavior in people, the way he is dealt with by the management hierarchy will determine the quality of his contact at the level of production.[3]

Recognition of this fact has resulted in many health departments' employing the techniques to be described below upon themselves. The aim is to enrich understanding of interpersonal relationships within the department in order to increase the efficiency of the work at the effector level, contact with individuals and groups in the community itself. Some health departments take this into consideration in planning the administrative position of the mental health consultant. In California, for example, he is an adviser to the health officer.[4] Appointment at such a level was considered to be an aid in his establishing contacts with bureau heads, none of whom would directly outrank him. From this vantage, the mental health consultant could conduct discussion groups with any level of personnel in the department. This sort of thinking is most appropriate when the basic aim of the mental health program is the horizontal one of influencing the way the whole department does its work through influencing attitudes of personnel. It may be less appropriate when the aim also includes a vertical program of clinical service and mental health education for the public. In this instance, it may be more efficient to have the mental hygiene leader in the "line" organization rather than a "staff" position, and have his program under the general supervision of some chief whose interests include a number of other "vertical" or direct-service programs. Such a chief will be able to help the mental hygienist to find his way administratively in developing his service program. This sort of administrative arrangement does not necessarily interfere with horizontal influencing of other bureaus or divisions of the department, providing, of course, that staff meetings of the whole department are held frequently enough to maintain acquaintance with the various leaders and the development of genuinely common departmental aims.[5]

The horizontal program in mental hygiene in the health department may be carried out through many different techniques. Some have used publications, posters, bulletin boards, etc. Some use series of seminars on interpersonal relationships, a technique also used widely in other industries as will be described in Chap. 15. Some have used the institute or workshop, a series of sessions extending from 3 days to 2 weeks of intensive learning, consulting, and group discussion around some central theme.[6] Some are designed to meet the needs of the health officer, who is then expected to carry his newly found knowledge and attitudes into the leadership job he holds in the department, thereby influencing the attitudes and behavior of those he leads.[7] Some institutes bring together selected groups from the local departments, e.g., health officers and their chief nurses.[8] Nurses, being particularly avid for aids to increase the efficiency with which they meet their case loads, have perhaps been most active in intensive training projects. In some instances meetings, including small group discussion sessions, have been planned to bring together the established health department professionals and the newer addition, the mental hygiene clinic teams.[9] In still other instances, local health departments have organized series of meetings in which all the personnel of the health department, including secretaries, clerks, telephone operators, and janitors, get together regularly with a skilled leader to discuss current troublesome cases. Such complete staff meetings are likely to be helpful in establishing the primary concept that everyone in the department has a contribution to make to its total aims.

The type of content for such institutes and discussion groups will be detailed in later chapters. The point here is that the techniques and

methods to be described are not always to be considered "for somebody else," but may be useful also within the department itself. In one
health department it was found that the physical examination for
nurses, regardless of their age at employment, had omitted a pelvic
examination. At the same time, the department was running cancer-
detection clinics. This sort of rejection by the health department of
what is good for the public is not contemplated in the discussion of
techniques of nonclinical mental hygiene methods.

NONCLINICAL TECHNIQUES

These techniques range from those which do not involve direct contact between personnel and audience, through such relatively impersonal contacts as the lecturer before a large audience, to the most intensive type of attitude-changing work known, the interview between two
people.

Posters. Posters have been used in mental hygiene for two general
purposes: (1) to gain attention for the field; (2) to put across some particular idea. The poster is cordially distrusted by many health educators; it appears to be quite unpopular. Nevertheless it is a time-honored
technique and will be discussed briefly.

In general, it is accepted that posters should attempt to get across one
single and uncomplicated idea. Posters designed to gain attention for a
field usually seek some symbol that will crowd a maximum of context
into a very small space. Thus the mailed hand and attacking sword of
the cancer group is designed to mobilize all the associations of knight-
errantry with their high-minded attack upon evil and, of course, also
the concept of self-sacrifice to gain the grail of the control of cancer. The
National Association for Mental Health has recently adopted a ringing
bell as its symbol. Here, the aim was to carry a message of joyous hope-
fulness into a field long dominated by stigma, "snake-pit" hospitals, and
public neglect. Such symbols attempt to condense around a health field
as many preexisting helpful contextual ideas as can be managed.[10]

Frequently, posters attempt to attach some idea of urgency to the
symbol. This often takes the form of a simple, stark statement of the
toll the disease in question is taking from the population. Mental hygiene, also, has made use of its terrifying statistics for this purpose. A
few years ago it was a fact that one person out of 20 would spend some
time in a mental hospital during his lifetime, or, using four as the
average family, one family out of five would have a member a patient in
a mental hospital sometime during the family's life. Actually, these
figures are too low for some states; in New York in 1949 the correct

figure was that one person in every 12 would spend some time as a patient in a mental hospital.[11] This more modern figure is now being used.[12]

There has been a great deal of argument over whether or not these techniques are actually effective. Their immediate purpose usually is raising money but also may be helping people to decide to have some diagnostic procedure carried out. If effective, do they arouse so much anxiety that their total and long-range effect is bad? No definite conclusions can be drawn, but Aesop pointed out long ago that monotonous frightening of people led to disastrous distrust eventually. The public will tolerate only just so much of scare technique; thereafter they will make a joke of it or resent it and reject the program arousing it.

Another symbol frequently used is less abstract—a patient who arouses pity. The crippled child under treatment has been used with tremendous effect by the National Foundation for Infantile Paralysis. Such a symbol has not been found very useful in mental hygiene, though for some educational purposes a talented artist can produce pictures that will bring out desire to help relieve loneliness and suffering.[13] But it is hard to portray the suffering inherent for patient and family where the crippling is mental deficiency, and this sort of poster has not been used very extensively in mental health work.

The content poster has been used to some extent, but there are many difficulties, largely related to the issue of facts and related attitudes referred to earlier. The situations to be dealt with are too complex and too delicate to yield to the simplification demanded for effectual presentation on a poster. It is no more effective to say "don't worry" to a worried mother on a poster than it is in a superficial interview. The interview may be deepened and enriched by further talk and continued contact, but the poster can go no farther than the blatant suggestion. Posters teaching the limits of some feature of child development have also been used, but again it is hard to make so simple a statement as is demanded by the poster technique stand up to a test of scientific accuracy. Too great compromise with accuracy will inevitably defeat any poster; no one will long respect the oversimplification of what is obviously complicated.

Although effectual content-type posters are certainly not impossible in the mental health field, no very successful ones have as yet been produced. On the other hand, the attention-attracting devices of the symbol, particularly when used as a means of raising money, would appear to be as applicable in the mental health field as elsewhere.

Pamphlet Literature. Pamphlet literature in mental hygiene has been used very widely and with some success, at least so far as getting pamphlets read is concerned. The pamphlet is a much more flexible device than the poster. It can be a very short, "punchy" piece, almost posterlike in its effect, or it can be a much longer document or even a series of pamphlets directed to the same audience. An example of the first type is *Mental Health Is* 1, 2, 3, published by the National Association for Mental Health.[14] The second type is perhaps best illustrated by the Children's Bureau booklet, *Your Child from One to Six,* which has obviously met the needs of mothers over the years, since it has sold millions of copies.[15] Another pamphlet of this type is the school mental hygiene pamphlet published by the American Medical Association.[16] The best examples of the third type are the multiple pieces produced for parents of young children. Of these, the best-known is the "Pierre the Pelican" series produced by the Louisiana Mental Health Association and distributed by many health departments to new parents at monthly intervals through the child's first year.[17] A second series has been developed for the pregnant woman to prepare her for the events of the advancing pregnancy and for delivery.[18] Some evaluative studies have been done on the "Pierre" series which indicate that it is likely to be carefully read by those who receive it.[19,20]

It will be noted that the last types of pamphlets are directed at specific audiences—the mother of a child from 1 to 6, the parents of an infant, the couple actually in the process of producing a child. There appears to be no longer any doubt that if a pamphlet is to be maximally effective in doing more than attracting attention to the general field of mental hygiene, it will have to be directed to a particular audience with known and rather specific needs that it attempts to fill, in terms both of knowledge and of attitude to be taken toward the problem and the knowledge given. This point will come up again in the discussion of anticipatory guidance technique in Part 2.

Another sort of pamphlet in mental hygiene, not yet used very extensively, is the comic-book type. This technique was first used in venereal-disease health education, where it appeared to show satisfactory results, though no thorough evaluative studies were done.[21] In 1950 the New York State Mental Hygiene Commission produced a comic book in the mental health field which appears to have had fair success as measured by sales. It was based on the "Blondie" series of cartoons and was drawn by the artist who originated that series on the comedy of everyday family happenings.[22] There is some doubt whether the somewhat moralistic conclusions the author and sponsors present as mental hygiene principles in this series is as good practical mental health as the daily promotion of the understanding of human foibles by this artist that appears in the newspapers.

There is an immense literature of pamphlets in mental hygiene. Many agencies tend to feel that they must produce their own material in this field, that nothing already written will quite do the job they need done. In some instances this may be true, but in many it reflects inadequate study of what is already available and results in unnecessary duplication of effort. It seems wise for a department or agency that is, as most are, short of funds to concentrate on a few items for distribution to specific audiences who have problems that are likely to give rise to a need for specific information. Such pamphlets may be made available through appropriate clinic services, e.g. in the prenatal clinic and furnished to practicing obstetricians, or in well-baby clinics and furnished to those physicians in the community doing well-child care. Finally, there might be one general piece for distribution through the literature racks that most health departments still have in evidence. These remain because literature does disappear from them, probably taken by people who find there something that meets their needs but who are unable to bring themselves to ask for help more directly. It is obvious that this general piece should contain references to other more specific materials which can be obtained.

Newspapers and Magazine Literature. It is in this field that there is the greatest difficulty in distinguishing between public education and the stimulation of public interest, sometimes called propaganda. Unlike pamphlets which remain on the shelf or can be replaced, newspaper and magazine material is very evanescent. It must make its point in a day or a week or a month, after which it will no longer be available to influence anyone. In some cases, even in newspapers, it will be possible to run several articles that may be followed as a series, but even here each article must be able to stand alone and the missing of one article must not vitiate the sequence. It appears next to impossible to sustain interest in serial articles in monthly magazines, however successful this technique has been in presentation of novels. For the most part, each article must be complete in itself and must be arresting enough to catch initial interest and carry enough continuous impact to ensure its being read to the end. As such writing requires great skill, it frequently is done collaboratively by a mental hygienist and a writer, rather than by either alone.

Usually, newspaper publicity is confined to announcements and reports of special activities. The latter can be longer, combined with pictures and otherwise made appealing so that the reader will be encouraged to add his efforts or contribution to the program reported. Such feature stories are not difficult to place provided there really is something to report that is newsworthy or appealing. Editors are usually easily persuaded to print material that is for the good of the public when they can put it into a form that will attract readers as well. They are also usually willing to print announcements of meetings and will frequently report a meeting quite fully when it is on a matter of general interest.

The range of articles in magazines is extremely wide, from authoritative and carefully prepared statements by leaders of the field, in the more responsible magazines, to the trash of some of the pulps. The latter usually are weighted heavily with articles on sex, which is frequently almost exactly equated with psychology and psychiatry. Hypnosis is another popular subject, as are articles purporting to be helpful for increasing the effectiveness of personality functioning. The effect of such material is entirely unevaluated. It must meet some very definite and poignantly felt human needs, since it appears to sell in profitable quantities. It would probably be a worthwhile project for some reputable mental hygienist to attempt to compete in appealing to the public which reads such magazines with scientifically sound material.

This has been done in at least one instance with the "advice to the lovelorn" type of column that appears in many newspapers. Many of the letters received by the authors of such columns reveal genuine and deep concern on the part of the writers, and the advice given is acted upon in some instances. The psychiatrist or other responsible person in mental hygiene usually will have nothing to do with such situations, arguing that he cannot get enough information from a letter to make a reply and remain within the ethical requirements of his profession. Mace,[23] however, came to the conclusion that this offered an opportunity, and he has managed such a column, along with more traditional type of marriage counseling service, for several years. No strict evaluation has been possible, but he does reach the conclusion that the task is a worthwhile one and that professionally ethical advice is probably superior to that of a cynical newspaperman.

Mental hygienists with talent for writing generally reach somewhat the same conclusion—that someone is going to satisfy the public's desire for information, and it had better be done by a qualified and ethical person than by unqualified ones. Physicians frequently are hesitant about writing for the public, fearing criticisms from their colleagues, who may accuse them of attempting to build up their reputations in ways that violate medical codes of ethics. Generally speaking, these erstwhile very strict codes are tending to be relaxed in order that public education may be furthered through responsible magazine articles.[24] Here, too, there is real need for leads and for subject matter that is eye-catching and interest-arousing; this fact is frequently disturbing to the carefully ethical physician. There are undoubtedly a few physician mental hygiene writers who are not bothered by such considerations, but there are many also who have to force themselves to the decision that public education is necessary and that a certain amount of dignity may have to be forgone in supplying the need.

The Exposé. This type of newspaper and magazine mental hygiene writing requires special discussion. Usually, the public official has little or no control over it; it is generally imposed upon him from outside, though he may have invited it as a means of arousing public opinion. Thus far, such writing has been vivid reporting in words and in pictures of the unfortunate conditions that may be found in mental hospitals, particularly those that have been neglected by the public. (This discussion applies equally to training schools for delinquents, schools for mental deficients, detention homes, and the like.) The newspaper or magazine sets off an orgy of recrimination, usually directed at the public officials in charge of hospitals and often unfairly costing them their jobs. In many cases this is merely a displacement of guilt the public feels because of its own neglect, on a convenient scapegoat, though in some cases gross inefficiency and, much more rarely, clear venality may be uncovered. In exposé writing, the reporter usually is not concerned with making a balanced presentation. His interest in accuracy is only to the extent that he does not underestimate the bad; the good about the institution he is exposing does not concern him, and he is quite frank about this usually. The actual situation may include many devoted people who spend their lives in serving patients. Those in the community who know this are often in a quandary. Should they defend these employees publicly and thus tend to assuage the public furor? Or should they allow it to run its unfair course in order that maximal improvement of conditions for the institution shall result through increased appropriations and more generous personnel assignments? Shall the informed person point out the good the hospital does, even with its faults, and thus help restore the confidence of patients and their families in it, though risking at the same time the dilution of pressure for improvements at the level of political action? These are exceedingly difficult questions to answer. It would appear wise, however, for the administrator of an institution under such exposé procedure to see to it that his staff understands the dynamics involved in the usual public excoriation and that they can be understandingly content to "take it" for a while in the hope that the hospital system will eventually be improved. Similarly, physicians, nurses, and social workers—in fact, all the personnel who come into contact with patients and their families—should make redoubled efforts to help these recipients of hospital services also understand the situation.

Thus far, probably because they are too new and too small to attract such intense public interest, outpatient treatment and mental health promotion programs have not been the the subject of public exposés. It might be hoped that one day they will be important enough so that their operations would attract such attention; for the properly managed exposé does frequently result in long-term improvements and extensions of service, though at considerable cost to hospital morale and the confidence of patients and their families.

Books. The most consistently popular books in mental hygiene are those on child care which deal with the everyday happenings of the home during a child's development. One pamphlet, almost of book size, of this type has already been discussed briefly—*Your Child from One to Six.* A decade or two ago the mothers' bible was Holt's book, *The Care and Feeding of Children,* which had a tremendous readership.[25] Spock's excellent work, *The Commonsense Book of Baby and Child Care,* has filled, in recent years, the need formerly satisfied by Holt.[26] Its easy, reassuring style and lack of rigidity appeal to and help many mothers in the throes of learning how children behave and about their own reactions to some of the behavior that is difficult to take. There are many other less comprehensive works and also a group that takes up some particular behavior item very thoroughly. These are usually effective in proportion to the matter-of-fact, nontheoretic position they take. Inasmuch as such works relieve baseless anxiety and thereby remove a stress upon the parents, leaving them free to deal realistically and appreciatively with their children, they contribute much to mental health.

Most books of the guidebook type are about children and their care, but other problems are covered as well. An excellent example is Ross and Stern's *You and Your Aging Parents.*[27] Some of the books on marriage attempt to satisfy a need in this way also. Books on adolescence for adolescents represent another example, though no such book has achieved the success of a child-care manual. However, there is no obvious reason why this technique might not be applied to any period of life or to any situation commonly encountered in living.

Some books attempt to interpret behavior in terms of one or another psychological or psychiatric theory. These books are usually read only by the highly literate public and probably have little mass effect directly, though they may be widely influential through their effect on key leaders in the community. Social and cultural changes may be introduced and are certainly furthered by books. Halliday has summarized the evidence that changes in the culture may radically change patterns of mental and other illnesses, witness the decrease in hysteria in Western cultures between the two world wars.[28] It is hard to point out the exact effect of a particular publication in such a situation, if only because to have such effect their influence must extend over a long period, during which many other factors operate simultaneously. Nevertheless it now can hardly be denied that the publication of Freud's work has had a strong effect on Western cultures. There are very difficult problems involved in making the decision as to when a new psychological theory is ready for assimilation by the culture, and when it is still too immature for this and should be confined to discussion in learned journals.

Another type of book takes up mental mechanisms, explaining projection, sublimation, identification, etc. Such books make for glib use of terminology by their readers, but whether they increase insight remains an open question. They may not actually reach personalities to such an extent that the person involved could recognize the unhealthy use of such mechanisms, or having recognized them, could control them.

There are also books which deal with various types of mental illnesses. Some of these, e.g., Karl Menninger's *The Human Mind*,[29] have remained popular for many years. They probably are reassuring in their general effect because they outline the limits of the normal and the borders of the mental illnesses rather clearly. The fear that one has a mental illness is probably more widespread than is mental illness itself; the reassurance such books afford is needed by many. To the sick, they at least offer the consolation that their illness is a recognizable one and not unique. Someone knows how they think and feel, and there is a physician to whom they may turn for help. Such books also probably help families to recognize that illness is responsible for the extraordinary behavior of the patient and thus avoid a blaming attitude toward him.

There are irresponsible books that ride some psychological hobby or attempt to teach some trick guaranteed to relieve distress or increase happiness. Somebody finds an understanding that gives him relief and greater efficiency in living and jumps to the conclusion that if only everyone else lived by his technique all would be well with everyone. These books are bursts of enthusiasm reminding one of the output of the recovering manic patient. It is extremely disquieting to the person whose whole effort and total persistence are devoted to keeping a precarious, borderline adjustment reasonably satisfying to himself, when an uncritical, ideal existence is flaunted in his face.

The books that are records, usually autobiographical, of severe mental illness form another large group. They acquaint the public with the fact that mental disease has understandable areas and that, in general, it is a terrifying, sad experience for which sympathy, understanding, and active treatment in good hospitals are vitally necessary. That they actually influence others to solve their own problems satisfactorily appears to be at least questionable.

The health officer who must select a library in mental hygiene for the public will do well to consult bibliographies prepared either by a committee of responsible mental hygienists in his own community or by some unbiased lay group such as the local, state, or national mental health associations. The literature is vast, and its quality spreads over a large range from what is probably harmful to what is probably good. It is wise to recall that the public is more interested in what happens and what to do about it, whereas the responsible professional person will want to know the factual or theoretical reasons.

Using Drama to Increase Participation. Mental hygiene educational work must always have a dual objective, to teach facts and to mold attitudes. Constant research, largely of the trial-and-error sort, therefore goes on into the ways and means by which the public can be emotionally involved during the learning process. Emotional involvement itself, of course, is not the goal; if it were, all good films and plays would have to be classed as mental hygiene efforts. The method, in this case the emotional involvement of the audience, should not become confused with the aim.

Plays lead the audience into identification with one or another of the characters so that each member lives through an experience as if it were his own. This technique has been widely used in radio, on television, and by actual playing of situations before groups, either with trained actors or by selecting members of the group at hand to play particular parts.

Radio. Radio programs appear to be effective in proportion to the extent they promote identification of members of the audience with the persons speaking. Thus, lectures and speeches appear to be the least effective method of presentation of content material. The panel discussion, allowing a larger interplay of emotion between members of the panel while they discuss the situation before them, apparently allows a greater emotional involvement of the audience and is more successful. When the lesson to be taught or the matter to which attention is to be directed can be presented as a play with the illusion of reality strongly reinforced by skilled actors, the effect is probably maximal. Perhaps the most successful series of plays based on clinical material was *Doorway to Life,* done several years ago.[30] This carefully planned series used actual clinical cases as the basis for its plays. After being reduced to anonymity, these were discussed with highly skilled script writers and then written as lifelike episodes in which tension-producing situations were recorded, investigated, and resolved during the course of the program. Similar series have been presented effectually by social agencies seeking foster homes or adoptive homes for children. The National Foundation for Mental Health, now integrated in the National Association for Mental Health, produced several series of recorded plays for radio presentation.[31] These use a common pattern, that of having a nationally known figure comment on the play at the end, pointing out its lesson and the need for its being taught, or simply lending prestige to the presentation. This technique has the great advantage that the public-service time of local stations can be capitalized upon with low expense to the sponsoring agency.

On special occasions the national networks have presented single impressive programs around the mental hygiene theme, usually on the problems of the use of psychiatric hospitalization and the attitudes surrounding this. These programs have apparently had large listening audiences; aside from this, their effectiveness has not been evaluated. They also occasionally use famous personalities in introduction or closing.

The use of "spot" announcements has proved very effective in money-raising campaigns. Perhaps they have been most effective when they come at the end of a comedy show, when the principal suddenly drops his show personality to become serious and intimate and speaks directly to his audience in an appeal to help some unfortunate group. The force of the "spot" appears to be related to the emotional effect of the dropping of the theatrical role, whereby the actor appears as a person in his own right, and presents not entertainment, but a deeply felt personal appeal. Independent "spot" announcements, not tied in with longer programs, are probably less effective. The "spot" announcement, like the newspaper article, must have its message very much condensed and in forceful language. It is better adapted to getting attention or attracting contributions than to teaching.

Radio programs have been used as stimuli to promote group discussion. The most extensive use of this method was a cooperative effort of the Canadian Mental Hygiene Society and the Canadian Broadcasting System.[32] The network broadcast a series of situations at a regular time each week and the Society gathered groups, frequently of teachers, but also others, to listen and then elaborate on the situation as it applied in their community and to work out a local solution for it.

This appears to have worked quite well in Canada and might be expected to be effective where there was some governmental control of a broadcasting system so that regularity of public-service broadcasts could be depended upon. This sort of technique might well be used at a local level, making use of the platters mentioned above, though these programs attempt to "tie up" the package at the end, whereas the Canadian ones left the resolution of the situation to the local groups in their discussion.

Television. The advantage of television over radio is that it shows the actor or speaker and thus makes identification and consequent emotional involvement more complete. Much of the discussion of radio technique and problems applies equally well to television without very much alteration. The impact of a play or incident is greater when seen; the facial expressions of panel members enhance the possibility of identifying with them, and the lecturer has the whole range of gesture and expression to add to his vocal skills. The same caution, that emotional involvement not become the only end sought, needs to be made for television as for radio.

Series of educational broadcasts appear to be effective when televised. *Ding Dong School,* a televised nursery school, is said to have a wide and devoted following among preschool children who respond to the program's appeal to do certain handwork and obey certain rules of decorum.[33] The Baltimore public schools used television teaching for a short period during a strike in 1952 and feel that the medium was effective in helping children learn while the school buildings themselves were closed.[34] Various groups interested in the teaching of child development have conducted series of programs in that field with evidence of continued audience interest, and further evidence of serious study as evidenced by the fact that recommended books were more frequently withdrawn from the library.[35]

Plays and Playlets. In recent years, largely through the cooperative efforts of the National Association for Mental Health and the American Theatre Wing, several series of playlets have been produced for use as introductions for discussions.[36] These deal with various social and family situations in such a way that identification with the characters is easy for the audience. Members of the audience are then drawn into the subsequent discussion, identifying themselves first with one character and then with another. The fact that they are not really the characters, however, makes possible an admixture of objectivity that usually leads in the end to a rational but feelingful solution of the situation presented.

Such playlets need not be so elaborate as to have been printed at all.

They can be outlined almost on the spur of the moment, and there are advantages in obtaining the plot locally since it then is certain to allow identification on the part of the local audience. The whole technique of playlet presentation and discussion has been used as the format for radio and television series. In this case, the discussion is usually carried by a small panel, of course, rather than through participation of a large studio audience. As will be discussed more fully a little later, movie excerpts may also be used as stimuli for group discussion.

The play "My Name is Legion" is the one full-length play written to have direct mental hygiene educational impact.[37] It is based on the life of Clifford Beers, the founder of the citizens' mental hygiene movement in its present form, and presents some of his experiences as he lived through the harrowing ordeal of a severe psychotic episode. The aims of the play are to make the psychotic episode understandable to the audience, thus reducing the public's feeling of isolation from the mental patient. It attempts to engender sympathy for the psychotic patient by making understandable the type of pain he is suffering. It makes clear the importance of an appreciative and patient family in helping the sick person recover. It shows that the attitude of hospital personnel toward patients is a tremendously important factor in recovery from mental illness. Unfortunately, the play requires expert and talented acting, and its usefulness as an educational medium is therefore reduced.

Plays and playlets with real actors allow a more intimate identification of the individuals in the audience with the characters on the stage or, more usually, simply at the front of a meeting room. Locally devised playlets have the advantage of coming closer to recognized local problems; the technique of writing and producing short sequences as a stimulus for discussion is not usually difficult. There are prepared playlets that use situations of general and widespread occurrence for their subject matter. These may be used as scripts for local presentation or as models to be adapted to local conditions.

Motion Pictures. The film as a device for public health education received a tremendous impetus during World War II, when it proved an effective tool for all types of education. Before this, it had been used as a technical device in certain experimental work, e.g., for the full recording of particularly interesting cases of psychiatric or neurological disease, for the study of child development, and for the analysis of reactions of groups. Excerpts from commercial films had been used as stimuli for discussion also, but few were produced specifically for public education. Many of those produced for the education of specialized groups, particularly the series on the mental mechanisms produced by the National Film Board of Canada,[38] for the instruction of medical students and psychiatric specialists, were purloined for use in educational efforts directed toward the lay public, and rapidly became popular and widely used. There were added to them very rapidly films on particular aspects of child behavior, particularly food-refusal problems and problems in sibling rivalry. Following these there began the series by the Mental Health Film Board (United States), which has produced films aimed both at general issues of the effect of life experience on later personality structure and function, and at issues particularly concerned with special periods of development. In addition to these there are films commercially made to illustrate and complement certain books in this field and for other purposes, e.g., the news reel sort of venture. Films have become so numerous that a special appendix listing them and telling something of their content and usefulness has been added at the end of this volume.

At one time it was hoped that films might be produced which would stand alone and not require elaboration or discussion after the showing was finished. To a very large extent, this ideal has been given up; it was found that the audience was likely to leave tense, anxious, and guilt-laden unless discussion was encouraged. In such discussions it becomes possible for the members of the audience to recognize that they are not alone in these feelings, that others also feel anxious because they were not in the past able to achieve the satisfactory attitudes usually portrayed at the end of the films. Discussion usually brings out technical faults in the film itself, so that it is robbed of any magical authority that may have been imagined for it. It can then be discussed as something having no more authority than any other human statement. Then its teachings can be discussed realistically and the members of the audience can leave with the concept of a desirable adaptation to some problem or problems, but not feeling that, having failed to make exactly the adaptation depicted, they have in that measure failed in their own lives and in guiding the development of their children.

As an example of a film discussion, let us take the very popular 20-minute production of the Mental Health Film Board, "Preface to a Life." [39] This film starts with an infant at birth. His mother holds an ideal for him of devotion to her, an obviously unhealthy type of ideal for a boy in the American culture. The father has an equally unreal ideal, depicted on the screen as marching up the steps of the Supreme Court building in Washington. The confusion and unhappiness of the boy caught between these two ideals is beautifully depicted in the film, and the effect of them on the parents is also clear. The father becomes more stern and demanding as the story moves on; the mother, less attractive for loving as she demands more attention than the healthy boy can give. The boy becomes more unsure of himself, being unable to be as good at everything as the unrealistic goals of his father require, or as unassertive and dependent as his mother asks. This story ends with the lad alcoholic and unhappily married. There is a second ending, however, in which the parents learn to give and take, adapting to the boy. This version ends with the boy a budding success in architecture and happily married.

Shown to parents of adolescents, this film can generate guilt feelings of some magnitude, since it leaves them with the feeling that they may have failed. They see themselves often as the parents with unreasonable ideals and demands and feel that, since they failed early in the child's existence, the die is cast. In the story there is a beautiful presentation of a child's confusion when his parents argue. A food-refusal episode is so ludicrously accurate that it almost always brings out ripples of laughter, indicating embarrassment at the inevitable identifications almost any parent must make. An adolescent dating scene, repeated for both stories, frequently is followed by a silence in the audience that seems to indicate bafflement in the face of such powerful adolescent drives. Depending on the audience, it is possible for the discussion leader to focus attention on some one episode as the subject for the discussion or for beginning it, at any rate. It is, of course, taken for granted that he will have seen the film and done some analysis of it before the meeting so that he can, if desirable, direct the group's attention to certain episodes. This technique tends to withdraw the power of the "bad-ending" story, if this seems desirable. This film contains some parts that are rather heavily over-acted. These scenes can be held up to mild ridicule to cut down on the magic frequently attributed to the film by the emotionally stirred audience. This can puncture the film's dramatic appeal and make its discussion possible, yet leave it strong enough to change attitudes as the content of the various situations is further discussed. When a member of the group brings up a subject for discussion, it is likely to be closely related to a real-life situation in that person's experience. It may be wise, depending upon the intensity of emotion apparent in the telling of the story, to identify it as part of the feeling or experience of others; this can be done by the raising of hands or by asking for other experiences of a similar type to be added for discussion. When the situation is too intensively brought out and it is feared that others may not be able to identify with it, the leader may use a personal experience of his own or, usually a little more dangerous technique, an experience from a case he has seen to broaden the situation before carrying it on. Generally speaking, few leaders can risk building entirely fictitious situations for this purpose; the audience will pick up the falsification and frequently completely devalue the leader, often so cleverly that he does not realize he has lost his status at all.

At times, situations will arise which are too intense to be allowed to run their course in discussion. The trend of the discussion must be changed suddenly to avoid embarrassing and damaging overexposure of personality needs and difficulties on the part of a member of the group. Perhaps this is best handled indirectly and, if possible, without the group's realizing that the change in direction is taking place. Humor is one way of dealing with such a situation, bringing in an appropriate funny story that will relieve the general tension and free the audience to take up another trend of thought. Frequently, there is possible a play on words that will "kill" tension the same way yet leave open a new path for discussion. Sometimes, the problem must be tackled directly, simply making the statement that this appears to be a problem that might best be gone into after the meeting. This is usually not a good technique, because it does not disperse the tension in the audience and, of course, it leaves the member of the group who introduced the situation in a conspicious and uncomfortable position, even while offering him help. Finally, it is hard on the discussion leader, who usually would like to get home after the meeting and not spend too much time with members who wish to discuss particular cases in detail.

From this example of how films may be used, it is clear that the effects of such work are extremely hard to evaluate. It is not difficult to get statements from the audience that they have enjoyed the film and the discussion, not difficult to see that they have been emotionally involved. It is very difficult to know whether there is any difference in their lives afterward because of the experience, though most authorities agree that for a proportion of the audience there probably is lasting effect. Certainly, there is no question that the excellent films now being made have extraordinary capacity to stir audiences deeply and to stimulate lively discussion of problems, from maternal neglect of the newborn [40] to the profound feelings of rejection of the retired skilled workman.[41]

Excerpts from commercial films have about the same value as the especially prepared films. They have certain advantages in some situations because they do not need to tell a story in themselves. For this reason, they may lead to more pointed discussion than films burdened with the need for some measure of completeness.[42]

Personal Contact with the Leader. It is clear that, although the film has been grouped with techniques not involving direct personal contact between a leader and the audience, in practice it is most effective when discussed. This requires a leader, even though he be secondary to the film in the eyes of the audience. There are situations, however, in which the personal contact with the leader is the prime issue. There are many different types of this work, involving single or multiple leadership. These will be discussed under the classifications of lecture, discussion series, institutes or workshops, and finally special techniques used in discussion leadership.

The Lecture. Lectures are, in general, rather unpopular at present, largely because they allow a minimum of audience participation. Nevertheless, there are opportunities to use this technique where no other can be used. The program arranged to allow a large number of people to see and hear a famous figure in the field, for example, can hardly be other than a lecture in which the leader speaks and the audience listens. Such meetings are frequently used to add prestige to an organization, as at the annual meeting, or in connection with fund drives.

Lectures usually are carefully structured discourses, aimed at solidly supporting some hypothesis or at popularizing some idea. As such, they are not primarily intended to involve the audience emotionally. As in general education, the only use of emotional involvement is to ensure the audience's attention. The danger that mental hygiene may mistake emotional involvement for an end in itself rarely arises in the lecture, which gives structured thinking its day in the field. It is directive thinking, not the frequently irrational sort of meandering discussion, that leads only to an indefinite and undefined end. Unemotional, rational thinking is highly necessary in this field, and the scheduled lecture, be it a "one-night stand" or a planned series, has a real place in public education in mental hygiene. Even when the primary purpose of a lecture is inspirational, there remains a need for the structured thinking that characterizes this technique. Dr. William Menninger, a very talented inspirational and instructive lecturer, frequently interrupts his applauders by leading them to action at once, inviting them to join their local voluntary mental health association or to take some other desirable action. Evaluation of the effectiveness of lecturing is difficult, but many a mental health association has been founded on the effectiveness of lectures, and many a campaign for funds has been launched on the basis of them.

Discussion Series. Discussion sessions may be single or multiple. The example of the use of a movie above may be considered a sample of a single discussion group. Such a session should be summarized by the leader at the end, listing the topics taken up and the various types of solutions offered by the group. Such discussions can be carried out with groups of 10 to 30 persons—occasionally many more, if the stimulus is a good one and the leader adept.

Discussion groups of this sort are usually organized to function as part of a general program of an organization. The audience may be a PTA group, a church group, a service club, or a woman's club, which wishes to include mental hygiene in a series of programs covering other topics as well. Special groups may be organized for the specific purpose of mental hygiene learning. Some mental health associations make the organization of special groups for this purpose the basis of their public education program, planning with groups of people and furnishing leadership for 6 to 10 or even more sessions. Such sessions do not usually need stimulus material presented; they recognize that there is time available so that subject matter can be allowed to arise from the actual experience and pressures within the group. While there is a general end in view in such series, it is usually left somewhat unformulated so that there will be no temptation to force it on the group, but rather let the group formulate its own end as it moves along. Frequently, members are lost because of this; not everyone can endure working without a defined end in view, and these leave the group rather than "waste time" in what is essentially nondirective discussion. In such a situation, the leader and his helpers have a responsibility for summarizing the discussion so that there can be some recognition of movement for those who are dependent upon structure to stick to the procedure at all. The multiple-group-discussion method requires more highly skilled leadership than most other techniques of mental health education. Perhaps because of this, it is frequently unsuccessful in carrying through a completed series of meetings. Many such groups fail to attract the members for more than a few sessions. Not infrequently this is blamed on the sensitivities of the group members, and it is easily said that those who drop out are unable to stand looking carefully at their own problems. Perhaps equally often the leadership has failed, or perhaps the group really had no problems it wanted to discuss.

Properly carried out, however, the small group, no more than 15 persons, meeting at regular intervals over a period of time, is probably the most efficient technique for learning the insights that mental hygiene has to offer and for attaining the attitudes necessary to make them effective in daily living.

The technique of working with groups in this manner is the subject of a vast literature. In brief, the leadership team generally consists of three persons: the leader, a recorder, and an observer. The leader keeps the discussional ball rolling, referring questions to specific persons occasionally, but more often simply directing them back to the group, which learns to accept its responsibility for answers rather than looking to the leader for this function. Occasionally, "resource persons" are added to furnish facts when they are needed. The recorder keeps a running record of the discussion so that a study of the group's step-by-step progress can be made. The observer attempts to grasp the general trend and to contribute to the postdiscussion analysis examples of failure or satisfactory function of the leader in terms of stifling discussion or, conversely, of involving previously silent members. The observer is also called upon by the group to give a history of the discussion at any time. This elaborate leadership and analysis team appears rather heavy and cumbersome, but it is the result of a great deal of research and, like the therapeutic clinic team, may be expected to work when trained.[43] Sometimes this elaborate instrument appears to be used to deal with subject matter too trivial to justify it, and again, the techniques become uppermost and the subject matter secondary, sometimes to the irritation of the paricipants in the group. The technique is fairly new and may be expected to show changes as it continues to be used. It is a method suitable for committee work, for the insistence of the chairman that the group take the responsibility rather than the leader does bring out a representative report, frequently one enriched by real group creative thinking. The technique is to be avoided by those who like to dictate the results of committee meetings.[44]

Institutes or Workshops. The institute is a continuous meeting lasting from 3 days to 2 weeks—occasionally longer, when large projects are undertaken. The participants usually live under the same roof, eat most or all of their meals together, and spend much of their recreational time in each other's company, as well as spending most of the working hours considering common problems. The institute generally has a basic educational aim; the workshop, usually the aim of producing some statement or document. However, the terms are loosely used as synonymous.

This popular mental health teaching method was, like film production, greatly stimulated by the military educational practices during World War II. In 1948 the Commonwealth Fund financed an institute in psychiatry or psychosomatic medicine for general practitioners of medicine which took place in Minnesota.[45] This institute had a large faculty, case-method teaching was used in very small groups, and much time was left free for essentially nondirective group discussion of case material or of material set forth in lectures, of which there was no more than one daily. The objective of the institute was to make the physician aware of the psychiatric opportunities in the sort of cases that appeared in his practice. Follow-up studies years after the institute indicate that it had a marked effect on many of those who attended it, and that this effect was apparent in their practice, particularly the handling of convalescent patients, hypochondriacal patients, and patients with certain types of endocrine disorders.[46]

In 1949 the technique was adapted for a group of health officers. Here, too, clinical case teaching was used, but the aim was not therapy but simply the appreciation of the emotional and social implications inherent in such diagnoses as syphilis, tuberculosis, pregnancy, and childhood behavior disorders. This institute was reported in the book, "Public Health Is People." [6] This general pattern has been followed in many other states and regions, including Maryland (for health officers and their chief nurses) and New York State (for health department executives, for local health officers and nurses, and educators). Other institutes for health officers have been held in Utah, Washington, Illinois, Missouri, and other locations. In some cases, not here listed, the pattern has been lost in favor of the old-fashioned type of lecture instruction, neglecting the discussion-group technique and the intensive association of the group.

The institute usually throws public health and psychiatric personnel together in intimate association. Frequently it is the first such association in the experience of either group, though as the method is more widely used this becomes less true. There is an initial period, its length depending on the pressure of time, in which each group investigates the other. Following this period of getting acquainted and allaying suspicions, there begins to be some hard work. By the end of the third or fourth day of a two-week session, everyone is discouraged and fears failure. Then the curve of optimism gradually begins to rise, and by the end of the session, all seem happy and enthusiastic about the result. This sort of curve of emotional satisfaction appears to exist whether the institute is 3 days or 3 weeks long. Its significance is completely unknown, but knowledge of its existence, by the faculty at least, before the event helps to get over the anxious doldrums toward the end of the first third of the conference.

The effectiveness of these institutes has been extremely difficult to evaluate. Most people who attend them feel they get a great deal from them, and this feeling lasts for years after the end of the institute. There is considerable cultural pressure against criticizing such efforts, and if criticism is really desired, it must be asked for repeatedly and insistently. Otherwise, there will be false impression that everyone was happy about the whole affair.[7] It appears likely that a few people attending institutes of this sort are fundamentally changed in their habits of thinking and working. These give the impression of a real "conversion experience" having taken place. As might be expected, changes are less radical with most, but are usually in a positive direction in the sense that they see the other fellow's point of view more clearly and are able to operate more on the level of winning cooperation than at the authoritarian level. A few people are disturbed by the experience sufficiently to seek psychiatric treatment, which they may well have needed previously but could not ask for. One result that is very hard to evaluate is that frequently someone is seduced from his own profession to seek training to become a psychiatrist!

The institute procedure has been modified and adapted to serve many different types of groups, both lay and professional. Regardless of the group for whom it is designed, it will probably be successful in direct proportion to the care with which it is planned. The general aim must be clearly defined, though always with recognition that it may have to be altered when the institute is under way. The lead-off lecturers each day must be selected very carefully, since their sincerity and clarity in the statement of issues has much to do with the effectiveness of later discussion in small groups. Group leadership must be carefully worked out so that biprofessional representation is attained, with neither group setting out to learn together either slighted or pushed into undue prominence. Group members should be known by some of the faculty and the smaller groups made up in such a way that difficult persons are either scattered or concentrated in one group under particularly competent leadership. Because topics of discussion are frequently allowed to arise spontaneously in the group, anxiety will arise. One way of offsetting this is to have time carefully and accurately scheduled and to keep to the schedule; the anxious student will then at least know where he will be, even if he does not know what he will be discussing at the specified time. Simple as it sounds, this does appear to be an important technical consideration. Leaders should have had the opportunity to discuss objectives and methods of the institute beforehand, at least once some weeks before the beginning and again immediately before, though this is often difficult because of the expense involved. In any case, several meetings of a planning group are desirable, and the faculty should meet immediately before beginning the institute for a day or at least an evening. Faculty meetings during the institute introduce difficulties, since they accentuate the differentiation between faculty and students and thus undermine the feeling of all working at the problem together under an agreed leadership.

Frequently there are problems of communication between groups where the large body is broken into smaller sessions. This may be solved by the recorder's preparing an abstract for mimeographing and distribution as soon after the day's sessions as possible. This means a secretarial staff and an editing committee working far into the night throughout the period of the institute, an expensive but frequently necessary procedure. The alternative, of verbal reporting of the discussion groups before the entire institute, results in deadly dull meetings which satisfy no one, as a rule, and do not relieve the intergroup envy. Such envy seems to be a part of good morale, unfortunate though the association may seem. Reporting technique deserves further study, but at present frequent mimeographed reports appear to be the best method available.

Generally speaking, no member of an institute should be accepted who cannot attend the whole session. Occasionally, of course, this rule must be broken, but this should be done as infrequently as possible. Only under the most unusual circumstances will a discussion-group member wish to change groups. In general, this also is to be avoided as much as possible. While methods of organization of institutes and techniques of management are important, probably the most important issue is to have a clear idea of what it is hoped will be accomplished and a flexible structure that will allow modification in midstream if it appears desirable.

Perhaps no method has had so great an impact on mental health education in the last 10 years as the institute for professional personnel. The technique has not been adapted in many instances for the public, largely because it is quite expensive and is too time-consuming and confining to be used for other than intensive in-service training. Perhaps future development will make it more suitable for general public education.

Two Special Techniques. The use of playlets designed on the spot to illustrate a point or to stimulate discussion on an issue has already been discussed. This technique can be used in a wide variety of situations. If the subject is how to do a good prenatal home visit by nurses, it can be played out for the criticism of the watching group. After the criticism is all in, the same "actors" or new ones may be selected to play it again, and if necessary the process repeated as new aspects of the situation develop. A great many situations "too hot to handle" by direct attack can be brought under discussion in this fashion, the stress being on "how to do it" rather than the attitudes involved. The attitudes follow or are implicit in the design of the best way of accomplishing an objective. Role playing is a technique which can save many an otherwise dying discussion.

With large groups it is sometimes desirable not to impose subject matter on the group by prior decision, but rather to let the group itself decide what questions are to be discussed. This may be done without special techniques if an audience is aware of why it has come together, or it may follow the use of some stimulus—a playlet, a film, a talk. The "buzz-session" technique is frequently useful, particularly with an audience of more than 30, to accomplish this purpose. The audience is divided by rows or half-rows, or other convenient arrangement that will throw 6 to 12 people into each group, and is instructed that these groups are expected to come up with appropriate questions within, say, 3 minutes. The acceptability of this suggestion or direction is remarkably high. People waste little time in greetings and organiza-tion but rather sail into the discussion at once. The noise of the im-promptu groups in discussion rises almost at once, giving the name to the technique. At the end of the time, the questions are called for. If the audience is small—five or six groups—all suggestions can be recorded, with what abbreviating may be necessary, on a blackboard or easel chart. With a large number of groups, duplications will soon appear, and it is possible to ask for those with questions not already covered to speak, thus assuring representation but avoiding duplica-tions. While this is a most effective and quick technique, it is no end in itself; when it is finished, the subject matter the audience has se-lected remains to be discussed. It is certainly a very quick way of gain-ing audience interest and ensuring genuine audience participation.

The Interview. There is no clear-cut distinction to be made be-tween educational interviewing in mental hygiene and psychotherapy aside from the fact that in the one the subject comes with a complaint to a physician, while in the other the contact may be sought and the awakening of the desire for enlightenment may be a part of the aim of the interview. The seeking for psychotherapy involves a greater com-mitment on the part of the seeker and allows a more thorough review of his history, a more direct attack on the unhealthy attitudes. The educational interview must usually be more tentative and cautious. The objectives of the subject may have to be channeled in a direction not originally in his thinking in order to approach the central prob-lems and opportunities as seen by the interviewer.

SUMMARY

Techniques in mental hygiene range from the relatively impersonal printed article or pamphlet to the intensely personal relationships that can develop in recurrent shall discussion groups under trained team leadership. Techniques should never be allowed to become the central issue; this must always be to accomplish the educational aim set. Various stimuli for discussion are available, but role playing and films are perhaps the best and most popular. Lectures are useful when dealing with large groups, for inspirational purposes and for teaching the rational structure of mental hygiene, while small-discussion-group techniques are probably better suited to the attitude changing that makes it possible to use knowledge gained.

REFERENCES

1. Cartwright, D., and A. Zander: *Group Dynamics Research and Theory,* Row, Peterson & Company, Evanston, Ill., 1953.
2. Hanlon, J. J.: *Principles of Public Health Administration,* chap. IV, The C. V. Mosby Company, St. Louis, 1950.
3. Lemkau, P. V.: "What Can the Public Health Nurse Do in Mental Hygiene?" *Pub. Health Nursing* 40:299–303 (1948).
4. Zimmerman, K. A.: "The Beginnings of a Preventive Mental Health Program in a State and Local Department of Health," *Am. J. Pub. Health* 38:811–816 (1948).
5. Lemkau, P. V.: "Mental Hygiene in the Public Health Program," in *Administrative Medicine,* Haven Emerson (ed.), Thomas Nelson & Sons, New York, 1951.
6. Ginsberg, E.: *Public Health Is People,* The Commonwealth Fund, New York, 1950.
7. Miller, A. D.: "The Institute of Interpersonal Relationships in Public Health; An Evaluation," *Ment. Hyg.* 38:85–106 (1954).
8. Unpublished material, programs, group discussion reports, etc., of the Frederick Conference, 1949, Division of Mental Health, Maryland State Health Department, Baltimore, Md.
9. Lemkau, P. V.: "The Mental Hygiene Program of the Maryland State Department of Health," *Maryland Health Bulletin* 23:79–87 (1951).
10. Maxcy, K.: Rosenau's *Preventive Medicine and Hygiene,* 7th ed., chap. XX, p. 782, Appleton-Century-Crofts, Inc., New York, 1951.
11. Tietze, C.: "A Note on the Incidence of Mental Disease in the State of New York," *Am. J. Psychiat.* 100:402–405 (1943).
12. *Twelve Facts about Mental Illness* (pamphlet), National Association for Mental Health, Inc., 1790 Broadway, New York, 1954.
13. Sopher, Aaron: Drawings reproduced as covers for *Spotlight on Mental Health,* vol. 1, nos. 5–12, 1949; vol. 2, nos. 1–12, 1950; vol. 3, nos. 1–12, 1951; vol. 4, nos. 1 and 4, 1952; vol. 5, no. 1, 1953, Maryland Mental Hygiene Society, Inc., 317 East 25th Street, Baltimore.
14. *Mental Health Is* 1, 2, 3, National Association for Mental Health, 1790 Broadway, New York, 1951.
15. *Your Child from One to Six,* Children's Bureau, Publication 30 (revised 1945), U.S. Department of Labor, Washington, D.C.

16. *Mental Hygiene in the Classroom,* American Medical Association, Chicago, Ill., 1951.
17. Rowland, L. W.: Pierre the Pelican Series, Louisiana Society for Mental Health, New Orleans, La., 1947.
18. Rowland, L. W.: Pierre the Pelican Prenatal Series, Louisiana Society for Mental Health, New Orleans, La., 1950.
19. Rowland, L. W.: "A First Evaluation of the Pierre the Pelican Health Pamphlets," *Louisiana Ment. Health Stud.* 1:1–23 (1948).
20. Greenberg, B. G., M. E. Harris, C. F. Mackinnon, and S. S. Chipman: "A Method for Evaluating the Effectiveness of Health Education Literature," *Am. J. Pub. Health* 43:1147–1155 (1953).
21. Hinnant, Bill, and T. E. Billings: *Little Willie,* V-D Graphic, Health Publications Institute, Raleigh, N.C., undated.
22. Young, Chic: Blondie in *Scapegoat, Love Conquers All, Let's Face It, On Your Own,* New York State Department of Mental Hygiene, Albany, N.Y., 1950.
23. Mace, D. R.: "An English Advice Column," *Marriage & Family Living* 12:100–102 (1950).
24. Committee on Public Education: *Report on Public Education,* Group for the Advancement of Psychiatry, Topeka, Kans., Report No. 29, 1954.
25. Holt, L. E.: *The Care and Feeding of Children,* D. Appleton and Company, New York, 1894.
26. Spock, B.: *The Commonsense Book of Baby and Child Care,* Duell, Sloan & Pearce, Inc., New York, 1945.
27. Stern, E. M., and M. Ross: *You and Your Aging Parents,* A. A. Wyn, Inc., New York, 1952.
28. Halliday, J. L.: *Psychosocial Medicine,* W. W. Norton & Company, Inc., New York, 1948.
29. Menninger, K.: *The Human Mind,* Alfred A. Knopf, Inc., New York, 1930.
30. Doorway to Life, series of radio programs in 1946–1947 season, Columbia Broadcasting System, New York.
31. The Kopecs' Dilemma (and other titles), National Association for Mental Health (formerly National Foundation for Mental Health), 1790 Broadway, New York, 1948.
32. Stogdill, C. G.: "Summary of Mental Health Activities in Canada as a Part of Public Health," unpublished data prepared for meeting of the Committee on Public Health of the American Psychiatric Association, Nov. 15, 1948.
33. Quinn, E., and J. Barrow: "Ding Dong School," *Coonet* 53:46–50, November, 1953.
34. "Freezeout Adds 3 R's to T.V.," *Life* 34:22–23 (1953).
35. Ginsberg, S. D.: Bringing Up Baby, series of television programs on station WAAM, Baltimore, Md., sponsored by the Johns Hopkins University and the Enoch Pratt Free Library, Apr. 6 to May 25, 1952, unpublished.

36. Temperate Zone series, National Association for Mental Health, 1790 Broadway, New York.
37. Ridenour, N., and V. Sterling: *My Name Is Legion,* National Association for Mental Health, New York.
38. Mental Mechanisms Series (films), National Film Board of Canada, 620 Fifth Avenue, New York.
39. "Preface to a Life" (film), Mental Health Film Board, New York.
40. Spitz, R. A.: "Grief" (film), available through New York University Film Library, Washington Square, New York.
41. "The Steps of Age" (film), Mental Health Film Board, New York.
42. Human Relations Series (films), Commission on Human Relations of the Progressive Education Association. See also *Film Forum Rev.* 2:63–64 (1947).
43. Cartwright, D., and A. Zander: *Group Dynamics Research and Theory,* Row, Peterson & Company, Evanston, Ill., 1953.
44. Strauss, F., and B. Strauss: *New Ways to Better Meetings,* The Viking Press, Inc., New York, 1951.
45. Witmer, H. L. (ed.): *Teaching Psychotherapeutic Medicine,* The Commonwealth Fund, New York, 1947.
46. Evans, Lester (The Commonwealth Fund): Personal communication.

CHAPTER FIVE

The Attack on the Problem:
National Mental Health Services

An organized attempt to solve any public health problem as large and as menacing as that presented by the mental illnesses and offering as many and varied opportunities as the promotion of mental health will require a high order of organization, involving both governmental and voluntary agencies. Chapters 5 to 7 discuss this organization as it may be observed at various governmental levels, using the usual pattern of national, state, and local administration in the United States as the primary model, though referring also to other countries and cultures on which information is available.

The end of World War II saw all the nations of the world, both victors and vanquished, in a state of administrative unrest as regards public health services, and particularly in respect to mental hygiene services. In those countries where contending armies had fought, hospitals were destroyed in some measure. Even if facilities were not directly damaged, funds, personnel, and materials had been diverted to military purposes so completely that psychiatric hospitals suffered neglect. Furthermore, almost all nations had become alarmed by the high rates of rejection of personnel for military service because of psychiatric disability. Many nations suffered relatively high rates of discharge from the military services because of mental illnesses. For the first time, extensive research, both epidemiologic and clinical, was done on the psychiatric breakdowns under combat conditions. The pressures of neglect of civilian problems, reinforced with the obvious need for preventive services, has led to great activity and to considerable advance in mental health programming since the end of the war in many parts of the world.

Psychiatric illnesses are peculiarly associated with the culture in which they occur, though the ramifications and the significance of the associations are not by any means as yet completely understood.

Enough is known, however, so that it is clear that no general pattern of administrative or, particularly, clinical, practice could be devised to fit any and all circumstances. In earlier studies, it appeared impossible to reach generalizations in this area. To deal with this field at all it seemed wise to collect all the available information about operating programs and discuss them seriatim, risking generalizations rarely. With the passage of the years since the war, programs have accumulated more experience and stabilization has occurred, to some extent at least. While it is still true that "field experiments change with surprising rapidity" and "a shift in personnel is often followed by a shift in emphasis so that a program may look very different after the passage of a very few months," these statements are not so true as they were in 1948.[1] The quality and interests of the personnel immediately involved often control what is done more than accepted scientific generalizations, but this is less the case than it was a few years ago. It appears possible now to generalize programs of operation into various patterns rather than simply recording multiple examples. The experience on which the generalizations are based has accumulated with extraordinary rapidity. Caution must still be observed in assuming that the patterns to be outlined may be duplicated under other personnel conditions and in other geographic areas, but nevertheless patterns are discernible on which recommendations may be based.

HISTORY OF MENTAL HYGIENE ORGANIZATION

Almost every social, welfare, or health movement begins in one man's mind or at least originates from the thought of a social group. When communication was not as easy as it now is, the possessor of the idea had to do his first work at home, in his native village. It might take many years for his idea to become known outside his area and extend to the state, the nation, or the world at large. Perhaps history is changing in this respect. Certainly the speed of dissemination of ideas is now radically different from what it was when the first hospitals that cared for psychiatric patients were established centuries ago. Perhaps now a new idea in administration might be promulgated at a national level, but it would probably not get much of a hearing unless it had been tried out locally first.

The earliest large-scale mental hygiene program was entirely therapeutic in intent; indeed, the concept of prophylaxis did not become at all apparent until approximately 100 years ago. In ancient Greece, about 500 years before Christ, there developed religious shrines and temples with staffs of priests especially prepared to carry on religious ceremonies intended to cure the insane. The temples did not maintain hospitals in the sense that people were cared for continuously in them; if treatment was not successful, the patient went his way. In many places in the world today this is, of course, still the general practice. It is not known how much the government was involved in this system.[2] Prior to the organized society of ancient Greece, mentally ill patients apparently were expected to be cared for by their families. In the *Republic,* Plato appears to have been concerned that some families did not do this and that society was burdened by neglected insane persons. He says, "If anyone is insane let him not be seen openly in the city, but let the relatives of such a person watch over him at home in the best manner they know of, and if they are negligent, let them pay a fine." [3] Plato indicates governmental concern with the problem; presumably the government would collect the fine. That political leaders were subject to mental illness, and that the action of insane absolute monarchs is something to be deeply feared, is apparent in the stories of kings Saul and Nebuchadnezzar about 1000 B.C.[4]

Ancient Rome, following the lead of Hippocrates and others, managed a reasonably clear distinction of the treatment of mental illness from religious exorcism, though there was still much discussion about the location of the soul in the body and about the function of the brain. Erasistratus speaks of treatment procedures that sound quite modern—dietary measures, hydrotherapy, music, pleasant companions. Apparently little is known about what sort of places were used to carry out such treatment or what interest government took in them. It is, however, worth noting that Erasistratus was once physician to the king of Syria.[5]

General hospitals first appeared about A.D. 300–400, and since mental and physical illness were not distinguished clearly then, it is probable that all sorts of cases were admitted. The isolation of mentally ill patients in separate institutions apparently was first carried out in Jerusalem in 490.[6] It is perhaps pertinent to speculate that this was a very serious mistake that brought tremendous suffering in its wake in the generations since. In any case, the first psychiatric hospital appears to have been founded some 1,500 years ago. The next was in Cairo, in 870. This was clearly a governmental institution, the founder being Ahmed Ben Tuleen, the ruler of the land. The Arabian era of medicine (1000–1300) was marked by separated hospitals also.[7]

During the Middle Ages general hospitals multiplied and usually had psychiatric sections. The prime impulse for the founding of hospitals lay in the Christian doctrine, and orders of religious persons furnished the physicians and nurses to a considerable extent. These hospitals were supported by the rulers and the rich, though the administration of them appears to have been private—in this case, of course, religious. In this period hospitals were founded all over Europe. The first one exclusively for psychiatric patients was in Spain; the second, Bethlehem, later Bedlam, near London. The latter was founded in 1247, but it is not known when it began to receive psychiatric patients and these were apparently cared for in earlier hospitals, now forgotten, prior to this time. The first psychiatric hospital on the American continent was established in Mexico in 1566. The first in what is now the United States was the Pennsylvania Hospital in Philadelphia, of which Benjamin Franklin was clerk, in 1709.[8]

During the prehospital period patients collected themselves about famous religious shrines, so that some cities and villages became psychiatric centers. The best-known of such places is Gheel, Belgium, which established a small medical institution to care for and prepare patients for religious "treatment" at the shrine very early, perhaps about A.D. 700.[9] The patients refused to leave if they were not cured, and the householders of the town apparently took them in as boarders. Now almost every family has a patient living in its midst and doing such work as is possible for him, medical supervision being supplied centrally. The success of this sort of foster or "family care" at Gheel has given rise to family-care programs all over the world, particularly in the United States in the last fifty years.

State mental hospitals, which now care for about 90 per cent of all mental patients in the United States, began in Virginia, the Williamsburg Hospital beginning its work in 1773. Before this, patients were cared for by paid "keepers" who frequently profited from the cheap labor they could get from the patients. The state-hospital idea spread rapidly. Just before and during the Civil War in the United States the movement was pressed by Dorothea Lynde Dix. Beginning with prison reform, she moved on to efforts to relieve the insane, many of whom she found in the prisons outside the care of physicians. She pleaded for Federal subsidy of mental hospitals, and had not President Pierce vetoed her bill, mental hospitals would have had the exclusive profit from the sale of large tracts of national lands in the United States.[10] Many of the then existing states owe their first hospitals to her, and all were greatly improved by her investigations and her "memorials" to legislatures that seemed so frequently to be successful.[11] Read today they are still moving documents, and they related conditions still all too familiar.

In most of the world, as public health programs became established, the health needs of psychiatric patients were included with other health needs, apparently as a matter of course. Psychiatric hospitals were government hospitals, in some countries paid for governmentally but still receiving nursing care through various religious orders. In the United States this did not take place, and there has remained until very recent years little contact between public health and care of psychiatric inpatients and outpatients. At the present stage of evolution, the care of outpatients and the prophylaxis against the mental diseases are among the objectives of almost every health department, and the interest of public health officers in psychiatric hospitalization is rising.

DEVELOPMENTS IN LEADING NATIONS

United States. It is traditional in the United States that the Federal government is primarily interested only in national and interstate problems, and has power to interfere in intrastate affairs only when that power is granted by the states themselves. For this reason the first Federal services in psychiatry had to do with the exclusion of psychotic immigrants, the psychiatric care of merchant seamen and military veterans, the psychiatric care of prisoners in Federal penal institutions, and finally, the care of narcotic addicts. The furnishing of care to veterans and military personnel is outside the scope of this book. The other functions listed were incorporated in the U.S. Public Health Service, first and partially in the Narcotics Division, in 1929, and the next year as a Division of Mental Hygiene. In 1946, the National Institute of Mental Health replaced the Mental Hygiene Division. The two hospitals for narcotic patients were transferred to the Division of Hospitals in 1949 also, though the National Institute of Mental Health maintains an active interest in problems of addiction, and psychiatrists from the Institute man these hospitals. In 1950 the collection and analysis of statistics on psychiatric conditions over the nation was removed from the Bureau of the Census and became a responsibility of the Institute of Mental Health.[12] The Children's Bureau, founded primarily to prevent the injury of underaged persons employed in industry, was established in the Department of Labor in 1912. In 1946 it became a part of the Federal Security Agency, and in 1951, along with the Public Health Service, a part of the Department of Health, Education, and Welfare. This Bureau has operated primarily as an educational, demonstration, and research service in the health field, operating to a large extent through state health departments. It does not offer direct field service with its own personnel. The Bureau early became interested in the mental health of children, and it financed some early demonstrations in getting psychiatric services to rural areas. One of the demonstrations was in Colorado and was organized in collaboration with the health department and the University of Colorado Department of Psychiatry in the 1930's.[13]

The National Institute of Mental Health came into being with the passage of the National Mental Health Act in 1946. This act provided for three functions. Two were essentially new ventures for a Federal agency: (1) financing of education for psychiatrists, psychologists, psychiatric social workers, and psychiatric and mental health public health nurses; (2) financing of psychiatric and mental hygiene research.[14,15] The third function, that of providing incentive funds to the states for the establishment of mental hygiene programs, was greatly broadened by the act, but this had been carried out earlier on a small scale under other grant-in-aid provisions.[16] In addition to these three objectives, the Institute has planning functions, the statistical service already mentioned, and certain demonstration and research responsibilities. In 1953 the research hospital for the National Institutes of Health was opened. The Institute of Mental Health has its share of bed and laboratory space here to carry on its own research program.[17]

Training under the National Mental Health Act has been divided into two administrative functions: (1) the granting of stipends to trainees; (2) the granting of funds to universities and other establishments where psychiatric personnel may be trained to make possible the enrichment and expansion of teaching programs. Originally, training funds were restricted entirely to postgraduate specialty education, but later grants were made to medical schools to improve psychiatric education at the undergraduate level as well. The Institute, operating with the advice of a well-selected committee on training, has attempted carefully to avoid dictating the type of training to be given, and stipendees and fellows are selected by the training center.[18] In the few years of experience under the act, this program has succeeded in training a large number of psychiatric personnel, a surprisingly large percentage of whom have remained in public service, usually at state and local levels.[19] This has never been a large program; the maximum appropriation under it has been about $3,500,000. The Congress has been kindly disposed toward it, showing a tendency to expand its operating budget, though only very gradually.

Research proposals in psychiatry and mental health were at first cleared by an Advisory Board to the National Institute of Mental Health but more recently have become a part of the whole research grant program of the Institutes of Health. This tends to apply the strict scientific judgment characteristic of these committees to projects in psychiatry and mental health, just as to requests for grants in other fields of medical science—certainly a healthy move. Requests for research funds—always far larger here, as in the training section, than the monies available—are screened, and grants for those believed to be most promising are made to persons or institutions. Great care has been exercised to avoid dictating what areas of research are considered important by the Institute itself so that Federal dictation of the direction of research will be avoided; it would appear that this effort has been generally successful.

The grant-in-aid program for the states has presented fewer administrative problems to the Institute than have the training and research functions. From the start, grants have been made on a formula basis to all states and territories fulfilling the minimal requirements of a merit-system personnel policy in the agency designated by the state to receive the funds. This agency is called the "mental health authority." The funds must be matched by the state. While in the first few years of the functioning of the act this presented some difficulties, as time has gone on these stimulus grants have called forth a tremendous response in state and local matching funds—a trend that is still continuing. The grant-in-aid funds are entirely outside the control of the Institute once they are granted, except that auditors have the right to examine accounts to see that the funds are not misappropriated to fields other than psychiatry or mental health. The act specifies that the grant funds may not be used to defray expenses of hospitalization, but the state may use them for training, research, service, or public education as it sees fit, and a reasonable amount may be used to offset the general administrative costs of the department as well. Table 1 indicates the effectiveness of the grants in mobilizing funds from the states and territories.

Although a great deal of money has been drawn into the expansion of mental health programs under the grant program, the Congress shows a tendency to reduce funds under it. The first reason for this reflects a popular political trend of the day, to keep the Federal government out of responsibilities that are considered fundamentally to belong to the states. The second is based on the rather weak argument that, since there are personnel shortages, reduced appropriations for services and education are reasonable—a peculiar interpretation of the economic law of supply and demand.

In 1952 there was an attempt to eliminate Federal grants-in-aid to the states for the control of particular diseases or groups of diseases and to change to a pattern under which block grants were to be made to the states, the state itself determining which of its health programs would receive the funds. The aim was to reduce the problems of administering large numbers of "categorical" grant programs at the Federal level. This movement was defeated so far as funds for mental hygiene programs were concerned. It was feared by the opponents of the move that the level of public education and the education of the mental health authorities in the various states was too low to ensure that mental health programs would receive their rightful share of the proposed block grants. They felt that mental hygiene programs would fare better under the restricted categorical fund policies.

TABLE 1. United States appropriations for grants-in-aid to states and territories and matching funds, 1948–1953 [20]

Year	United States appropriation	Matching funds from states and territories, including local funds
1948	$3,000,000	$2,500,000
1949	3,550,000	5,350,000
1950	3,550,000	6,250,000
1951	3,200,000	8,500,000
1952	3,100,000	9,000,000
1953	3,100,000	11,400,000
1954	2,325,000	12,275,000

Canada. Unlike the United States, the Canadian Department of Health and Welfare administers funds not only for extramural psychiatry and mental hygiene but for the improvement of hospital services in the provinces as well. This program is carried out by a Division of Mental Hygiene, established in 1945. It operates with a nongovernmental advisory council which, however, has persons representing the provinces among its members. The Division has funds available which are far larger in proportion to the population than is the case in the United States. It has extensive grant responsibilities, as well as the assignment of arranging coordination and standardization of practices through interprovincial conferences and consultation services. Research and teaching grants are made to appropriate institutions, and the Division may conduct surveys and researches in its own right as well. The Division is represented on the Dominion Council of Health, an official body made up of all Federal governmental agencies concerned with health, through the Deputy Minister of National Health.[21]

The National Film Board of Canada has produced excellent educational films in mental hygiene in collaboration with the Mental Health Division. The Division has also established extensive loan libraries of films in this field which have been produced elsewhere.[22]

Collaboration with the Canadian Broadcasting Company has been close in the preparation and presentation of radio material, as described in Chap. 3.

United Kingdom. The extensive development of the National Health Services in England, Wales, Northern Ireland, and Scotland has included mental hospitals and other services to a considerable extent. Psychiatric hospitals are included with other hospitals under the regional boards, not without some complaint by some mental hospital administrators.[23] In general, the impression is gained that the balance of local public health services to medical care services generally has been disturbed to the detriment of local health authorities at the moment and that this has contributed to make the growth of outpatient psychiatric services slower than in Canada or the United States. The teaching hospitals have strong outpatient departments, of course, and apparently this system of hospital and specialist care for psychiatric patients is the basis for future development.

The United Kingdom has been particularly active in research and in providing psychiatric services in the field of industrial mental hygiene.[24] A national scheme for outpatient services was evolved in 1948 [25] but does not appear to have been put into effect. The present national health program, which tends to include so much of health as public health, has made the identification of the traditional public health organization difficult and its functions in mental hygiene rather vague. There are, however, numerous and active research centers concerned with social, cultural, and physiological factors that may be influential in lowering the incidence of the mental illnesses.

Scandinavian Countries. The Scandinavian countries have tended to include mental health as an integral part of public health for many years. In some of these countries the local health officer is responsible for the hospitalization of psychiatric patients and for their rehabilitation after release from hospital.[26] This fact, in addition to the relatively small population concerned and the extensive vital-statistics records, both governmental and ecclesiastic, have made possible studies of heredity in mental illness and in its demography which are probably unequaled.[27]

Japan. Japan includes its mental hygiene functions under the Ministry of Health and Welfare. There is a Division of Mental Health, which functions as a statistics-collecting and consultation service and has budget responsibility for the several national hospitals. As in the United Kingdom, support for mental hospitals is drawn mainly from national medical insurance systems, though in Japan there is less unification than in Britain and central administration and local integration is far less elaborate. The Children's Bureau of the Ministry is very active in the mental hygiene field. Unlike its prototype in the United States, it is an operating agency and its child welfare stations, independent in the local health organization, also offer outpatient psychiatric service, typically including child psychiatric clinics among their facilities. Psychiatric hospitalization is administered through prefectural departments of health, though the level of integration is, generally speaking, rather low. As is usual in the Orient, psychiatric hospitalization is far less prevalent than in North America and Western Europe. Since primary support of all hospitals depends upon insurance payments, the direct Federal and state contributions are relatively small. Perhaps for this reason, more than half the psychiatric patients in Japan are hospitalized in institutions under the control of private boards, which are not, strictly speaking, governmental hospitals.[28,29]

The Japanese National Institute of Mental Health, established in 1952, is a relatively small teaching and research institution and is not in the administrative line in the Ministry. It has produced studies of importance in the field and has provided consultation services to various government departments.[30]

U.S.S.R. The discussion of medical facilities within Russia is beset with many difficulties, and the sources of information in English are few. Wortis reports an extensive national program involving hospitalization, outpatient care at the local level, and family care or patronage. Policies are national and are carried out through associated organizations within the republics and districts. Outpatient treatment is, for the most part, done in centers shared with other specialties and a general-practice sort of service. There appears to be a strong tendency to avoid psychiatric hospitalization whenever possible, under the theory that patients do better under extramural treatment.[31] The rate of hospitalization in Russia in 1949 was approximately one-tenth of that in the United States, approximately the same as that in Yugoslavia, for example, and about three times as high as that in Japan. The relation of rate of hospitalization to extent of outpatient psychiatry practiced is unknown, but it would appear that at the moment, outpatient psychiatry in the Western world has not developed sufficiently to be able to reduce hospital rates. It is therefore likely that the low rate in Russia is to be ascribed to cultural and economic factors rather than efficiency of outpatient or inpatient treatment.

Mental hygiene is actively cultivated in Russia. Public education through industrial organizations and other groups is allegedly carried out in accordance with national aims and planning.

SUMMARY OF NATIONAL ORGANIZATION

These few descriptions of mental hygiene organization at the national or Federal level are hardly sufficient to be used as a base for generalization and recommendation; nevertheless, this step will be risked. Any national unit containing within it other semiautonomous subunits should have a national mental hygiene service as an integral part of its national health organization. This organization should not be responsible for the care of the mass of psychiatric patients of the nation. These will be cared for by the subunits more efficiently, since these can be closer to the particular cultural, social, and economic factors that are important in providing service.

The prime functions of a national mental health service will be as follows:

Planning to Meet the Mental Health Needs of the Nation. A competent statistical section will be necessary to establish uniform or comparable reporting from the various subunits of the nation, both on hospital patients and for outpatient and educational services. This section should have a staff considerably larger than that necessary merely to process incoming data. It should also have active field consultants to promote the accuracy and uniformity of reporting from the subunits and should sponsor research projects in the epidemiology of mental illnesses. It is only through the operation of such services that the nation can know the prevalence and incidence of the mental diseases and discover any changes taking place. It may be said that no nation has at the present time developed the complete program of statistical services envisioned here.

A staff will be needed for planning to meet the needs of the nation and to determine those areas most needing stimulation or subsidy. This staff should have available to it some sort of advisory council representing nongovernmental and nonprofessional interests. This body may be combined with or separated from a second body designed for the coordination of the mental health functions of other governmental agencies, i.e., education, labor, welfare, veterans' agency, the military service, and other sections of general health service. The size of such a staff is extremely difficult to gauge, since its duties cannot be exactly determined, and the need for coordinative and consultative services will vary widely from country to country. In most nations, such a service will probably not have very great political power, but will rather work in a consultative pattern. In some cases it may have power to make financial grants given it by the national government in order to induce the subunits to develop certain needed functions.

Powers to Carry Plans to Fruition in Action. How this shall be accomplished will depend upon the political philosophy of the country. In nations characterized by very powerful national governments, this might be accomplished through legal coercion of the subunits. In nations with a Federal national policy this will be accomplished by other means, such as consultation and education, of financial inducements proffered to the subunits. The precise needs outlined by the planners will certainly not be the same for all nations, but will probably include research, personnel training, and some services.

Organization to Supply Needed Psychiatric Services That are National and International in Scope. This will include immigration and emigration examination and advisory functions, the hospitalization of nationals not eligible for care by subunits, the psychiatric aspects of narcotic traffic, the psychiatric care of prisoners convicted of federal offenses, etc. Such a section might conceivably be assigned the psychiatric care of veterans and military personnel, but so far as is known no nation has established such a pattern.

Secondary Functions. Among these might be the development of educational materials for the public and the professions, and the stimulation and support of in-service training programs for personnel already at work. Basic research in psychiatry and mental hygiene might become a function, in addition to the applied research by the statistical section, which has primary status. Other similar functions would be the development of recommended standards for the operation of various technical procedures in the field and suggested standards for training and other requirements for personnel, as guides or for immediate action, depending upon the political philosophy of the country concerned. Objectives and standards for medical education as regards psychiatry might also be set up.

INTERNATIONAL MENTAL HEALTH SERVICE

Of the functions just described for a national health service, the first two are the same for an international service. They are, to a considerable extent, presently functions of the Mental Health Section of the World Health Organization. The organizational character of W.H.O. is such that it has little or no power of enforcement. It must work, and is working, largely on the basis of consultative, advisory, and standard-setting services. Unlike most nations which have a measure of uniformity of culture in their subunits, the W.H.O. deals with all the differences between member nations in culture, economic security, religion, and general health attainments that the world supplies. Its power to influence is at present confined to three possibilities: (1) the education of leaders in professional groups through the granting of fellowships; (2) grants for demonstrations; (3) the influence of its own personnel as consultants and advisers to governments. The W.H.O. Mental Health Section relates itself primarily with national services in countries to which it is invited, its consultants reaching to the subunits within a nation only with the express permission of the national government concerned.[32]

Like many national mental health services, W.H.O. is in active collaboration with a voluntary mental health agency at the appropriate level, the World Federation for Mental Health.[33] This is a loosely coordinated group of national voluntary mental health associations banded together to promote international exchange of knowledge in the field and to stimulate action for the improvement of the mental health of the whole world and for the alleviation of the suffering of all patients with psychiatric illnesses.

SUMMARY

A national mental health service should be a planning agency with appropriate means for encouraging subunits to collaborate in the planning and the carrying out of plans. In addition, it will serve the indispensable national psychiatric needs that are inappropriate to the function of a lesser political unit. International development is being carried forward in the W.H.O. through consultation services and fellowship programs.

REFERENCES

1. Lemkau, P. V.: *Mental Hygiene in Public Health,* 1st ed., McGraw-Hill Book Company, Inc., New York, 1949.
2. Zilboorg, G., and G. W. Henry: *A History of Medical Psychology,* chap. 3, W. W. Norton & Company, Inc., New York, 1941.
3. Plato: *Republic,* quoted in Lewis, Ref. 5.
4. The Bible—I Sam. 16, Dan. 5.
5. Lewis, N. D. C.: *A Short History of Psychiatric Achievement,* W. W. Norton & Company, Inc., New York, 1941.
6. Zilboorg and Henry, Ref. 2, p. 561.
7. Lewis, Ref. 5, p. 61.
8. Zilboorg and Henry, Ref. 2, chap. 14.
9. Sibbald, J.: Gheel and Lierneux: "The Asylum Colonies for the Insane in Belgium," *J. Ment. Sc.* 43:435.

10. Deutsch, A.: *The Mentally Ill in America,* chap. 9, Doubleday, & Company, Inc., New York, 1937.
11. Dix, Dorothea Lynde: "Memorial of Miss D. L. Dix to the Honorable, the General Assembly in behalf of the Insane of Maryland," Reports of the Maryland Hospital, 1849–1852, Document C—by the Senate, Feb. 25, 1852.
12. Federal Security Agency, Public Health Service, National Institute of Mental Health, a Unit of the National Institutes of Health: Mental Health Series, no. 42 (revised), Government Printing Office, Washington, D.C., 1950.
13. Ebaugh, F. G., and R. Lloyd: "The Role of a Mobile Clinic in the Educational Program of a State Psychiatric Hospital," *Mental Hyg.* 11:356 (1927).
14. Pub. L. 478, 79th Cong., chap. 538, 2d Sess., H. R. 4512.
15. Hearings on H.R. 2550, 79th Cong., National Neuropsychiatric Act, Sept. 18, 19, and 21, 1945, Government Printing Office, Washington, D.C., September, 1945. (This bill later designated H.R. 4512.)
16. Sec. 314, Pub. L. 410, 78th Cong., chap. 373, 2d Sess., and earlier laws which this superseded.
17. Topping, N. H.: "The United States Public Health Service's Clinical Center for Medical Research," *J.A.M.A.* 150:541–545 (1952).
18. Department of Health, Education and Welfare, Public Health Service, National Institutes of Health: Letter IMH-TN, Jan. 26, 1954.
19. Vestermark, S. D.: "Training and Its Support under the National Mental Health Act," *Am. J. Psychiat.* 106:416–419 (1949).
20. Lowry, James V.: Personal communication, Apr. 1, 1954.
21. Emerson, H. (ed.): *Administrative Medicine,* chap. 23, by J. L. Little, "Federal or National Health Organization in Various Countries," Thomas Nelson & Sons, New York, 1951.
22. Stogdill, C. G.: "Progress of Mental Hygiene Programs in Public Health in Canada," *Canad. J. Pub. Health* 40:497–507 (1949).
23. Stern, E. S., and K. A. Spratley: "Hospital Administration with Special Reference to Mental Hospitals," *M. Practitioner* 229:276–279 (1953).
24. Ling, T. M., J. A. Purser, and E. W. Rees: "Incidence and Treatment of Neurosis in Industry," *Brit. M. J.* 2:159–161 (1950).
25. Blacker, C. P.: *Neurosis and the National Health Services,* Oxford University Press, New York, 1946.
26. Bremer, J.: "A Social Psychiatric Investigation of a Small Community in Northern Norway," *Acta psychiat. et neurol.,* Supplement 62, 1951.
27. Stenstedt, A.: *A Study in Manic-Depressive Psychosis: Clinical, Social and Genetic Investigations,* Ejnar Munksgaard, Copenhagen, 1952.
28. Lemkau, P. V.: *Report of Consultant in Mental Hygiene, June 2 to July 14, 1953* (mimeographed), World Health Organization, Regional Office for the Western Pacific, Manila, 1953.
29. *A Brief Report on Public Health Administration in Japan,* Ministry of Health and Welfare, Japanese Government, Tokyo, 1953.

30. The National Institute of Mental Health, Tokyo, June 1953: typewritten document.

31. Wortis, J.: *Soviet Psychiatry,* The Williams & Wilkins Company, Baltimore, 1950.

32. Expert Committee on Mental Health, World Health Organization: *Reports 1, 2, and 3,* Geneva, Switzerland.

33. Rees, J. R.: *A World's Eye View: Mental Health as Seen in the Report to the United States Committee for the World Federation for Mental Health,* privately printed, Nov. 23, 1953. Available through the National Committee for Mental Health, 1790 Broadway, New York.

CHAPTER SIX

The Attack on the Problem: State Organization

In large or populous countries, health services are usually provided by subunits, designated as republics (U.S.S.R., Yugoslavia), provinces (Italy), prefectures (Japan), departments (France), states (United States), or other similar units. Depending on the political philosophy of the country, the subunit will have degrees of autonomy from the semiautonomy of the states in the United States and the provinces of Canada to the strong central control said to characterize Russia. In the United Kingdom the various subunits have varying powers; Scotland, for example, has separate health laws from those of other subunits. Whatever the power of the subunit, however, it usually is the administrative agency furnishing psychiatric care and the major source of income to finance these services. It is also, of course, the main administrative and financing unit for public health services in the preventive area as well, though there is much variation in administrative pattern.

ORGANIZATION OF STATE SERVICES

This is practically the only country in which mental-hospital services are separated from other health services provided by the state. Until fairly recent years in the United States it has not been the practice for government to accept responsibility for medical care other than mental hospitalization; general hospitals were either supported by voluntary gifts to finance needed services the recipient could not pay for, or were supported by the payments of patients themselves. Under these circumstances, there was no need for hospital administrators in health departments, and the public health administrative organization developed separately from the mental hospital program (see page 84). More recently, hospitalization has increasingly become a function of health departments in subsidies to general hospitals, the operation of tuberculosis hospitals, and, still more recently in an enlarging number of states, the operation of chronic-disease hospitals. As this trend moves forward, it seems probable that eventually there may be a unification of hospital services, probably within the health department or some even more inclusive unit.

There are many different types of organization now operating in the United States as regards health functions at the state level; the same is true in other countries as well. In New Jersey, for example, all state institutions from prisons to hospitals are in a Department of Institutions and Agencies. This pattern combines in a single unit a very wide range of administrative problems and has the defect of inevitably linking medical curative and custodial hospitals with penal institutions. It also has the defect of separating public health activities outside hospital, carried by the health department, from inpatient services, the responsibility of the Department of Institutions.

Other states combine health and welfare in a single state department, frequently including the mental-hospitalization administrative unit as well, though this service may be entirely separated and stand as a state department of its own. This combination of all health and welfare services in a single department appears most logical, since the problems are highly interrelated everywhere. In practice there are many problems in making a coordinated attack on the two fronts. Frequently, the appointee in the top administrative post is a layman with more political prestige than technical training in either of these highly professional and technical areas. If he is technically trained, it is usually in one field or another, and few appear to achieve real unity of purpose and coordination of effort. In those states which have included mental hospital and public health functions in a single department, there has not as yet been any more notable integration of the two than in other states.

Other states operate with public welfare, mental-hospitalization, and public health functions as separate departments, each with its own commissioner or director responsible to the governor. Under this arrangement, the departments are usually headed by technically trained men in their own fields, and most states have evolved to a level where these positions are protected, either by law or by publicly supported tradition, from discharge because of political changes that may take place. This means, of course, that the governor is expected to be able to grasp at least some of the technical problems in each of these fields along with the many other problems such as roads, taxation, education, conservation, and recreation that also may be reporting to him.

It is the virtual impossibility of this task that led to combination of these services under a single head.[1]

The tendency to neglect mental hospitals and their patients appears very easy to slip into. This tendency is, in the belief of many, best off-set when mental hospitals are a department apart, with their own head reporting directly to the chief executive. This is the type of organization generally preferred by the voluntary mental health associations, since under this plan they are able to make their opinions felt more directly than through a person preoccupied with many different responsibilities.[2]

In only two instances in the United States has the administration of mental hospitals been made a responsibility of the public health department. The first was in Vermont where the move was not made primarily for administrative reasons but for political ones, and the experiment ran only 2 years before it was followed by another reorganization which again removed the mental hospitals from the department's control. During these years no insoluble problems of integration were encountered, and some integration appears to have occurred, but there was not enough experience gathered to allow any real judgment of the advisability of this administrative pattern.[3] This pattern of organization is an attractive one. It was adopted by Indiana in 1952 and still operates, not escaping the criticism of some, however, and has been considered by other states.

Outpatient and Educational Services. With the passage of the National Mental Health Act in 1946, the states and territories of the United States were required to designate a "mental health authority" to be responsible for the development of a program of services to the population. Of the 53 states and territories, 29 designated their health departments as this authority; 9, the department responsible for the mental hospitals; and 8, the department of welfare or a combination department as described above.[4] The explanation of this distribution is not easy, since health departments had not, in too many instances, previously begun work in mental hygiene. Connecticut had begun this sort of work in 1920, establishing it with bureau status in 1931.[5] Maryland began its work in the health department in 1934 as a function of a then Bureau of Child and Maternal Health,[6] a pattern followed by New Jersey the next year and by Wisconsin in 1944. Oregon established a division of mental hygiene under the state board of health in 1941.[7] Similar ventures were carried on in certain large cities under health-department auspices. The pattern was not by any means universal, however, whereas every state had a functioning mental hospital system, regularly employing psychiatrists. Probably the stimulating consultation services provided by the then Division of Mental Hygiene of the U.S. Public Health Service in the decade before the passage of the act had prepared many health departments for taking on mental hygiene programs, so that they were ready and anxious to do so when the opportunity for funding them arose.[8] The fact that the correspondence concerning the designation of an authority was with the Public Health Service probably also brought the public health department clearly before the state executive and led, in some cases, to designation merely because of this.

It was also probably important that mental hospitals were not identified in the minds of many people as public health services. Most of the 12 states in which the administrator of mental hospitals is designated the authority had already been operating outpatient clinical services, at the hospitals themselves, but also at a distance from it, in genuine attempts to extend service to all the population. In no state in which the hospital administration was active in outpatient work was the health department designated the authority. In a few states, welfare departments were already furnishing psychiatric services, and in these this department was designated the authority. Since the establishment of these authorities in 1946, a few states have changed their designations. The trend, if such it is, apparently is toward removing the authority from health departments, probably because of dissatisfaction related to unavailability of personnel, and perhaps also because some health-department administrators demonstrated that they did not have the necessary training.

There has been considerable discussion as to whether the health department or the mental-hospital department should be responsible for the development of preventive and outpatient services. In 1950, the Council of State Governments, in spite of the fact that the majority of the states were actually functioning otherwise, recommended the unification of all mental health services in the department responsible for psychiatric hospitalization.[9] The reasons advanced for this recommendation were that in most states the hospitals had psychiatrists already in their employ, that personnel was in very short supply, and that greater economy and availability of personnel would result if services were completely unified. Unification within the health department was discussed but discarded as not appropriate at that time. It was pointed out that encouraging extension of psychiatric hospital service through outpatient and educational programs would tend to break down the isolation of the hospital and its personnel from the community.

This recommendation was opposed when it became public and is still the subject of debate. It is argued that new personnel will need to be trained and developed regardless of the department furnishing service. Many psychiatrists, even though thoroughly experienced in the care of psychiatric patients in hospital, are not trained for the services to the less severely ill in the community. They would have a great deal to learn and would not be able to step into their new role, any more than a public health–trained person could fill hospital responsibilities. It was pointed out that the furnishing of community health services is a task requiring special skills and that psychiatrists could not perform it without the aid of competent and trained public health administrators. The point was made that in local communities public health had numerous nurses and physicians already at work, and that these offered an available source of help in the establishment of clinics and the possibility of increasing the number of persons who could be involved in therapeutic and educative programs. It was also pointed out that there were marked personnel shortages in every hospital system in the nation and that the withdrawal of this personnel, for outpatient service, would make this shortage even more acute. In those states in which outpatient services had developed within hospital systems, at least part of the psychiatric personnel was specialized for this service and had lost its identification with the hospitals to a large degree. Finally, the local health departments frequently had space in use only part time. The mental hygiene clinic could use such space at less cost than if separate space had to be found; though, of course, it could be used for health purposes regardless of the source of the personnel employed.[10,11]

The general conclusion reached from a review of these arguments is that both the public health department and the mental hospitals have a stake in the development of psychiatric diagnostic, treatment, and preventive-educative services to the population. These can best be obtained through integration of the technical personnel of the two medical specialties involved. It is probable that this integration can be obtained under many different types of administrative organization provided leadership is available. Such leadership should be developed through the education of the psychiatrist in public health practice and theory— and, vice versa, the training of the public health officer in psychiatry and mental hygiene. Such persons are as yet relatively rare and are not being trained very rapidly in any country. Schools of public health in the United States [12] and in Europe [13] are giving increasing attention to these issues.

A great deal of thought has been given to whether or not the leadership for psychiatric services to the population requires personnel actually trained in the two specialties. Such training is, of course, expensive. It requires under present American standards at least 5 years following graduation from medical school, and such a schedule allows no time for acquiring field experience before assuming a highly responsible administrative position. It has been speculated that a combined training might be worked out that could shorten this training period, and, indeed, psychiatric standard-setting bodies in the United States are pressing toward broader education of psychiatrists in community organization and sociology.[14] Basic sciences of public health such as biostatistics and epidemiology are gaining recognition as tools for research in psychiatry and have received some recognition in the training of psychiatrists. This trend will probably be extended as a larger number of communities realize that a psychiatrist cannot suddenly change his pattern of operation and grasp the technique and philosophy necessary to think and work in terms of total populations merely by accepting a position in a health department.

Neither is the converse true. Public health–trained personnel at the present time have, generally speaking, a fair appreciation of the need for mental hygiene services in their communities. But they are not able to achieve the technical skills necessary actually to carry out programs as presently conceived. Specialists appear necessary if programs are to be carried out. Nevertheless, the health officer should have enough knowledge of psychiatry and its techniques and traditions to be able to work smoothly with his psychiatric clinicians and educators. Occasionally, a public health–trained person finds that mental hygiene is an attractive specialty and chooses to enter psychiatric training in order to be able to work within this specialty and to bridge the remaining chasm between the two.

In some states, notably New York, the variety of state departments concerned with the development of mental hygiene services to the population led to the conviction that no one department ought to be administratively responsible for such services. The result was the establishment of a commission consisting of the heads of the departments of health, welfare, education, and mental hygiene; this last department operates the hospitals and for years has operated outpatient services over the state. This commission employs an executive and staff to carry out the mental health mission assigned. The designated mental health authority remains in the Department of Mental Hygiene, but the funds under the Federal grants and state appropriation are expended by the commission. The commission has operated no psychiatric diagnostic or treatment services; these are supported through grants to clinics. It carried on an extensive educational program for public health workers and educators, as well as an important research program in the field.[15,16] This commission was replaced in the development of the Community Mental Health Services Act of 1954.

In most countries, outpatient services have been historically associated with teaching-university outpatient departments, and in some countries these remain the mainstay of service. For the most part, such clinics are oriented toward the diagnosis and treatment of individual patients, though there has been some extension into consultative services to social agencies. Development of outpatient services in the United States and Canada have followed a somewhat different pattern, adding other types of clinics to the usual university-sponsored ones. The first type developed about the mental hospitals for the continued care of patients discharged from the hospitals; these operate either at the hospital itself or in locations more convenient to the former hospital patients. In many areas, these clinics were the basis for later development into more general outpatient services. The second line of development has been the independent clinic supported by contributions or tax funds, established frequently to function without direct association with any medical institution—public health, mental hospital, or other hospital. Just as the trend has been for the clinics for posthospitalized persons to expand to do general outpatient work, so these independent clinics, frequently established to furnish service exclusively to children and as consultants to social service, judicial, and other agencies in the community, have frequently—and healthily—developed into "all-purpose clinics" with direct associations with more general medical institutions.

ORGANIZATION WITHIN HEALTH DEPARTMENT

Mental hygiene as a function of the health department is a fairly new concept and cannot even yet be clearly defined. Perhaps partly because of this, there is uncertainty as to where it should be located organizationally. Is mental hygiene all-pervasive, affecting the procedures of every activity of the health department, or is it primarily a specific service to the public which might be provided by a division or section? The former has been called the "horizontal" function of mental hygiene; the latter, the "vertical." [17] Few question that the mental hygiene program of the health department must have both types of objective. The amount of accent upon one or the other will determine to a considerable extent the level on which mental hygiene is placed in the organizational scheme of the department.

If the horizontal function is stressed, the program will probably find a place high in the administrative organization, at the bureau level or above.* In California, the mental health unit does not offer service directly to the public; this function is carried by the state department operating the hospitals. The prime function is the spread of mental hygiene information throughout the department in all its units, both local and central. This aim requires that the status of the leader in mental hygiene should be high enough to command the respect of the highest ranking officials in the department, and that he be able to cross administrative lines with ease. In order to achieve these ends, the mental hygienist was established as a consultant to the health officer. This is a "staff" type of position, involving no "line" or operating responsibility, yet with a position in the organization which would achieve the ends set for the program. Under this system, the consultant has been able to hold seminars and discussion groups with all appropriate levels of personnel in the department, both locally and in the central administrative group.[18] The location of the position has, in all probability, also led to increased acceptance by the other state and voluntary agencies with concern for an integrated mental health program in California. While it is true that the highest administrative level position can be made impotent by inadequacies in the personality or professional training of the man holding it, it is also true that the best man may be hindered in his work if his administrative position is not one that can command respect.

The Connecticut Health Department has the distinction of being the first in the United States to have included mental hygiene as an integral part of the organization. In 1920, a division of mental hygiene was established and was made a bureau in 1931. This program was at first entirely directed toward the education of the public but was, after a few years, reorganized to include clinical services to the public as well. The influence of the division in the operation of the central department became sufficiently great so that the promotion to bureau status appeared not only justified on the basis of importance in the total program of the health department in the state, but also necessary for the best development of the horizontal mental hygiene functions.[5] In Connecticut, progression was from service or vertical program to a point where its influence as an in-service educational agency or horizontal function justified administrative placement at a higher level.

In Maryland, mental hygiene is represented as a Division of Mental

---

* Nomenclature in health department hierarchy varies widely. Here by "bureau" is meant an administrative unit reporting directly to the state health officer; by "division," a unit reporting through a bureau; and by "section," an administrative unit reporting through a division.

Health within a Bureau of Preventive Medical Services which also includes as divisions maternal and child health, crippled children's programs, venereal disease, and communicable disease, some of these being further divided into separate sections for administrative purposes. The Division of Mental Health includes a Section on Alcohol Studies. The mental hygiene division employs two mental health nurse consultants who are administratively attached to a Division of Public Health Nursing but receive technical direction from the chief of the Division of Mental Health. One of the nurse consultants is employed in in-service educational services, usually in the local health departments, but also centrally. The other is employed to carry on an intensive educational program for public health nurses and supervisors in connection with a psychiatric institute. These contribute greatly to the horizontal aims of the Division. Other functions of this type have been institutes for local health officers and central office personnel and a continuous availability for consultation regarding problems involving psychiatric, personnel, administrative, and other problems. While the chief of the Division of Mental Health does not sit as a member of the bureau chief staff conferences, the influence of the division is actively felt because of the informal consultation practices in operation. This exists to some extent also with regard to the newer Section on Alcohol Studies, which has also influenced the in-service nursing educational program as well as the thinking of the Bureau of Medical Care in regard to the operations of the chronic-disease hospital program in the state.

Both the Division and its Section on Alcohol Studies operate vertical or service programs. The Section is relatively new, but it operates several evening clinics for the treatment of alcoholics and is expanding in the direction of sponsoring a program of hospitalization for acute alcoholics and in combination research and treatment clinics with the two medical schools in the state.[19] The Division of Mental Health operates clinics with the immediate aim of providing one day a week of psychiatric-team service to each 50,000 of the population of the state. In some cases reaching this level involved the subsidy of already operating clinics. In most instances, however, new clinics had to be organized under the administration of the local health officer, to whom the chief of the division acts in a consultant capacity.[20]

The politicogeographic organization of the state is important in considering the organization of the clinical services of mental hygiene under health-department auspices. There is tremendous variation in the size of the basic administrative units as well as in their population. Maryland, for example, has about 2 million population, roughly half of whom live in Baltimore, which is less in area than any of the 23 counties making up the rest of the state. These counties vary in population from 300,000 to below 20,000. Georgia, with a population of roughly 3,000,000 has 157 counties. The county with least population boasts less than 3,000 people; the one with the most, almost 400,000. A further problem is that the county is not the primary political unit in many states, particularly New England states. Here, the effective unit is the town, which may be very small both in area and population.

Regionalization of some type or another is the obvious answer in the administration of programs where the political unit is not of such a size as to allow efficient use of services. This presents great difficulties, however, for the different units are likely to have considerable local pride and tradition. Pride of possession in "their" clinic or other service makes them unwilling or unable to share with other units. There are likely to be travel difficulties as well. In Maryland, for example, it seemed logical to group three counties totaling about 50,000 population for service, but this meant that patients from one of the counties had to bear the cost of toll over a bridge. This factor materially reduced the possibility of their making equal use of the service compared with patients from the other collaborating counties.

Another possible solution to the problem is the traveling clinic, meeting in the various political units at longer intervals. Such clinics may be full-time teams meeting in different areas or may be part-time teams that serve a population unit requiring less than full-time service. The traveling full-time team has certain disadvantages; it has no home-base unit that it can call its own, with which it can achieve real familiarity, knowing the people well and the community organization of the community served. The part-time team, utilized perhaps one day a week in a particular location, can become familiar with "its" community through repeated visits; the team adopts the community and the community the team. The team members have their professional contacts in, usually, only two areas, their home and their "adopted" locality, whereas the community has the opportunity of seeing them at work frequently enough to feel it knows them.

A traveling clinic, depending on the level of service it has been decided to supply, should meet for the service of a population not less than once a week in the same location. Experience indicates that less frequent visits to a community tend to make treatment almost impossible. Psychotherapy appears to become much more difficult and slow if intervals between treatment sessions are longer than a week, particularly during active phases of treatment. Diagnostic functions of clinics, which are of great importance to a community, can be carried out by visits at longer intervals where necessary. Under these conditions such treatment as is within the competence of local personnel may also be possible.

The traveling clinic will not answer the problems of the necessity of regionalization for service in most areas of the United States. Where regionalization to obtain a suitable population unit is impossible, it is unlikely that a treatment service can be provided. It is clear that one of the functions of the leader of a mental hygiene clinic service at the state level will be to plan regionalization and to resolve the problems of local pride, morale, and tradition so that the regional plan will actually work. This requires skill in community organization of a high order in many instances and also needs the intelligent cooperation and help of the local health officers concerned. Voluntary mental health associations can be of great help in the making of regionalization plans for furnishing clinical service.

Personnel. The central mental hygiene office will also usually have recruiting responsibility, since local health officers will not have, in many cases, the access to the psychiatrists, psychologists, and psychiatric social workers necessary to operate clinical services. The local health officer should, however, have the opportunity to interview any prospects for employment in his county or for serving the people of his community. He should be able to reject them if he chooses, since it is he who will have administrative jurisdiction over them once they are at work.

Recruitment of psychiatric and auxiliary personnel is frequently a very discouraging task, for in many parts of the world they are in extremely short supply. Health-department recruitment is particularly difficult because salaries are frequently low. The public demand for psychiatrically trained people is so high that they can frequently command greater salaries in other than public service, and consequently they do not fit into the levels of salary on which the rest of the health department specialists function. Recruitment is very difficult for full-time positions where the psychiatrist must be paid no more than a pediatrician or venereologist at the same administrative level, when the psychiatrist knows that elsewhere his specialty commands a premium wage. Clever administrators have found ways of subventing some of the rules that exclude the operation of the laws of supply and demand, but the rules still stand in many areas as bars to successful recruitment. There are psychiatrists, just as there are other specialists, who are willing to sacrifice financial advantages for work that they know is important, but unfortunately few of them have discovered public health psychiatry as a field offering these compensatory satisfactions. It is likely that as psychiatric postgraduate education expands in the direction of knowledge of community needs, more psychiatrists will make this discovery. Probably as health officers gain more knowledge concerning mental hygiene programming they will be able to present the opportunities more attractively. Some full-time personnel will probably be necessary for planning and administration in most programs. It is at least doubtful that this responsibility can be carried by personnel of less training than the psychiatrist, and it is highly preferable that the leader also have public health training, even if he must be paid full salary while obtaining it. These requirements appear high, but mental hygiene is a relatively uncharted area and the only insurance the administrator can have against inadequate work is the personality and training of the leader selected to plan and carry out the program.

Part-time personnel is in some areas, particularly near centers of psychiatric training, somewhat easier to secure. This is often true in the United States and Canada, where there has been a great increase in the number of psychiatrists in the postwar years. Generally speaking, rates of payment for part-time service more nearly approach an adequate recompense to the specialist, and administrative restrictions on part-time employment are somewhat less onerous than on the employment of full-time personnel. Even if payment is low, the psychiatrist may find it possible to give a day a week as his recognition of the traditions of his profession for furnishing public service. Generally speaking, part-time service of less than a full day has been found unsatisfactory—too many interruptions take place for planning that part of the day for which the psychiatrist is not employed by the department. Whenever travel time is of any consequence, less than full-day employment is distinctly unprofitable for the department. When the psychiatrist is assigned the care of a particular population unit, he becomes a member of that community for his day there. He becomes surprisingly attached to it and, sometimes, defensive of its rights in the total program. This identification tends to decrease the turnover of personnel. In Maryland, at least, the turnover has proved to be surprisingly low, probably mainly because of this identification with the adopted community.

In the case of auxiliary personnel, psychologists and psychiatric social workers, the employment for part-time service is also likely to prove possible and economical. In many communities people trained in these two professions may be found among the housewives of the community. Women who worked in these professions before their marriages are unable because of their family responsibilities to hold full-time positions but can arrange to take a day or two each week for clinic work. Such employment not only furnishes personnel for the mental health program but salvages professional education for the community that would otherwise not be used. This is a personnel resource frequently over-looked in recruitment efforts. It involves, of course, some lost time through maternity leaves and family emergencies, but such interruptions can be well tolerated by communities where friendly relations exist among the team, the local health department, and the community.

PUBLIC EDUCATION IN MENTAL HEALTH

This function of the state health department varies widely, depending principally on the planned aims of the mental health group and the strength of the voluntary mental health association. Usually, the department will maintain a film library for free loan or low rental and will supply pamphlet material for distribution through local departments and at other places. It may maintain a library of books and journals for use by the clinic teams and health-department personnel and perhaps for the general public. Over and above these basic functions there is very wide variation in program. In many instances there may be need to educate the community for the use of some specific service, such as preparation for the opening of a new clinical service. There may be special demands by professional groups to be satisfied so that institutes or courses for teachers, clergymen, juvenile court officials, rehabilitation workers, etc., may be planned and carried out. There are almost always demands for lectures or film discussions for parent groups, parent-teacher associations, service clubs, etc. Much of this latter type of demand may be satisfied by the voluntary mental health association, if such an organization exists. It is frequently more healthy for the community if a voluntarily supported organization can carry on this type of education, not only in such organized groups as have been mentioned, but in newspaper, radio, and television publicity and education as well. One educational program that cannot be neglected is the cultivation of appropriating bodies. This must remain an object of both the voluntary association and central and local official departments, and it is best carried out with some joint planning.

RELATION WITH VOLUNTARY ASSOCIATIONS

In some states the voluntary mental health association is directly, sometimes completely, supported by public funds. Such arrangements are usually considered unwise by both official and voluntary bodies.[21] The citizens' group is robbed of some of its freedom to criticize the official agency when its existence is threatened by the possibility of withdrawal of financial support. This does not, of course, negate the possibility of a public body's making a contract with a voluntary association for carrying out some particular service or research program, but even here care must be exercised that contracts do not restrict the freedom of action on the part of the voluntary agency. This paragraph applies particularly to areas operating under democratic philosophies of government and with a standard of living that makes it possible for the citizens of the area to support voluntary health associations. It should not be forgotten, however, that costs are lower in countries with low standards of living, and that poverty is not too easily to be brought forward as an excuse for direct governmental support of what are purported to be voluntary agencies. The slow processes of education of the public which are necessary to make an active voluntary association functional and dependable are not to be avoided by granting financial independence to a body that has not actually become representative of genuine public interest and concern.

The criticism of public officials and their programs by voluntary health agencies is not always easy to bear, and there is a tendency for the official to withdraw and keep his plans secret from voluntary agencies where he is under criticism. It may, at times, be necessary to keep plans relatively secret in order to avoid premature action by voluntary agencies, but generally a frank statement of position in planning and financing is a more successful policy than establishing a distant, separated relationship. Voluntary agencies, when healthy, generally want to move more rapidly than the public official will feel is practical. They will be more certain of ability to influence appropriating bodies favorably than is the public official. At times, the public official will be certain that a full statement of needs as seen by the voluntary agency will frighten appropriating bodies so that they will hesitate to begin on the program at all. In general, some compromise can be reached or, if not, there can be amicable disagreement with full understanding on both sides, the decision to be made by the appropriating body itself. It is certainly true that public officials act more quickly and positively when pressed by voluntary mental health organizations than when they are forced to generate all the pressure for financing of program themselves.

SUMMARY

The primary political subunit (state, prefecture, province, department) will usually furnish psychiatric hospitalization and be responsible for some outpatient clinical and educational preventive services. These services are in many nations combined with other services within the health department, but in the United States they are more or less separated under two departments of the government, one concerned primarily with hospitalization, the other with the more traditional public health functions. Preventive and outpatient clinical services may be administratively assigned to either department, depending on local tradition and the interest of the two departments concerned. These services usually have two aims: (1) a horizontal one of spreading the concepts of mental hygiene through all the activities of public health and other agencies; (2) a vertical one of furnishing clinical services to the population. The place of the central mental health administrative group in the hierarchy of the department will depend somewhat on whether emphasis is to be on the horizontal or vertical aim. Recruitment of personnel is difficult but may be facilitated by the planned use of part-time personnel. Voluntary mental health agencies are best not supported by public funds, since this compromises their freedom of criticism of public officials. Such organizations may be able to carry much of the load of public education, thus saving public funds for the more easily demonstrated clinical services for which appropriating bodies are usually more willing to grant financial support. The planning of public programs in collaboration with voluntary agencies is wise policy whenever possible. Differences of opinion between public officials and private agencies are better faced directly than by retreat into secrecy and the isolation of the official in charge of public programs.

The central office administrative group will have planning, recruitment, supervisory, and consultative functions, but, in general, actual administrative responsibility should rest in the local health officer, regardless of whether the department operating the program is health, welfare, or that responsible for psychiatric hospitalization.

REFERENCES

1. Ballard, F. A., and R. G. Fuller (eds.): *Mental Hygiene Laws in Brief,* National Committee for Mental Hygiene (National Association for Mental Health), New York, 1941.
2. "CMHA Urges Separate Department of Mental Health. Mental Health and Our Community," *Bull. Cleveland Ment. Hyg. A.,* Winter, 1950.
3. Fuller, R. F.: *Study of Administration of State Psychiatric Services: A Further Informal Progress Report to Members of the Advisory Panel,* Sept. 15, 1952. See also Laws of Vermont, 1949, Public Acts, No. 184.
4. *The Mental Health Programs of the Forty-eight States,* p. 86, Council of State Governments, Chicago, 1950.
5. Cunningham, James C.: "The Connecticut State Department of Health Mental Hygiene Program," *Am. J. Pub. Health* 32:606–610 (1946).
6. Newell, H. W.: "The Development of Mental Hygiene Clinics in the Counties of Maryland," *Ment. Hyg.* 31:426–435 (1947).
7. Haugen, H. B.: "An Approach to the Mental Hygiene Public Health Problem," *Pub. Health Rep.* 58:1211–1214 (1943).

8. Vogel, V. H.: "Mental Hygiene in the State Health Department," *Pub. Health Rep.* **56**:1–10 (1941).

9. Ref. 4, p. 7.

10. Lemkau, P. V.: "Mental Health Programs of the States," *Am. J. Psychiat.* **107**:470 (1950); **107**:788 (1951).

11. Russel, W. L.: "Mental Health Programs of the States," *Am. J. Psychiat.* **107**:709–711 (1951).

12. *Report of the Conference on Mental Health in Public Health Training Programs, June 2 and 3,* 1952 (mimeographed), The Harvard School of Public Health, 1952.

13. *Lehrplan der Akademie fuer Staatsmedicin,* Hamburg, Sept. 1, 1952.

14. Whitehorn, J. C. (ed.): *The Psychiatrist, His Training and Development,* American Psychiatric Association, Washington, 1953.

15. *Progress toward Mental Health . . . for Fifteen Million People,* New York State Mental Hygiene Commission, State Department of Mental Hygiene, Albany, 1952.

16. Gruenberg, E. M.: "The Syracuse Study of Mental Health Problems of Aging," paper read at the 109th annual meeting of the American Psychiatric Association, Los Angeles, May 5, 1953, to be published.

17. Lemkau, P. V.: "Public Health Administration in Mental Hygiene," *Am. J. Pub. Health* **41**:1382–1387 (1951).

18. Zimmerman, K. A.: "The Beginnings of a Preventive Mental Health Program in a State and Local Department of Health," *Am. J. Pub. Health* **38**:811–816 (1948).

19. Dellinger, Joe B. (Chief, Section on Alcohol Studies, Maryland State Department of Health): Personal communication, 1954.

20. Lemkau, P. V.: "The Mental Hygiene Program of the Maryland State Department of Health," *Maryland Health Bull.* **23**:80–87 (1951).

21. *Report of the Policy Committee to the* 1953 *Annual Meeting of the Membership and the Board of Directors,* National Association for Mental Health, Oct. 10, 1953; revised report, Jan. 5, 1954. The policy is still in process of codification and will eventually appear in manual form.

CHAPTER SEVEN

The Attack on the Problem: Local Administration

Mental hygiene programs at the local level (county, city, regional, or district unit) bring public health and psychiatric personnel into close working relationships. Some of the problems of attaining a mutual understanding and regard between these two groups of personnel have already been detailed in Chap. 3. There remain to be discussed the ways the two groups may evolve to function together for the improvement of the mental health of a population and for the diagnosis and treatment of the psychiatrically ill members of it.

MENTAL HYGIENE PROGRAMMING

Mental hygiene is not yet one of the "basic six" [1] services of local health departments, and it is indeed a question whether it will ever rank as a basic lifesaving measure. Probably it would be a mistake to allow funds to be diverted from any direct service such as safe water supply, milk protection, basic nutritional program, or disposition of sewage to be dispensed for the alleviation of mental illness at the present stage of knowledge. As has been said frequently, one cannot do mental hygiene on dead people. It has also already been pointed out that the proper control of the communicable diseases and of nutritional deficiencies are in themselves powerful mental hygiene tools. Thus mental hygiene comes as a by-product of absolutely fundamental lifesaving procedures; they inevitably carry with them mental hygiene aspects much to be desired.

In order to achieve maximum efficiency in communicable-disease control and nutrition, however, the horizontal type of mental hygiene program may be essential. Mental hygiene offers particular skills in the management of attitudes, and attitudes determine the success or failure of all programs for the promotion of the health of the people. The use

111

of its principles and group skills may be an essential element in the administrative functions of the health department. On such grounds as this, it is quite probable that mental hygiene is practiced in every successful department, whether it is recognized as such or not, and whether or not personnel designated as mental hygiene specialists are employed. This is not to contend that mental hygiene and effective administration are the same, or that the former can replace the latter. The latter borrows heavily from the former, however, and administrators familiar with the literature of and philosophy of mental hygiene are probably more effective than those ignorant in the field.[2]

The Health Officer and Mental Hygiene Information. Every health officer should be informed concerning mental hygiene to some minimal level, though it is extremely difficult to determine just what this level should be. In many communities, the health officer will be required as a regular part of his duties to determine, usually in concert with a local practitioner or consultant, who shall go to psychiatric hospital. Frequently he will have to decide what sort of commitment shall be used in a given case, depending upon the laws of state or province.[3] Presumably knowledge sufficient for this task is gained in medical school, but experience shows that frequently medical-school training is insufficient and that health officers suffer considerable anxiety in the performance of this function. As an aid to its more effective discharge, the Appendix summarizes the symptoms of the principal psychiatric syndromes. One of the best means for gaining diagnostic skill that makes for efficient and kindly use of the commitment powers of the health officer is for him to form a liaison with the mental hospitals to which the patients he commits are sent. By this means he can check his impressions against those of psychiatric specialists in the hospitals and also learn the outcome of his cases. In some instances this has led to the development of a follow-up service by public health nurses of patients previously hospitalized; this is a normal function of local health departments in some countries but is only just beginning in the United States.[4] In any case, an alliance with the psychiatric hospitals serving his area will serve as an educational resource for the health officer and probably also net him some helpful friends.

Secondly, the health officers should be informed concerning industrial mental hygiene, since he has the responsibility of maintaining a smoothly running organization. It is no accident that some of the earliest industrial mental hygiene programs were developed in retail merchandising and in large clerical operations.[5,6] It should not be overlooked that the health department "sells" health and that record keeping constitutes a significant part of the work and is one of the few functions used to gauge its efficiency. Again, this represents the horizontal mental hygiene function in the department.

Thirdly, the health officer will need to be familiar with the techniques of interviewing particularly useful for his "front-line" personnel actually in contact with the people of the community—clinic physicians, nurses, sanitarians, receptionists, and others. No maternal and child health program can be maximally effective with personnel educated to pay attention exclusively to physical functioning, neglecting the personality concerned. For example, basic principles of child development and management must be known by nurses and clinic physicians, and the health officer will need a genuine concern and interest in this knowledge if it is to be put into practice by personnel under his control. This is another part of the horizontal function.

Finally, if the time and situation are ripe for it—and this is becoming true in larger and larger sections of the world—he will need a familiarity with the vertical program of furnishing early diagnostic and treatment services to the population. Obviously, each of these functions integrates with the others. On the other hand, aims must be stated and priorities assigned, even though it is recognized that if any one goal is set, it is highly probable that the others will inevitably be involved and furthered to some extent.

IN-SERVICE EDUCATION IN MENTAL HYGIENE

Fundamental to any in-service educational program is a pattern of free communication within the department. It should be possible for anyone in the local department to make his needs known to a person superior to him, certain that this need will be carefully considered and that he will receive a report of the decision reached. Depending upon the size of the department, much or little of the needs felt at the phase-junction of department personnel and the public will reach the health officer himself. But regardless of the size of the department, personnel working directly with the public should know that they can, if necessary, make their needs known to the top executive. In small departments this may be through the medium of the general staff meeting with free and spontaneous discussion, plus an open-door policy maintained by the health officer. In larger departments, staff meetings will be regional. Generally speaking, there should be staff meetings that cross all the professional lines within the department rather than, or in addition to, those for specialists. Nurses, social workers, or sanitarians may need conferences for the discussion of technical problems, but these cannot replace general conferences in the department. In any case, free communication is essential to determine needs for in-service education. With such communication, problems of relationship with persons and groups in the community and problems of clients can become known and ways and means available for meeting them within the department can be mobilized. If necessary, outside authorities can be brought in to help solve problems. The development and maintenance of such a communications pattern is by no means a simple task. Among other things it involves personality characteristics of security and open-mindedness on the part of the executive and his staff which can only be developed through constant care as well as on the basis of adequate administrative training. Some mental hygiene functions can be assigned to specialized staff, but this one must be carried primarily by the leader or leaders of the department.

With this condition operating with some measure of success, needs for in-service training of a realistic and practical sort can become known. Nurses will want to improve their interviewing techniques. They will want information on what to do about the rejecting mother, the dosage of reassurance to give under particular circumstances, how to handle a difficult district health committee, what to say to the mother who asks about masturbation, how to handle the tuberculosis patient who is recalcitrant about going to hospital, etc. There may be people who can help in some of these issues where the department itself cannot furnish experts and cannot call on the next higher echelon for them. There may be a psychologist who can help with problems involving child development, a psychiatrist who will lead a discussion on the rejecting mother or on the way to observe during interviewing. There may be social-service workers who can share their special knowledge, making the discussion a mutual learning experience and a basis for close cooperation of social and health agencies. There may be an educator who can lead discussions regarding particular learning problems connected with the nurses' health-education function. This can, and frequently does, lead to enrichment of the school health program. Sales executives can help sanitarians with their problems in some instances, and psychiatrists can contribute reassurances and knowledge regarding the frequently encountered litigious person.

It is only on the basis of satisfying real needs that most effective in-service education can be done. There is a place for programs planned to meet needs that the group may be assumed to have, even though the mechanism for bringing questions to the surface may not be perfect. New workers need orientation, which may be planned to take place before the employee has had opportunity to grasp the need. Furthermore, situations may arise when a specific course of instruction is necessary to meet some particular need observed by a superior but not yet felt by the staff. It is generally agreed that such planned courses are not as efficient in procuring learning, but availability of teaching personnel and other reasons may dictate a sacrifice of efficiency in this respect.

In-service education may be conducted by visits of state consultative staff, at the request of the health officer or with his acquiescence, the request originating at the central office.

CLINICAL SERVICES

There are many advantages, administrative and educational, in the plan of organization under which mental health services are part and parcel of the other services of the health department. On the theoretic side, the advantages lie in furthering the general principle that man is a unitary being. On the practical side, rent, heat, and other service costs can be saved by multiple use of health-department clinical space if the clinic operates only part time. The community organizational skills of the health officer and his staff are available, and the therapeutic aids of the clinical staffs of the health department are also at hand for the service of the patient and for liaison in the community.

It has been said that the sterilizers, examining tables, x-ray machines, etc., of the clinic may furnish an unsuitable environment for psychiatric work. Perhaps in such a situation the patient may expect to have "something done to him," whereas in psychiatric treatment the watchword is collaborative work of staff and patient on the problems at hand. The setting may lead the patient to expect definite, clear-cut advice rather than a counseling relationship. Some effort may be required to change the expectancies of the patient and to protect the staff from being seduced into more advice giving than is therapeutically wise. Nevertheless the difficulties are usually quickly overcome, and the end result is not interfered with. There are disadvantages in that multiple use of space involves storage problems for the bulky play and psychological testing materials necessary for psychiatric work, particularly with children, but these problems are also not insuperable.

Another difficulty concerns the keeping of psychiatric records. These records frequently must contain private and intensely personal material that cannot be open to the risk of being bruited about by gossips in the community. The records ought to be kept locally where they can be most useful; in fact, on purely medical grounds there is every reason to believe that they should be an integral part of the family case folder. Aside from reasons of confidentiality, the bulk of psychiatric case records makes this inadvisable, and no one has yet solved the problem of how to keep psychiatric records brief; the necessary facts simply are too numerous, and any adequate record is long. The usual compromise is that the working case record is kept in a separate locked file open only to the psychiatric clinic team; it is open to others, including the health officer himself, only upon the permission of the psychiatrist. It is hoped that some day medical philosophy will have advanced to a point at which it will be as reasonable to put in the record how a man got syphilis as to state the fact that he has it, and that the fact that he is cruel or emotionally gauche in his attitudes toward his children will be no less an important medical fact to be known to health personnel than the record of the bruises on the child. But this time appears to be in the future still, at least in most communities in the United States. In any case, the family case record usually contains only an abstract of the psychiatric history and therapeutic record. Especially composed letters convey such information to the community agents involved in the cases, including the physician, as is essential for them in carrying out their therapeutic responsibilities. This is felt to be somewhat immature, but it seems necessary at the present state of development in all types of psychiatric work, public as well as private. One of the really difficult problems of the separate, confidential psychiatric record is that it gives rise to jealousies and sometimes real dislike between the "classes" within the health department—those who have access to the locked file and those who do not. Such jealousies are easily aroused anyway, for several people must share rapport with the patient. The locked file tacitly forces the assumption that the psychiatrist, the psychologist, and the psychiatric social worker are in some way special medical vessels who can contain corrosive information without leaking, whereas others are made of less resistant material. Experience leads to doubt of this conclusion, but tradition nevertheless maintains the separated and restricted record in most places.

Secretarial work for psychiatric clinics is a heavy burden. When a clinic operates full time the problem is not so difficult, since obviously a full-time secretarial staff is necessary and must be financed. With a part-time clinic the problem is more thorny, for the bulk of work is not sufficient to justify a full-time employee, and part-time secretaries are difficult to procure and to train in the medical ethics involving confidentiality. In such situations, usually one secretary is assigned the job of keeping the psychiatric case records in addition to other duties. Uncooperative health officers—or office managers—can easily sabotage a clinic's effectiveness by shifting the stenographic task from one person in the office to another, for there is much new technical jargon to master for a secretary just beginning to take and transcribe psychiatric records. The use of recording instruments, so that dictating can be done apart from the secretary and transcribing done on the days the clinic is not operating, offers one satisfactory solution. When a new part-time psychiatric clinic is set up, it will be wise to plan rather carefully how the secretarial burden is to be carried. It is easy to say that the extra work can be absorbed by an existing pool of clerical and stenographic help, but if this is done it will require careful consideration. The keeping of the records may prove as difficult a problem to solve as the finding of a psychiatric leader for the clinic team.

Cases for the mental hygiene clinic are referred from various sources, varying from community to community, depending partly on the type of educational program that has preceded the opening of the service. If explanatory talks are given to teachers and school administrators, cases will come in large numbers from the schools; work with medical societies will result in an increased percentage of cases from practitioners in the community; and so forth through the social agencies of the community. Curiously enough it is impossible to gauge the extent of need in any of these areas by the number of referrals from them; nowhere has the need for service been saturated so that the real pressures can be evaluated. In several years' experience in Maryland, approximately 15 per cent of cases were referred by practicing physicians, 30 per cent by health department personnel, 30 per cent from the schools, 20 per cent from departments of welfare, and the rest from other scattered sources.[7] In some cases, clinics have allotted a "quota" of admissions, except for emergencies, to each of the various sources. Some offer only consultative services for cases beyond the quota; others simply refuse to accept further cases from that agency. This latter policy seems unwise except in case of absolute necessity.

In some areas, local health departments have found it wise to insist that every case be considered a referral by a private physician, or at least to secure the permission of the patient's physician before any diagnostic or treatment procedure is carried out. Treatment is refused if permission to communicate with the physician is denied. There are many advantages in this, and they extend beyond the extremely important one (in the United States, at least) of maintaining good relations with medical organizations. The physician may have valuable helpful information on the case that will clarify diagnosis and speed treatment. Furthermore, the reporting to the physician of the findings of the clinic is one of its very important educational opportunities.

Other clinics insist that every case be cleared by the public health nurse in whose district the patient resides. Usually the nurse is required to make a home visit, reporting her impression of the people and environment to the clinic team. This function is expanded to include a more or less extensive history of the case in clinics operating without a psychiatric social worker. This procedure prepares the nurse to accept such therapeutic assignments in the case as she will be asked to carry. There is frequently cause for complaint by nurses who function in this way that the clinic never turns back to them the result of its deliberations and therapeutic work—it devours all the information they can give it but never gives them anything in return. Psychiatrists and their professional helpers are not likely to be informed concerning the intensive rapport the public health nurse frequently maintains with the people she serves. They are likely to underestimate the value of her information, the extent of her therapeutic opportunities, and the persistence of her interest in her patient. This ignorance may well make the nurse feel frustrated and angry if the opportunity to follow through on the cases is not offered her. Perhaps this is particularly true when she has cases which are as severe as the ones she has referred already, but which cannot be managed by the clinic by any other stratagem than putting them at the end of a waiting list. As is the case with her tuberculosis patients, if she cannot get definitive treatment, she does want help in how to manage the case as effectively as possible during the waiting period. This opportunity for interim service is one of the main advantages of integrating mental hygiene clinical services into existing health departments.[8]

The problem of the management of appointments in part-time clinic operations has already been discussed in Chap. 3.

The Inauguration of New Clinic Services. In many countries, mental hygiene work has been highly publicized, and there will be demand for service on the part of some groups in the community. The problem in the United States, at least, is not to generate demand; this can usually be found ready-made among groups of educators, in social agencies, in the juvenile court, and among public health nurses. Demand does not usually originate with medical practitioners, though the pediatric specialists may be vocal to this end. On the other hand, organized medical societies rarely oppose the starting or expansion of clinic programs in psychiatry when they are properly approached. There exists in many communities—and this is becoming more true over the United States, at least—a local mental health association and, perhaps, an association of parents of retarded or otherwise handicapped children. These organizations are also in the forefront in demanding some psychiatric support, once the possibility for obtaining service becomes known.

The focusing of the demand from these various types of groups into a program that can meet the realities of financial possibility, and the adjusting of what are usually inflated expectancies to the actual possibilities for delivering service, is one of the first tasks in the establishment of a new clinical service. Psychiatry is heavily publicized at the present time in much of the literate world. Almost magical powers of solving human problems are ascribed to it by many people. These are certain to be disappointed with a new clinic set up if they do not know its ways of working and its limitations beforehand. On the other hand, overstress of the limitations leads to discouragement, which is dangerous, particularly when local financial support must be obtained. It is very difficult both to be honest about the amount and effectiveness of service likely to be available and also to preserve the community demand at the level necessary to establish and finance a new service.

Many local health officers are severely embarrassed when local demands are only for clinical service to patients, whereas financial resources available seem to make the horizontal type of program the only one conceivable under existing circumstances. Such a program is likely to seem to the demanding group to be a very poor second choice to a solid clinic service, which could relieve the discomforts of patients and which would help the people who must teach and care for them in the community. Frequently, the harsh financial facts will, however, help the community to take their second choice rather than no help at all, though the health officer and his consultants may have a stormy time before this conclusion is reached. These problems cannot be solved by health department personnel alone. They must be thrashed out with some sort of health council containing representatives of the population to be served.

Demand may be latent in the community and deliberately left latent because there appears to be no early possibility for satisfying it. Emergency cases may be sent, with as little fanfare as possible, to some neighboring area or city for diagnosis and treatment, the persons "in the know" avoiding the inadequacy of local services' becoming a subject of general information. The same situation, however, may be the subject of newspaper articles and public meetings when it appears likely that an aroused and vocal public demand can lead to support for a local service previously recognized as needed. Where a long-term plan of extension of services is actually unfolding in response to known needs, community agencies will agree to accept minimal emergency service for a year or two in the light of what seems to be a sound plan, mobilizing the community's latent demand when it appears likely that service may shortly be supplied. Leadership in such situations may mean leaving a demand diffuse and sporadic, then bending every effort to make it enthusiastic and organized when the possibility of satisfying it ripens through state or local legislative appropriating action or voluntary agency support. When such mobilization of demand fails to bring forth the hoped-for appropriation, there must be an alternative plan that will leave the community more than it had before in educational program. Otherwise, there will result frustration and apathy that may not again arise to active demand should possibilities for increased service again appear. Generally speaking, a clinic service will not integrate well into a community in which need for its services has not been recognized. It appears to be an unwise policy to bring in any service unless the community feels a need for it and has some idea as to how to use it before it is brought. Nevertheless, once the service is assured, some intensive educational work will need to be done. The health-department personnel will need to learn to handle new record and reporting forms. The importance of recording interpersonal and environmental conditions in referred cases will have to be learned by the nurses with this new assignment. The local medical society, the acquiescence of which has been obtained much earlier, needs to have an explanation of how to refer cases, an invitation to attend staff conferences, and perhaps some education on the interpretation of the reports physicians will receive from the clinic. Schoolteachers, principals, and pupil personnel workers will need information of a similar sort, as will social workers and executives of agencies. Special educational work may have to be planned for the juvenile court. Collaboration with the psychiatric hospital serving the locality may need to be established if not already in existence. As already noted, the distribution of this educational program will, at least for a time, determine the sources from which the cases come.[9]

Usually when a new clinic service is inaugurated there ensues a discouraging period during which a great many severely defective children will appear. The clinic team and the health officer may feel such cases to be hopeless and see no opportunity in them. Many will prove to be imbeciles or idiots, depending upon the location and previous services available, and in some localities they will have been seen by many other diagnosticians. Their parents, unable to rest with the poor prognoses given by the others, will grasp at another straw, sanguine that a more hopeful prognosis may appear or that some "new treatment" will have been discovered that will cure the child. Every community has some such children; they are responsible for such severe unhappiness in their unfortunate parents that they are the first to appear in new clinics.

One of the great advantages of a clinic in a health department is that these cases can be followed continuously provided hospitalization is not absolutely necessary. There are nursing techniques that can make the load of care lighter, and suggestions for management that can reduce the emotional load. The very identification of the group may make it clear that special school classes are necessary, or that group therapy sessions with the parents will be helpful. Difficult as such cases are, they do offer opportunities for help, and not infrequently the new clinic's success will depend on the attitude taken toward them. The situation is something like that encountered in intractable cancer; the health services must be devoted to keeping the patient as productive as possible and the family comfortable even though being entirely honest about the poor prognosis. Cases with better prognosis come later if careful, helpful attention is given to these.

FINANCING LOCAL SERVICES

Mental hygiene programs are expanding and being established very rapidly at the present time and, like other new and expanding programs, are likely to show a hodgepodge of funding methods. The first clinics were almost entirely supported by nonofficial funds; the development of the clinic technique as it now operates in the United States is largely due to support during the 1920's by the Commonwealth Fund.[10] These were demonstration clinics, and it was expected that the host city would absorb their cost after some time. In most instances this happened, though some clinics were also allowed to die, the demonstration not being sufficiently successful to convince the communities that sacrifices should be made to maintain them. Where the clinics survived, their support was provided by tax funds in some instances, as through the budget of the juvenile court or an official welfare agency, or even a state university. In other instances—and this was perhaps more common—the funds came from voluntary agencies, sometimes a mental health association or a family case-work agency. Such groups also began clinics de novo, of course, once the technique became known. As the combining of fund-raising endeavors in North American communities became usual, community chests took in the clinics, either completely or granting support in combination with some tax monies.

As state health departments became interested in extending service to all the population of an area, local mental hygiene programs began to receive state subsidy. This expanded tremendously in the United States and Canada after the passage of national legislation providing subsidies on the basis of matching funds. For the most part, state and Federal funds were distributed in such a fashion that they could be used only to expand service and not to replace local funds.

The result is that funding of mental hygiene programs has grown extremely complex. Maryland (2 million population), for example, receives Federal funds which have varied from $22,500 to $45,800 between 1947 and 1952, and in 1953 received $32,000 (figures are rounded to the nearest $100). The first state appropriation of $25,000 was made in 1950; it was raised to $50,000 in 1951 and to $65,000 in 1952, where it continued in 1953. In 1954, to compensate for reduction in Federal grants and for expansion, the appropriation was $88,000. With a change in Federal policy in the direction of the reduction of grants to states, it is clear that increase in state or locally appropriated funds must take place.

Local contributions to the mental hygiene services vary widely, both as to source and amount. All counties contribute some local tax money, many both in cash and in services of generalized personnel and in building space, light, and heat. The amount of such contribution is very difficult to estimate; it is approximately $20,000 to $30,000 for the whole state. In addition there are voluntary funds. In one county this is a community-fund contribution of approximately half the cost of a full-time service. In another, the fund helps supply psychological and psychiatric-social-work service, on a basis beyond the relatively uniform per capita expenditure maintained by the state health department's division. In another area, private donations supplement certain salaries so that positions can be filled which are not sufficiently attractive at the level established under the standard salaries in the state. A supplementary film library is maintained by private contribution in one area. Another county pays certain travel expenses for clinical service; this has become more or less traditional since the clinical services were completely carried by volunteers.[11]

In addition to all this, there are further resources in Maryland. The teaching hospitals operate extensive outpatient services for children and adults; these are not a part of the state health department's budget, of course, but must be reckoned with in calculating per capita expenditures. One of these medical schools is tax-supported, the other is fundamentally a voluntarily contributed service. In one, a pediatric-psychiatric service on a demonstration basis is given supplementary voluntary support through the mental hygiene society,[12] which is responsible for other types of contributions to other clinics as well. In one county, a special demonstration service is supported by still another source of funds. In emergency situations various voluntary sources, such as lay health associations, service clubs, and women's clubs, may contribute for specific purposes. Small but fairly regular needs for play equipment are usually supplied by interested local groups.

Financing and financial planning in such a complex pattern requires a great deal of effort and time on the part of both the local health officer and his consultant at the state level. While administration would be far simpler if funds all came from a single, reliable source, it is also true that financing forms a solid ground of mutual concern that binds local, state, and even Federal authorities together in solving local problems, and voluntary contribution locally ensures genuine local participation that tends to keep services practical and adapted to local needs.

Local interest in mental hygiene is, under proper voluntary leadership, deep and driving. The public official in mental hygiene or psychiatry experiences both pressures and opportunities beyond those falling on officials concerned with programs that are intrinsically less emotionally disturbing. The management and proper direction of these powerful forces is a matter of considerable administrative skill and may be shared with the general field of public administration.

The Use of Volunteer Services. Voluntary support in money has already been discussed. In many cultures over the world, the concept of volunteer services in health, or indeed in any public program, has not developed to the extent it has in North America. The possibility of giving of one's personal time to such services depends upon many factors, including the political philosophy and the economic condition of the country in question. Where families can be supported by the work of the husband alone, the wife may give time to bring a service otherwise unattainable to less fortunate members of the population. A political philosophy that tends to place ultimate responsibility for control in the individual citizen tends to foster an attitude that, when the formal services are unable to accomplish their task fully, the individual citizen has an obligation to help personally. There are, of course, many other determinants, not the least of which are the ethical and religious tenets of the people.

Mental hygiene programs offer enormous opportunities to those with a drive to help their fellow man in direct ways. Most disturbances of mental health are marked by distress and sadness on the part of either the patient or his family, frequently both. Loneliness and a feeling of isolation are very common symptoms. These situations stimulate persons to want to help relieve them. This is the source of voluntary contributions and of volunteer time.

Volunteer services in mental hospitals have expanded greatly in North America since World War II. During the war years, patriotism was added to the factors leading toward citizen participation in health and welfare services. Under this urge, large numbers of people, particularly women of middle and upper economic strata, gave time to various recreational services in all types of military and veterans' hospitals. At the end of the war, need for such services decreased, the result being an excess of persons trained to work with psychiatrically and otherwise ill persons. This pool of volunteers was directed toward work in mental hospitals and has had a considerable impact on them.[13]

Several reasons for this can be quickly discovered. During the war years, the hospitals had been neglected medically and financially, and at its end they were badly overcrowded and understaffed. This was true practically the world over, particularly in countries such as Italy, Yugoslavia, and France, where buildings as well as personnel had been lost. As noted in Chap. 4, there followed, particularly in the United States, a series of exposés of conditions that did much to arouse public determination to improve the situation not only by increased appropriations, but also through the contribution of personal time. Psychiatric theory also had matured. Personality deterioration in patients had come to be considered the result of deprivation of social opportunities rather than exclusively of the progression of the particular mental illness involved. The expansion of social contacts for patients therefore came to have genuine therapeutic or prophylactic value. There were many other factors involved to make the time ripe for the broad development of volunteer services in mental hospitals. One of these that deserves special mention was that voluntary mental health associations were active in many parts of North America, at least, and were capable of organizing and carrying the considerable administrative load of arranging and operating such programs.

Volunteers are trained to perform certain types of services for patients. The most important and widespread of these is to furnish recreational opportunities. Women go to hospitals and get ward groups together to talk, play games, listen to music, sing, and have refreshments. This is a recurrent type of responsibility carried out with remarkable consistency by many groups of women. Other services require specific training; volunteers have been used as music therapists, to take patients for walks, as occupational-therapy aids, as letter writers, etc. Generally speaking, the policy has been not to use volunteers to replace any regular therapeutic service the hospital should supply. They provide the unique factor of bringing into the hospital interests from the "outside world," a contribution to the maintenance of the social skills of patients not usually possible to procure through the hospital staff alone.

Volunteers are usually available for work in outpatient clinics as well, but their function here is much more difficult to define, and, in general, their use has been much less widespread. As in the case of records, there is the problem of local gossip if it is generally known who attends psychiatric clinics; this is an unfortunate fact, but it nevertheless inhibits the use of volunteers in outpatient services. Clinic and playroom furnishings are often supplied by volunteers. Transportation of patients seems an ideal service for volunteers, but frequently has failed. Probably it represents too great a direct financial outlay, and even in the United States, automobiles are not common enough to be easily available for regular use outside the family.

Volunteers have been rather extensively used as counselors for juvenile delinquents in some areas, and with some success.[14] So far as is known, a similar use has not been made of them in mental hygiene clinics, but it would appear to be a possibility that might be developed. Many social issues and entanglements would undoubtedly develop, but it is conceivable that the child whose psychiatric problems are directly related to a broken home could profit by building an association with a responsible and stable father or mother figure. Many other situations come to mind in which such arrangements might contribute to the therapeutic plan. This would appear to be a field for judicious experimentation.

A much less dangerous field is the organization of volunteer services to furnish social opportunities for the elderly; this will be discussed in later chapters.

Mental health associations, of course, have tremendous need for volunteers, and recruit many. They are needed for the large programs of furnishing gifts to patients for holidays, particularly Christmas, for educational mailings, for the operation of financial campaigns, for the support of educational and service programs. Many professional persons are organized and trained to conduct discussion groups for the education of the general public in mental hygiene.

SUMMARY OF CHAPS. 5 TO 7

Mental health programs at the national level, in large countries that are administered as federations of states, republics, prefectures, departments, or other subunits, have developed to furnish certain types of services:

1. Organized leadership through consultation services to political subunits.

2. The collection of statistics necessary for planning and for certain types of research.

3. The financing of research programs.

4. The subsidy of training of personnel where shortages exist.

5. The furnishing of certain specific psychiatric services, such as immigration examination, psychiatric service to prisons, special services to seamen, military and veterans' services, etc.

6. Subsidy to political subunits for the care of patients, both in hospital and through outpatient and educational programs for the public.

The extent to which these functions are carried out in any particular country depends upon its political philosophy, its taxing structure, the state of public (and thereby legislative) interest in mental hygiene problems, and general economic conditions.

Programs at the level of the political subunits, the state, prefecture, department, or province, usually bear primary service responsibilities to the public and the psychiatrically ill members of it. Programs at this level have usually developed along the following lines:

1. Furnishing of psychiatric hospital services. When more than one hospital exists, this involves regionalization, both as to servicing cases from a given area and for follow-up services to discharged patients.

2. Furnishing or planning for psychiatric outpatient services. Such services may be supported by the state government, by university or other type of voluntary or tax-supported agencies, or by a combination of the three. The state administration of this program may lie in the health department or in the department of the government responsible for hospitalization, if these are not the same.

3. Furnishing a broad educational program, a horizontal program, within the state health-department staff and for local health-department staffs so that the general principles of mental hygiene that apply in all health work may be adequately known and used.

4. Furnishing consultation to local health departments in regard to the development and operation of outpatient services. Regardless of where responsibility is assigned at the state level, the ultimate function of tax-supported outpatient services should be administered by the local health department.

5. Furnishing materials such as library, film collections, and other educational materials for use and distribution throughout the state.

6. Furnishing educational subsidies to produce particularly needed personnel. This will probably be possible only in fairly large political units.

7. Stimulating and financing or actually performing scientific research. Since almost every move in establishing outpatient and educational services is likely to be more or less experimental, the planning and administration of such services is frequently of itself a research venture and should be treated in this light.

8. Collecting and coordinating statistical material applying to psychiatric and educational services and needs in the state.

9. Cooperating with voluntary agencies (where they exist) for the improvement, expansion, and support of programs.

Programs furnishing outpatient psychiatric service at the local level are difficult to administer unless the unit served has a population of 25,000 to 50,000. The arrangement of such units is itself a major administrative task in some areas, but unless it can be accomplished, therapeutic service is difficult to furnish, though helpful diagnostic services may be possible. Regionalization crossing local political boundaries is notoriously difficult but can be accomplished more readily if a considerable proportion of the cost of services is born at state or Federal level. Educational services may be planned independent of the size or population of the political unit. All services will be more efficient if coordinated by the local health department and if full use is made of its personnel for direct service to patients and for gaining the cooperation of other community agencies. To achieve this involves considerable educational effort at state and local level and joint planning by the health-department staff and the mental hygiene personnel, both state and local. Local mental hygiene programs will include the following:

1. Educational programs for health-department staff in such areas as are necessary to make its public health functioning maximally effective through the use of mental hygiene techniques and knowledge.

2. Educational programs regarding the use of outpatient psychiatric services. This will include case finding and investigation, and the carrying out of certain therapeutic responsibilities. It will also include material on how best to cooperate with the personnel of psychiatric clinic teams, and how to stimulate other voluntary and official agencies to make the most efficient use of the clinic services.

3. Cooperation with the voluntary mental health association in obtaining volunteer services and financial support and in planning services to meet the community needs.

4. Sponsoring or furnishing materials for a public educational program.

5. Depending on the laws of the area in question, the health officer may be a committing authority. Generally speaking, this function will be separated from the function of the outpatient clinic.

6. Cooperation with the psychiatric hospital receiving patients from the locality in educational programs, in the follow-up of discharged patients and in admission of patients.

7. In larger local units, planning will take on many aspects of state function in addition to the local ones detailed above.

REFERENCES

1. Emerson, H.: *Local Health Units for the Nation,* The Commonwealth Fund, New York, 1945.
2. *The Application of Psychiatry to Industry,* Committee on Psychiatry in Industry, Group for the Advancement of Psychiatry, Report 20, Topeka, Kans., 1951.
3. Ballard, F. A., and R. G. Fuller (eds.): *Mental Hygiene Laws in Brief,* National Committee for Mental Hygiene (National Association for Mental Health), New York, 1941.
4. Baltimore County Health Department, Towson, Md., unpublished plans and rules of procedure, 1954. The State Health Department of Georgia, Atlanta, has also plans for such activity, as yet unpublished.
5. Harrell, T. W.: *Industrial Psychology,* pp. 363 ff., Rinehart & Company, Inc., New York, 1949.

6. Giberson, L. G.: "The Technic of Listening to Troubled Employees," *Indust. Med.* 9:414–417 (1940).
7. Lemkau, P. V.: "The Mental Health Program of the Maryland State Department of Health," *Maryland Health Bull.* 23:80–87 (1951).
8. Maril, E. C.: "The Use of Psychiatric Casework Service in a Health Department Setting," *J. Psychiat. Social Work* 22:96–98 (1953).
9. *An Outline for Evaluation of a Community Program in Mental Hygiene,* Committee on Cooperation with Lay Groups, Group for the Advancement of Psychiatry, Report 8, Topeka, Kans., April, 1949.
10. Stevenson, G. S., and G. Smith: *Child Guidance Clinics, A Quarter Century of Progress,* The Commonwealth Fund, New York, 1934.
11. Thomas, Robert E. (Chief, Division of Mental Health, Maryland State Department of Health): Personal communication, 1954.
12. "Spotlight on Mental Health, The Mental Health Fund Supports New Clinic," *Ment. Hyg. Soc. Maryland* 6 (4) (1954).
13. *Volunteer Participation in Psychiatric Hospital Services,* National Committee for Mental Hygiene, New York, 1950.
14. Vedder, C. B.: *The Juvenile Offender,* Doubleday & Company, Inc., New York, 1954.

Part Two

THE DEVELOPMENT
OF THE INDIVIDUAL

CHAPTER EIGHT

The Study of Personality Development

BASIC PRINCIPLES

If the mental health of the population is to be improved, the methods used will be based on a knowledge of what people are in total personality, how they react, and what they react to. Chapter 1 indicated that personalities grow through a process of building up experiences around a constitutional base or core. Mental hygiene has the aim of arranging the kind of experiences encountered, the timing of experiences, and the setting so that the personality resulting will have maximum strength and maturity. So baldly stated, this sounds as though the body of knowledge that is mental hygiene were sufficient so that this task could be carried out if the scientist were but given sufficient power and resources. Actually, this is, of course, not the case. The mental hygienist works with those experiences that present themselves for study and within the narrow limits of power granted him under the social system in which he lives. Furthermore, each human being is unique, and each will integrate life experiences into the personality structure in his own unique way.

On the other hand, all health-promoting endeavors are based on the knowledge that human beings tend to react similarly to similar stimuli. Immunization programs would be impossible if the capacity for individuals to form antibodies were infinitely variable. Such programs depend upon the fact that a large percentage of persons will react the same way to the same physiological stimulus. The mental hygienist uses the same basic principle, assuming that most individuals will react in a similar fashion to certain psychological and physiological stimuli, which in this case comprise certain life situations and commonly shared obediences to basic biological laws. For example, all persons born have been subject to the laws of heredity and are subject to those of bodily growth and personality maturation. Almost all are exposed to an environment that includes parents and brothers and sisters. The vast majority of children attend school. Most men become wage earners, most women become mothers. Many men become soldiers for a period of their lives. People get older, and their patterns of reaction change as their years increase. Such commonly shared experiences must be integrated into the personality structures of most individuals in the population.

NECESSARY MATERIALS

The historical development of a situation is usually the key to understanding it. Certainly the history of an illness is essential in making a diagnosis, whether the illness is medical, sociological, or psychological. Suppose that the "disease" were lack of energy and high rates of mental deficiency in a population. The history of this "disease" might include the hereditary characteristics of the population, the historical development of its customs, the study of parasites in the soil, the chemical and physical state of the soil and the climate. These factors and many others would have to be recognized as contributory to the study of any individual in the population. What has preceded the present status must be taken into consideration when studying that status.[1,2,3]

Prophylactic programs must, of course, always be oriented toward the future. Frequently the present situation is evaluated in terms of that future. It is looked upon as a piece of history in the state of "becoming" —of maturing, as it were, before the eyes of the health worker. When the future goal is reached, the existing situation will be past history, to be studied as to how it contributed to the state then attained. The worker in prophylaxis will be concerned as to how his actions in the past affected the present, and how action now will affect what is still to come.

In order to influence the personality at any point in its development, it is necessary to have an idea as to how it came to this point. Furthermore, there must be a concept of a state in the future toward which the personality is progressing and developing. That goal is to be a mature, healthy person. A "mature, healthy person" is extremely difficult to define; indeed, a clear-cut and complete definition is impossible at this time. Suffice it to say that he is one who is able to live at relative peace with himself and with his neighbors; who has the capacity to raise healthy children; and who, when these basic functions are accomplished, still has energy enough left over to make some further contribution to the society in which he lives.

As noted above, although each human being is different, all pass through some relatively similar experiences. These generally encountered experiences, arranged according to developmental levels, as well as a discussion of the germ plasm so important in constitution, are to be studied in the following chapters. It is to be recognized that age or developmental levels are artificial and arbitrary. Development is not a succession of plateaus, each above the other; it is a continuous progression that cannot actually be broken into segments.[4]

As each experiential situation is taken up, the factors recognized as important in it will be discussed. The existing agencies in society—in the American types of living, in particular—which are useful in bringing influence to bear will be studied as they are encountered at the various ages. These agencies are the tools actually available for use in the programs outlined organizationally in Part 1. In general, the factors and agencies most stressed will be those which deal with social groups rather than with individuals, with family situations rather than with individual ones, with interpersonal rather than intrapersonal problems. Interpersonal issues are stressed because the principal environmental influences bearing upon the human being reach him through the other human beings with whom he lives. This does not mean that housing and other ecological factors are not important.[5] The developing personality will be affected by these relatively nonpersonal factors, to be sure, but the effect will usually be secondary; they will act upon a given child through their effect on his parents and upon the community in which he lives.

The intrapersonal biologic mechanisms through which impersonal environmental influences and interchange with other personalities change and modify the personality are given less stress. The adjustment of intrapersonal difficulties is primarily a therapeutic project, involving the reliving of poorly integrated past experience so that it can be successfully integrated into the personality structure. Prevention is the keynote of this work; therapy is given secondary emphasis throughout. We assume that if proper building stones are furnished and the proper mortar of attitudes is available, sound personality will result and intrapersonal mechanisms will not require attention or will require it less frequently.

The adjustment of intrapersonal problems deals in forces of great intensity and requires technical skill that is attained only through long training in dealing with sick people. Extensive readjustment of the personality that has become badly adjusted had best be left to the trained psychotherapist and not attempted by personnel who cannot be expected to obtain the necessary intensive training and who are primarily dedicated to more general preventive measures. It should be understood, however, that intrapersonal maladjustments of some severity may sometimes be dealt with successfully through the interpersonal relationships of the patient. Indeed, the establishment of relationships with other

people may be the therapeutic program prescribed by the psychotherapist, so that he calls upon the resources of the group worker as his prime
therapeutic instrument.

SOURCES OF DATA

The data used in the study of the development of the individual
are gathered from a wide variety of fields of science, and from literature and some of the other arts as well. Many of the basic concepts
come from the clinical study of normal children and adults. Some
material comes from the field of anthropometry, the measurement of
man. From this field come studies of the height, weight, reaction time,
muscle strength, all of which help to clarify the picture of the equipment an individual possesses as tools to solve life's problems at various
ages. From such data it is possible to calculate the changes in rate of
development taking place in the physical assets of the individual at
different life periods. Psychometry contributes to anthropometry in
making it possible to measure the capacity to learn. Through its techniques, one can define the differing patterns of thinking possible at
different stages of development. The response of the individual when
the culture demands that certain specific knowledges be acquired in
school, industrial, or other type of training is studied by the educational psychologist; his findings also contribute to the understanding
of personality maturation. Sociology and social work contribute information about the conditions and effects of group living. Anthropology endeavors to understand how cultures come to exist and why
they persist, and how their pressures mold personality; this science,
too, contributes to knowledge of how influences can be made to contribute maximally to healthy personality development.

Child psychiatry and pediatrics have discovered many facts from the
treatment of sick children which are applicable in the interpretation
of normal behavior. Adult psychiatry, seeking to cure people already
ill, has uncovered certain important etiologic factors that need to be
considered by the mental hygienist attempting to prevent mental disease by preventing traumatic early experiences. Geriatrics, the medical
care of the aged, has contributed data useful in preventing premature
personality disorganization.

In attempting to deal with the totality of human functioning, all
available material on human living must be considered. The mental
hygienist is the general practitioner of public health in this sense. This
concept is obviously too broad to be useful in practical application,
however. Not all experiences are of equal importance in the develop-

ment of the personality. Some must be selected for attention, while others may be neglected as less significant. The experiences dealt with in the discussion to follow have been selected on two bases: (1) they are believed to be important for a significant segment of the population; (2) they offer opportunities in some instances, at least, for modification through available knowledge and by available personnel.

PRESENTATION OF DATA

The development and function of the human personality does not yield easily to study by analytic methods, reducing the material to some sort of "elements" and subjecting these to particular study. Whatever the "elements" used, their sum seems always to be something less than the whole, intact personality with which the analysis began.* A concept of the whole cadaver can be gained by successive dissection of the head, neck, arms, etc. The personality cannot be subjected to such dissection and survive at the same time as a lively, interacting human being. There have been many attempts to determine and follow personality "traits" such as possessiveness, shyness, or tendency to aggression. Beginning with Jung's distribution of personalities along a line from introversion to extraversion,[6] there have been attempts to analyze personalities according to other criteria, including recurring patterns of behavior. All these methods present difficulties, since the criterion proves on further analysis not to be a simple "element" but to be complex, difficult of definition and, frequently, not stable for long enough periods to make longitudinal study possible. Such elements depend so strongly upon the environmental situation in which they appear that the student finds it next to impossible to say whether the "trait" is inherent in the person or in the situation under observation.[7]

Nor does the personality survive study by dissection by systems. One can get a reasonably satisfactory idea of the structure of the cadaver by dissecting the nervous system, ductless glands, vascular tree, etc. The analogous method will hardly give a complete picture of the personality. Intelligence might be studied as a "system," for example, tracing its earliest testable features through development to the maxi-

* "Analysis" is used here in the chemical sense and does not refer to psychoanalysis. In the latter, the attempt is not to analyze into elements of behavior, but rather to dissect the mass of experience that has entered the personality structure to identify those situations which have had marked and permanent influence on the structure. The aim is to bring any of these which appear to have resulted in continuing conflict into a synergistic relationship with the mass of experience so that a firmer structure that is more resistant to strain will result.

mum reached in late adolescence, and then following the decline in later age periods. Complex as "intelligence" is with factors of memory, capacity to make abstractions, ability to use symbols, etc., this pursuit would, even so, give only a very partial picture of the behavior of the subject. Similar studies have been done of the range of possible emotional reactions, from the simple evidences of painful and pleasurable tensions in early infancy to the more modulated reactions possible in later life. For a period psychologists attempted to deal with the problem of instincts as elements of personality; for many reasons this attempt has largely been abandoned as failing to present an adequate picture of the complexity of the interaction of inborn capacities and learning. The combination of the data of such systematic studies does not result in a personality. In some way or another, all these and other categories must be dealt with simultaneously if the reacting, living person is to be perceived in full perspective.

For these reasons the study of personality maturation that follows is not in terms of instincts, sentiments, emotions, and intellect, but in terms of epochs of development. This method allows orderly study without doing violence to the personality by breaking it into arbitrary parts. Development is a continuum of events taking place in fairly regular sequence but without clear-cut breaks. In the ensuing chapters, human development will be discussed as a succession of epochs, each dividing point being some developmental event such as walking, or some sociological event (based, of course, on the biological attainments of the individual) such as starting school. On the average, such events have a fairly close correlation with chronological age, though each such event has its own individual range of normal variation. In general, however, developmental events provide a safer guide for interpreting the actions of a child than the chronological age. In the case report later in this chapter, for example, chronological age would be an almost useless point of departure for mother or physician. The yardstick of chronological age is unyielding and applies its units equally to everyone. Developmental age is not a time unit, but one of accomplishment. Its units have a varying relation to the passage of time, the unit being different for each individual. Developmental age is the same as chronological age for the "average" child, but the average is a statistical fiction. The application of the statistical scores to any particular individual gives rise to great injustice; avoiding this procedure is one of the functions of mental hygiene. A "normal" 14-year-old child should be entering high school; to expect a 14-year-old child with a developmental age of 6 or 9 to accomplish this is obviously unfair.

Furthermore, chronological time proceeds at the same rate continuously. There are no permitted variations in it; it functions universally and equally and constantly for all. The basic sciences, physics and chemistry, for example, can be satisfied with such a time scale, but as the life processes are encountered rigid chronological time is less satisfactory. Difficulties become greater in the higher forms of life, and in man a concept of biological or developmental time is almost imperative. By the criterion of gain in weight, to be referred to again later, time passes eight times faster at birth than it does at the age of 3, for example, and for many time would pass extremely slowly as adults, for gains in weight may not occur at all. Language development presents similar problems of spurts in rate of learning at different life periods which, if graphed at a constant rate, would distort chronological time remarkably. Developmental scales tend to take into consideration some of these problems, making the succession of developmental achievements the criterion for the individual child. For dealing in averages and for establishing comparative norms chronological age is, of course, useful.

Judgment of individuals by their chronological age involves the assumption that the various human functions mature at equal rates; a "normal" 24-year-old woman, for example, would have attained the national average of education, would be recently married and relatively independent of her parental family. She would have made the emotional adjustments necessary to maintain a home of her own and have developed the capacity to care for children. Contrast this "normal" picture with that in the following case:

E. W. is a 24-year-old woman brought to clinic by her sister. She has four children for whom she cannot be trusted to care. She is unable to take a job as a maid because she cannot learn to use the gadgets in a home that can afford a maid. She often turns on the gas saying she will light it in a few minutes. She has held jobs as a field hand in cotton and tobacco fields. All four of her children were born in wedlock. The marriage is unstable, the husband leaving for a while each time a child is born. For short periods she has had a home of her own, but she manages very poorly and soon comes to live with some member of her family who supervises her and her children. She got through the second grade in a rural school in the South.

In this woman, maturity is advanced so far as sexual activity and reproduction are concerned—she even keeps the activity within the rules of the culture—but markedly retarded in intellectual growth and in ability to take responsibility. She demonstrates several different developmental ages that vary widely. She has a mental age, defined in terms of an intelligence test, of 6 years 6 months. Reproductively, she is in her thirties; in social responsibility probably in her early teens. The concept of developmental ages makes it possible to interpret her status far more clearly than if she were judged by her chronological age alone. To be sure, the woman described here is not "normal"; the case is used to demonstrate the situation of uneven development that may be seen with less extreme but no less important inequalities in personalities more nearly within the range of normal.

There are a few types of activity that can be followed in a logical study from birth to death. Intelligence as defined through the use of tests is one of the most satisfactory human functions in this regard. Motor activity is also reasonably satisfactory, although not so well standardized. Language development can be followed as a specific type of behavior available for repeated testing. Emotional development is a much less satisfactory one. The data to be used are almost entirely unstandardized and frequently do not yield to any form of measurement; no standard for comparison or unit of value has been devised. Attitudes must be interpreted on the basis of observed reactions to situations. Frequently interpretations must be made when not all the motives and stimuli involved in a given reaction are known.

The study of personality development includes material that depends upon the genetically based time schedule of the maturation of capacities and environmental factors, acting together. Temper tantrums illustrate the combination. This specific activity must be dealt with as it occurs in specific circumstances, with the hope that the activity may be understood even though it is impossible to standardize the situations in which it occurs or to estimate the intensity of the reaction in any measurable units. Wherever measurements and standardizations are available they will be used, but discussions will also deal with clinical material which, at the present state of our science, cannot be presented in this fashion. The public health officer is familiar with this problem of method. He can present a graph demonstrating that the percentage of the population with negative Schick tests is growing, is stationary, or is falling off and thus judge the effectiveness of a particular immunization campaign. But when he evaluates his health-education program, he is usually reduced to words rather than figures. The same problem confronts the mental hygienist. Intelligence, within limits, is in the same category as immunologic testing. Emotional reactions often must be evaluated in terms of clinical description and judgment. In the first case statistical techniques are useful. In the second, the statistical machine is the human brain; subject as it is to prejudice and error, it is the only machine available at this time for the solution of problems with the many immensurable variables encountered in dealing with emotional development.

REFERENCES

1. Crothers, B.: *A Pediatrician in Search of Mental Hygiene,* chaps. 9 and 13, The Commonwealth Fund, New York, 1937.
2. Plant, J. S.: *The Envelope: A Study of the Impact of the World upon the Child,* The Commonwealth Fund, New York, 1950.
3. Mumford, L.: *The Conduct of Life,* chap. 2, Harcourt, Brace and Company, Inc., New York, 1951.
4. Buseman, A., and L. Marburg: "Periodisität in Ablang der menschlichen Jugend, "*Kinderartzlich Praxis* 18:9–10, 443–451 (1950).
5. Cremieux, A.: "Paradoxes, Problems and Dilemmas of Preventive Efforts in the Mental Field," *Le Sud méd. et chir.* 81:980–984 (1949).
6. Jung, C. G.: *Psychological Types,* Harcourt, Brace, and Company, Inc., New York, 1923.
7. Spence, W. S.: "Theoretical Interpretations of Learning," in S. S. Stevens (ed.), *Handbook of Experimental Psychology,* John Wiley & Sons, Inc., New York, 1951.

CHAPTER NINE

The Preindividual Factors: Eugenics

The human being at birth is the product of innumerable forebears, each of whom contributed something to his constitution. These ancestors form the base of a vast pyramid, to most of which we pay little attention as a rule. For practical reasons, consideration is usually given only to the last few generations, on the assumption that they will show the principal elements concerned in the make-up of the individual. Furthermore, studies of human heredity in general tend to deal with specific items, such as the appearance of disease or defects, rather than with general characteristics, such as the social nature of mankind. There is also a tendency to stress the defects of stock rather than the assets of character that run in families.[1]

A discussion of the genetic background of the human race must take in far more than specific traits apparent at any moment. Genetic mechanisms have produced mutants from time to time which have enabled the human animal to adapt better to his environment or to control it more completely. For the most part, the distinctly human element in this genetic and selective process over the ages appears to be increasing capacity for the young individual to be molded by the people and things around him. Man appears to be different from other animals in this greater freedom to learn; the laws of heredity are less binding for him than for other animals. The recognition of this has led to the conception by some that man is infinitely variable according to the influences that are brought to bear after conception. This radical view holds that the fertilized ovum is a veritable *tabula rasa,* a blank slate that will contain only what is written upon it, that will be entirely passive in absorbing life's experiences, selecting later markings only on the basis of what has already been written. Other facts indicate that the state is not passive, that it changes with the passage of time, and changes in a reasonably regular pattern for all undamaged individuals.

HEREDITY SETS THE TIMETABLE FOR LIVING

Heredity, its pattern complete at the moment of conception when the sperm and the egg fuse, makes itself felt in the growth and development of the individual throughout life. Its function does not stop at birth; it sets the biological schedule for the major events of life, and, according to many geneticists, has a good deal to do with the time of death.[2] Together with certain modifying environmental conditions, heredity determines when an individual will walk, when he will talk, at what age his pubertal growth spurt will begin, when reproduction will be possible, and, for the female, when that possibility will fade. Heredity determines hair color, eye color, height, sensory acuity, and, in some cases, the loss of the last. It is only by heredity that human beings reproduce their human capacities at all.[3] All this is accepted as so commonplace that it may be thought of too infrequently.

HEREDITARY ASSETS AND DEFECTS

The magnificent intricacies of hereditary mechanisms that come out right are lost sight of, when viewed through the needle's eye of the occasional specific defect. The greatness of the whole of the working out of the hereditary process is lost in the study of particular changes. The inherited trait of albinism when observed in a passer-by is likely to blot out consideration of the fact that many characteristics developed quite normally, producing a functioning human being. It is, perhaps, worth stressing that heredity is responsible for the fact that most human beings develop normally and that only relatively few have "hereditary defects."

Medical geneticists have usually concerned themselves with the defects, errors, and accidents that appear in human development. This is only because nature is generally highly efficient and things usually turn out well. Transmitted defects are the rarity and attract attention, whereas cases reproducing within the range of normal are accepted without question. Medical men tend to look for things to cure; this undoubtedly contributes to the fact that the medical literature on hereditary defects is far larger than that on hereditary assets. Perhaps medical men find excuses for their failure to cure some conditions by crediting them to hereditary defect for which they cannot be held responsible. It is remarkable, for example, how much less is written about the hereditary character of diabetes mellitus since the discovery of insulin has brought this disease under control. The same may well happen to the discussion of the hereditary character of schizophrenia, epilepsy, and cancer, if and when these illnesses can be better controlled medically and when more about their causes has been discovered.

Physicians are rarely asked to "cure" a genius. The mother is proud of her son with musical talent and shows him off to her friends, but she does not take him to a physician because he is different from other boys of his age in this respect. The other slope of the curve gets much more medical attention. When the mother finds her son maturing too slowly and unable to pass in school, she is apt to conceal the fact from the neighbors but tell it to the doctor. Assets are rarely causes for complaint; defects usually are. This, too, contributes to the fact that defects dominate the medical literature on heredity. These reasons apply to medical geneticists, but they should not apply to biologists generally. In fact, the studies of hereditary assets are usually written by nonmedical authors.[4] Human biology is a relatively new and undeveloped field, however, as contrasted to medical science. It has not yet produced the volume of studies of normal or supernormal traits needed to balance the literature on hereditary defects.

Another reason that defects are more prominent in studies of human heredity than assets is that defects are more easily defined. There has always been a sociological definition of mental disease and deficiency which has made it possible to classify these traits for study in successive generations. It is always possible to see a supernumerary finger, achondroplasia, or cleidocranial dysostosis. The introduction of the intelligence test improved the definition of mental deficiency. Physical abnormalities are easily seen, and intelligence can be measured. But what of traits of character that are related to successful rather than unsuccessful living? Generosity, persistence, trustworthiness, responsibility—traits such as these defy clear-cut definition and measurement. This difficulty occurs less often in the socially undesirable traits. The law will eventually single out the profoundly untrustworthy and irresponsible, but the opposite traits may never come to official attention at all, much less be studied as possibly hereditary. Geneticists themselves are discouraged by these problems. Dahlberg says, "Among other characteristics which interest us most from the standpoint of heredity, we must include mental ones; and research on the latter is tremendously cramped by our lack of precise methods for measuring them. So no results of scientific value have yet been reached in this field." [5]

In the study of both assets and liabilities of personality, a large part of the difficulty lies in the tremendous capacity of the human being to learn. The acorn of possible hereditary transmission of traits is tiny compared to the giant oak of possibility for environmental modification. Even the most elementary genetically transferred traits, such as body size, are greatly modifiable according to the experience through which the individual passes. It is entirely impossible to separate the one from the other, and in many instances it is scientifically illogical to attempt it.

The problem of definition of assets presents few difficulties in animals, still less in plants. Such things as rapidity of growth, resistance to disease, ability to produce seeds or milk are sought after. These can be measured or weighed. Animals, particularly dogs and horses, are sometimes bred for certain "personality traits" like gentleness or alertness, but these are far easier to define in animals than are traits of the same names when observed in human beings. Definitions of the uniquely human functions of the human animal are so difficult, or, conversely, the traits are so complex, that their study across generations leaves a great deal to be desired, and is, in fact, probably logically indefensible.

Some Hereditary Assets. It is true that the human being is inevitably the result of genetic capacities molded by learning, and that personality assets and liabilities are impossible of clear definition because of their complexity and because they represent so small a sample of the entity, the human being. Still, certain studies have been made which have at least historical interest, and which will serve to illustrate some of the difficulties in the study of human genetics.

Intelligence was once a vague term defined only by reference to the state in which it is reduced, mental deficiency. The introduction of intelligence tests made possible a new clarity of definition in a positive sense; intelligence is judged by the ability to accomplish certain tasks that are comparable in difficulty for all members of a particular sociological group. The concept of intelligence is somewhat narrowed in its modern usage, but what is lost in breadth of concept is gained in achieving status as a complex of factors of the personality that can be measured with respectable reliability.

Prior to the use of intelligence tests, the hereditary nature of high intelligence was discussed in terms of fame or of creative genius. There are more modern studies, however, which show that intelligence in its narrow interpretation, as that capacity which enables individuals to do well on certain standardized tests, is also transmitted by heredity. We may refer to the study of 49 children by Grace Allen, in which she shows that the parents and siblings of her highly intelligent group were also of higher than average intellectual status.[6] There are many other studies of the problem, the more recent ones admitting the fundamental hereditary control as proved and moving on to the problem of how much environmental circumstance is able to change the intelligence-by-test. The weight of opinion at this time would appear to lie in the direction that hereditary factors determine the limits, both upward and downward (except in cases of extremely gross neglect of infants and injury to brain tissue), but that the kind of people and the cultural life surrounding the child have much to do with actual accomplishment in intelligence tests.[7]

Special artistic talent has been widely studied to test whether or not it is hereditary. These studies rather uniformly come to the conclusion that it is. Musical talent ran for five generations in the Bach family. Haydn, Mozart, Schubert, Handel,[8] Fauré[9] were all simply the most successful members of families that also produced other notable composers. The work of George and Ira Gershwin serves to illustrate another point, that frequently families showing talented individuals in one art form produce talented individuals in others. Indeed, individuals who are highly talented in one direction are frequently clever in several fields of endeavor as evidenced by Winston Churchill, known as a writer and painter as well as a statesman. Mathematics and musical ability appear to be associated genetically in some families; a study of Einstein might be of interest in this connection. The famous Darwin-Galton family presents evidence of the hereditary nature of the talent for scientific endeavor.

Having moved from a specific trait that is measurable, test intelligence, to talents definable only with great difficulty, we now arrive at a still more general trait, which may be called "social responsibility." The Edwards family has produced leaders of American governmental and religious thought over many generations. It took "seven generations of preachers and thinkers to produce Ralph Waldo Emerson."[4] The Lee family of Virginia is set forth as a prime example of the hereditary character of traits of social responsibility and leadership.

Special ability is a complex function, rarely appearing unheralded by some talent in the forebears yet appearing only when there is an environment at hand to foster its development. The two are inextricable in evaluating the final resultant, the person under study. Both capacity and the opportunity to develop it determine whether fruition will result. Modern geneticists and euthenicists, however much each may be wedded to his particular interest in the study of mankind, agree on this, and each would use the other's techniques so far as possible to improve the race.

Capacity to Accomplish is Inherited. Schubert did not inherit the "Erlking." What he got from his forebears was a sense of rhythm, an ability to hear the difference between various tones, a cerebral organization particularly acute in sensing the harmonic relationships of sounds, plus an indefinable urge and ability to create with these assets. To all this might be added the capacity to appreciate and be stimulated by the poetry of other men. Watching a first-grader struggle to learn that 2 and 2 equals 4, it is immediately clear that the ideas of numbers and multiplication are not inherited, but rather the capacity to grasp this sort of relationship. There are areas where the distinction between an idea and capacity to "have" the idea fades out.[10] The problem of instincts is an example. Sucking is present in the baby without its ever having been taught to him, though the function may improve in efficiency with practice. Sucking is an instinctive art, a pattern of movement that is genetically determined. It can be shown, however, that there is a great deal of emotional connotation connected with the sucking act. There are certain constellations of reaction related to sucking which appear in personalities over a period of years; thumb sucking for consolation is a case in point. Furthermore, it becomes extremely difficult to distinguish the point at which the instinctual muscle pattern of sucking becomes intermixed with the child's appreciation of mother love, where a presumably inherited capacity to feel mother love changes to the actual feeling of mother love. It is only a step further to the question of whether the idea of "mother love" might not be as much inherited as the sucking-movement pattern. This concept becomes even broader when one considers the work of anthropologists. They observe specific cultural patterns in various peoples but find many similarities when the patterns are compared. For example, the same plots recur in the myths of many different cultures, so much so that serious scientists have wondered whether these common patterns might not be said to be inherited for the human race. The ideas seem hardly to be separated from the capacity for creating them. Some have come to the tentative conclusion that perhaps both the capacity and the content are inherited. This concept has been discussed by Jung in terms of the "collective unconscious." [11]

Whatever may be the conclusion concerning these thorny problems, there is much truth in the adage "Like father, like son." When we wish to know around what sort of constitutional core a personality is built, it is worthwhile to look to the family pattern for data.

Some Hereditary Defects. Fortunately, nature turns out human beings who are usually within the range of normal. In terms of the mechanics of heredity, hereditary abnormalities are usually recessive, whereas normal traits are dominant. To have a hereditarily abnormal child, both parents must usually contribute genes carrying the abnormality; the presence of recessive-defect-carrying genes in one parent alone will ordinarily result in a normal child. The fact that many defects are recessive has definite implications as to their continuance in our society. There are defects that are uniformly fatal before the age of reproduction is reached. These certainly do not maintain themselves by any survival of the fittest, nor can they be eradicated by the successful functioning of that "law." The defect will not be lessened in the population by sterilizing the individuals affected; they die before they can reproduce. There is no way of knowing the normal carrier of such a defect unless we mate him with a known carrier of the trait and see if the offspring is defective in a particular way. This would involve the violation of recognized human rights and certainly could not be carried out within any human culture now in existence. It was not even attempted in the short-lived and unscientific Hitlerian regime.

The question of consanguinity comes up in this connection. Consanguinity is a special case of what happens in an isolated population. If choice of mate is restricted to a small group, the chances of recessives meeting are increased in proportion to the extent of the isolation and to the length of time the population has been isolated. Such groups often show larger numbers of defectives of many types than groups in which mating is less restricted. Again it must be pointed out that isolated populations are culturally as well as genetically isolated and that both types of restriction will probably make themselves felt. If recessive-defect-bearing genes are present in a family, the chance that they will meet is greater in consanguineous marriage than in the marriage of unrelated members of the general population. This concept of population isolates may well account for some of the findings in the people of isolated mountain valleys and even the common finding of lower mental ages in rural than in urban populations.[12] Perhaps it is best shown in the studies of hemophilia in the royal families of Europe.[4,13] On the other hand, if there are no recessive-defect-carrying genes, consanguinity is probably of no danger—witness the royal family of Siam, which is said to have been given to closely consanguineous marriage for over 4,000 years.

Specific hereditary diseases and the importance of heredity in mental disease will not be discussed here.[2] In the Appendix this will be taken up in relation to the particular mental diseases.

PROBLEMS OF EUGENICS

What can be done about the core on which the personality structure is built? There are two approaches: (1) to stop the continuation of defects; (2) to breed for assets. This categorization is not by any means completely satisfactory. We must take into consideration the fact that adverse and advantageous traits may be genetically associated. A case in point is the apparent tendency for people with the characteristic of personal responsibility of a high order to become mentally ill with symptoms of serious depression of mood.[2] It has been suggested that artistic genius is frequently associated with detrimental personality factors such as alcoholism and homosexuality. Probably Beethoven's ability to compose was at least partly dependent upon heredity; his deafness also may have been of hereditary origin. The large number of artists, poets, and composers who die young—Schubert, Mozart, Keats—might lead one to wonder whether some lack of physical stamina might not have been associated with their genius. Fortunately, such associations of high assets with severe defects are more spectacular than they are frequent; in people of lesser ability the defects are perhaps also less striking. In the main, there is little to fear in trying to breed out obvious and severe defects. If this were done, we should probably lose very few personalities of outstanding value to the race. As a matter of fact, however, even if the knowledge of heredity were complete and exact, breeding out of defects would be impossible from the practical point of view. The very grossly deficient and defective are unable to reproduce themselves. Healthy carriers of recessive-defect-laden genes are extremely difficult to discover, though some progress is apparently being made in this, particularly through the use of the electroencephalograph in connection with epilepsy [14] and a few other conditions. Even if there were accurate ways of spotting such carriers, however, they would be difficult to control. As knowledge of heredity improves, however, more people are becoming concerned about the fact that they may pass on an adverse hereditary trait to their children.[15] These patients are frequently a real embarrassment to physicians who lack exact knowledge of the hereditary character of various diseases.[1]

Although the grossly deficient do not reproduce themselves, many of the less severely deficient are fully capable of doing so. It is estimated that completely stopping reproduction of mentally deficient persons whose deficiency is suspected of being hereditary would result in only a 10 to 30 per cent decrease of this defect in a generation.[1] From a practical point of view, such a move is impossible, even if it were concluded to be entirely desirable. But elimination of the defectives is not the only advantage in sterilization or other means of reducing fecundity of the feeble-minded. Children born to a mentally defective mother usually are denied proper stimulation and guidance, even though the children themselves are of normal capacity. The family income will in all likelihood be low, the housing inadequate, the education neglected, the infant mortality and morbidity high, and venereal-disease and tuberculosis rates above the community average. It is not only because children are likely to be mentally defective that the feeble-minded ought to be discouraged from reproducing. It is also because the children so frequently receive inadequate care.

It has long been pointed out that sociological stratification is present in the United States in spite of our highly touted democracy.[16] To a large extent, these strata are based on historical and cultural factors, and they tend to become isolates in the genetic sense. Crossing the lines of these strata occurs, but there is great resistance to the crossings. The people in each group tend to marry people like themselves, and the fortunate or unfortunate traits are concentrated in the offspring. Inasmuch as social responsibility, which we have discussed as possibly having a hereditary factor, carries with it a high evaluation of children, and probably for less altruistic reasons as well, the socially responsible families of the last generation or so have tended to have small families. On the other hand, the lowest socioeconomic strata, where children may not be regarded as so highly valuable, and to which birth control is less available because of lack of intellectual curiosity and less used because it requires a certain emotional control, have furnished the bulk of the population replacements. In those strata, however, social responsibility, at least as defined by upper-class groups, is relatively low. What will happen in this situation is the reduction of the top groups and the relative increase of the lower ones. Since the lower socioeconomic groups are presumably of lower intelligence, this will be to the obvious detriment of the race. Sterilization of the most severe of the mental defectives will reduce the lowest group, but the top group will still not be reproducing itself. Under these conditions there is nothing to look forward to but a progressive decrease in the average intelligence of the race. There are some who believe on the basis of researches that this is already taking place, though by no means all geneticists accept this conclusion.[17]

What should be done about this? The first method of eugenics would appear to be the dispersion of population isolates, of social stratification. If "good" traits are dominant and "bad" traits are recessive, as seems to be the case to a considerable extent, dispersion will tend to lower the appearance of the "bad" in succeeding generations. It should not have the effect of lowering the "good," since we deal not with mixtures as a rule, but with dominants and recessives. Perhaps all this had best be summed up by saying that the best func-

tioning democracy in marriage would appear to be the ideal genetically. Whether or not this should include intermarriage of races is a
question that few can discuss scientifically at this time.

It was once fashionable for families of high social responsibility to
have large numbers of children. This is a fashion much to be desired
today, and it should be encouraged. In contrast, birth control should
be made available to the whole population, rather than only to the
upper strata as it now is to a considerable degree.[3] The very lowest
intellectually and socially, those who cannot survive without protective supervision, should be sterilized. Public health already bears responsibility in some states for the latter function,[18] and in some it has
included birth control directly [19] or indirectly in larger programs of
education for responsible parenthood.[20]

Eugenics is considered by some to be a medical responsibility; particularly the responsibility of public health. If it is, it must be admitted
that few are now concerned with it and that it has little part in the
teaching of graduate courses in public health. The experiences of
official population control in Germany have been so recently disclosed
and are so horrible that there is a tendency to link fascism with attempts at population management. On the other hand, in West Germany the public health agencies have the authority to clear all marriage licenses through their files of individuals known to have had
certain conditions thought to be hereditary. When such an individual
wishes to marry, the health officials have the right to call him in, to
persuade him to tell his proposed marital partner of the situation, and
to counsel with both regarding the possibility of passing on defective
germ plasm. Originally, the health official had the legal power to stop
the marriage, though this is no longer constitutional in West Germany.[21] No such program is known to exist elsewhere.

One reason birth-control devices are used more, and more effectively,
by the better-educated upper classes is that their use requires control of
sensuality by the use of intelligence and foresight. Patterns of sexual
activity vary widely according to the level of education, the better-
educated showing less total sex activity, fewer taboos, and more freedom for the partners to talk about their sexual activity. These factors
make birth control easier in their class than in those where cooperation
between the partners concerning sexual activity is likely to be confined
to coition itself. For this and other reasons, some nations have legalized
abortion as a means of preventing births that may be predicted with
reasonable certainty to result to the detriment of the family and society if they are allowed to occur.[22,23] Many serious students doubt the

wisdom of the use of abortion as a means of population control or of eugenics, even when the operation is done under the strictest of medical control.

England, France, Sweden, Canada, and other countries have programs subsidizing children, so that the socially responsible segment of the population will not keep their families small because they wish each child to have better educational and other opportunities. Tax relief given on the basis of children in the family is considered by many to be too low in the United States to have any eugenic effect, and direct subsidy for children is restricted to those who are already economically dependent. These programs are generally not the responsibility of health departments, and public health does not, in many parts of the world, appear to be reaching out very actively to take such responsibilities.

SUMMARY

The constitutional core on which the personality structure is erected is largely genetically determined. Man inherits the capacity to learn as a man can learn, to communicate as human beings communicate. His inherited capacities for growth and development can never be isolated for separate study. Even the most basic of them, such as those determining body size, are obviously greatly influenced by the setting in which the unfolding of the patterns takes place. For more complex capacities, the influence of the environment to encourage the flowering of capacities or the disuse atrophy of them is so great that the separation of inherent capacity and environmental stimuli and guidance is impossible. There are, nevertheless, obvious differences between people. Studies indicate that these differences run in families and, to some extent at least, are dependent upon inborn genetic capacities. The improvement of the constitution through the means of eugenics has not become as yet a major concern of public health, and indeed, it is doubtful if it soon will, in the United States at least. It is a field in which the health officer should have a measure of knowledge, for he may have the responsibility of premarital counseling and in some areas has direct responsibility in deciding conditions under which sterilization may be carried out.

REFERENCES

1. Osborn, F.: *Preface to Eugenics*, Harper & Brothers, New York, 1940.
2. Kallman, F. D.: *Heredity in Health and Medical Disorder*, W. W. Norton & Company, Inc., New York, 1953.
3. Stern, C.: *Principles of Human Genetics*, W. H. Freeman and Co., San Francisco, 1949.

4. Wiggam, E. A.: *The Fruit of the Family Tree,* The Bobbs-Merrill Company, Inc., Indianapolis, 1924.

5. Dahlberg, G.: *Race, Reason and Rubbish,* translated by Launcelot Hogben, Columbia University Press, New York, 1942.

6. Allen, G.: *Families Whence High Intelligence Springs,* Eugenics Records Office, Carnegie Institution of Washington, Bulletin 25, May, 1926.

7. Stoddard, G. D.: "Intelligence: Its Nature and Nurture. I, Comparative and Critical Exposition; II, Original Studies and Experiments," *Yearbook Nat. Soc. Stud. Educ.* 39 (1940).

8. Bauer, E., F. Lenz, and E. Fisher: *Human Heredity,* The Macmillan Company, New York, 1931.

9. Cordeil, A.: *L'Heredité musicale,* Libraire Le François, Paris, 1926.

10. Tinbergen, N.: *The Study of Instinct,* Oxford University Press, New York, 1951.

11. Jung, C. G.: *Psychology of the Unconscious,* Moffat, Yard and Co., New York, 1916.

12. *Report of the Mental Deficiency Committee,* part IV, H.M. Stationery Office, London, 1916.

13. Gates, R. R.: *Human Genetics,* The Macmillan Company, New York, 1946.

14. Löwenbach, H.: "Electroencephalogram in Healthy Relatives of Epileptics; Constitutional Elements in 'Idiopathic Epilepsy,'" *Bull. Johns Hopkins Hosp.* 65:25–137 (1939).

15. Groves, E. R., and C. H. Groves: *Dynamic Mental Hygiene,* The Stackpole Company, Harrisburg, Pa., 1940.

16. West, J. A.: *Plainville, U.S.A.,* Columbia University Press, New York, 1945.

17. Burt, C.: *Intelligence and Fertility: The Effect of the Differential Birthrate on Inborn Mental Characteristics,* Occasional Papers on Eugenics, no. 2, The Eugenics Society and Hamish Hamilton Medical Books, London, 1946.

18. Ballard, F. A., and R. G. Fuller (eds.): *Mental Hygiene Laws in Brief,* National Committee for Mental Hygiene, New York, 1941.

19. Stix, R. K.: "The Place of Fertility Control in Public Health," *Am. J. Pub. Health* 36:209–218 (1946).

20. Hollister, W. G.: "Parent Education, A 'First' for Mississippi, *Nat. Parent-Teachers* 41:34–35 (1946).

21. Ulrich, R. H. W.: Personal communication, 1954.

22. Blain, D.: *Report of Consultant on Mental Health to the National Institute of Mental Health, Japan* (mimeographed), World Health Organization, Western Pacific Regional Office, Manila, 1954.

23. *A Brief Report on Public Health Administration in Japan,* Ministry of Health and Welfare, Japanese Government, Tokyo, 1953.

CHAPTER TEN

The Prenatal and Perinatal Period

The moment the egg and sperm meet and unite their elements, the genetic fate of the individual is sealed. The limits of his capacities are set. The drama of the changing of capacities into behavior, of possibilities into accomplishment, begins then and continues until the individual ceases to live. The capacities develop only if the individual is nurtured, at first in the dark, warm, liquid environment within the uterus, where food is supplied merely through the beating of the fetus's heart. In adulthood the same need is filled only through labor involving the body and wits, including the capacity for planning that the individual has developed. The constitution may be very radically changed by happenings in the world in which it is nurtured. Some accident, the nature of which is not yet understood, can happen after 2 months of intrauterine life which will result in a settling of development leading to mongolism.[1] A good diet for mother and child in the last few generations has extended the height of human beings more closely to the upper genetic limit, so that men are considerably taller than they used to be. The timetable of development may be influenced; e.g., girls begin to menstruate on the average a year earlier than their mothers did. Infectious diseases can rob individuals of the chance to reach the limit of genetic capacity by destroying nervous or other tissue. Medicine and public health, using the broadest and most inclusive definition of these fields, will be alert to see to it that the life experiences develop the genetic capacities of the individual to the fullest extent possible, and mental hygiene will be alert as regards those experiences which affect the strength of the personality structure and its resistance to mental illnesses.

ENVIRONMENTAL INFLUENCES IN UTERO

The intrauterine life of the individual seems sealed off from the outside world. It has been idealized by some as an idyllic, perfectly comfortable existence. There are those who believe that there are memory traces of intrauterine life, not conscious memories but dream symbols, that indicate continued remorse throughout life that this earliest warm haven was lost. This sort of thinking tends to identify all positions in which the knees are brought up to the chin and the head bent over them as "fetal" positions, to be interpreted as an expression of longing to regain intrauterine life. Actually, the uterus may not be so comfortable as this dream picture suggests. At first the embryo probably never touches the limits of its aquatic empire with its minute writhing movements, but as the time for delivery approaches it is conceivable that the infant could feel frustration in not being able to extend his extremities. Newborn infants do not resent physical restraint to a very great degree [2]—perhaps swaddling clothes are a recognition that the infant is conditioned to a prisonlike existence and that too rapid dissipation of the reflex after birth might be harmful. Restrictive clothing under such an hypothesis could be defended as a means of making the transition from intrauterine to extrauterine life less abrupt. One might be led to question the present trend toward clothing that is entirely nonrestraining of the infant.

Maternal Physiology. The mother's condition affects the infant's environment only through her physiological processes or by transmitting infection. Maternal fatigue results in increased fetal movement [3]—an unfortunate association, since movement of the fetus can also keep the mother awake. An emotional state of severe anxiety in the mother can, in the opinion of Sontag, in some instances be related to feeding difficulties after birth.[3] If this is true, the relationship is probably through responses in the infant to hormones derived from mother's blood through placental interchange. When the mother suffers from an endocrine disease, there may well be an effect on the fetus. Hypoglycemia shortly after birth has been described in infants of diabetic mothers; the assumption is that the fetus was oversupplying insulin in order to provide an extra amount for its mother's metabolism and that the separation at birth allowed an excess to pile up. The evidence is apparently less clear for other endocrine conditions, though cases have been observed in which thyroid insufficiency or hyperfunction in the mother appeared to affect the infant.[4]

It was once believed quite firmly that only very severe disease or nutritional defect in the mother would affect the fetus. This concept is no longer accepted. The studies of maternal nutrition in relation to fetal death (abortion, miscarriages, or stillbirths) indicate that fetal loss is related to severity of maternal deprivation.[5,6,7] In general, death of the fetus occurs as a result of a completely intolerable insult, and there is a question as to whether there may not be less severe insults that result in imperfect development rather than in death.[8]

Obstetrical complications also influence the growth and development of the fetus. Anderson believes that bleeding during the third trimester of pregnancy is strongly related to the occurrence of cerebral palsy.[9] Toxemias of pregnancy in the mother occur with considerably more than chance frequency in the histories of epileptic, feebleminded, and other types of defective children.[10] It is probable that the basic insult in these instances is fetal anoxia, though directly toxic reactions may also be involved.

Other Influences. Richards, Wallace, and Sontag have shown that sounds influence fetal activity,[11, 12] and Sontag reports interesting observations of fetal overactivity after concerts attended by the mother.[3] Some mothers complained that the vibration of a washing machine produced fetal movements so severe as to be uncomfortable. The long-term effects of these stimuli, if any, are unknown, though Richards and Newberry have indicated that there may be a correlation between prenatal fetal activity and motor development in the first year of life.[13]

Drugs taken by the mother in some instances influence the unborn child. Very little is known about this point, though cases have been reported in which a child born of a morphine-addicted mother is also addicted to the drug.[14] There has, of course, been a great deal of discussion in the obstetrical literature of the acute effects of drugs administered immediately preceding delivery. The damage to the infant, if any occurs, is likely to be due to prolonged anoxia. The effects of alcohol and tobacco and of aspirin, the barbiturates, and the other commonly used drugs, are unknown to a remarkable extent; perhaps it is because these effects are too slight to be important.

Infections vary the intrauterine environment and influence development. This has been axiomatic for many years as regards syphilis, but more recently virus diseases have also been recognized as important in this connection. If the mother has rubella in the first trimester of pregnancy, maldevelopment of the fetus frequently occurs. Some authorities indicate frequencies as high as 25 per cent.[15] Cardiac anomalies, congenital cataract, and mental deficiency are the conditions most commonly observed.[16,17] Incidence of maldevelopment decreases the later in the pregnancy the German measles occur. It has been suggested that other virus diseases might act similarly, though the evidence as yet appears to be too scattered to draw conclusions.

Intrauterine accidents of a mechanical sort are rare, but they do occur occasionally and result in changes of body form that have psychological significance. A pair of identical twins who have been followed for several years bears out this point. These boys must have identical heredity, but one was born lacking the left forearm. The most probable explanation of such a finding is an intrauterine accident. It has been suggested that the differences in birth weight of monozygotic twins, a less spectacular but more common finding, is related to unequal sharing of placental area so that one gets more nutrition than the other. This circumstance may account for the differences that existed from birth in the genetically identical Dionne quintuplets.

These possibilities for hurtful influences reaching the fetus indicate that the picture of an idyllic existence *in utero* may need reformulation. Furthermore, the effects of nutritional deficiency and the various conditions that lead to damage through anoxia or other accident may well justify questioning the common belief that such conditions as mental deficiency are nearly exclusively genetically determined. It begins to appear that a considerable number of defective children may have been robbed of capacities through accidents during fetal life and delivery. This finding opens hopeful avenues toward the prevention of defects.

Responsibilities of the Health Officer. The health officer may have certain responsibilities in regard to some of the environmental influences bearing on the unborn child. Prenatal clinic care will include attention to syphilis in the mother, but there should also be in readiness a plan to put into effect in case of epidemics of German measles. Expectant mothers should be protected from contracting the disease in so far as possible. The question has also been raised as to whether therapeutic abortion at a period when such treatment is relatively safe ought to be advised in cases where the mother is known to have had German measles during the pregnancy.[18] Many feel that a special effort should be made to expose prepubertal girls to rubella in order to protect them from attack later when they may be pregnant. There is no accepted method as yet for safely inoculating with the disease,[19] a more certain way of securing immunity to protect the mother during the years she is likely to be exposed to the risk of pregnancy.

The allaying of the anxieties of the pregnant woman is also a matter of concern of the health officer in charge of prenatal clinics. The direct effect of this sort of work is difficult to evaluate. The child may itself be affected through fears in the mother that influence her appetite and her nutritional state. The relationship between mother and infant after delivery is certainly subject to conditioning on the basis of emotional attitudes held during pregnancy.

The common superstitions about prenatal influence, in so far as an expectant mother believes them, deserve discussion and sympathetic understanding on the part of the health officer. While superstitions may seem totally unscientific, they are often driving forces in human behavior. Also, some of them contain basic scientific truths, not always understood if not thoroughly studied and examined both from the physiological and psychological points of view. Folk ideas are worthy of study in the attempt to gain more healthful living for the clients of the health department. It is worth considering whether it is always wise to attempt to dislodge those pregnancy superstitions which, so far as is known, do no harm. In attempting to dissipate harmful superstitions, the educator replaces harmful beliefs by scientifically sound ones which, rationally at least, should be more reassuring to the anxious woman than the folklore. Thus when a mother is assured that the child will not have a strawberry mole if she eats strawberries, this superstition is replaced through teaching about the actual anatomy and physiology of the placenta and about the fixity of genetic patterns laid down at conception. The mother can honestly be reassured that if the child does have a strawberry mole it will not be because of fruit she ate. Dietary cravings, on the other hand, may be "all foolishness" but do no harm; it is even possible that they are an expression in appetite of some definite physiological need. This may even be true, though there is no proof one way or the other, of the habit of eating earth which is exaggerated in some women when pregnant.[20] The longing for special foods may well serve a social function in controlling the father. In the Virgin Islands, a culture where the relation between father and mother is likely to be somewhat casual, the pregnant woman is apparently able to exercise considerable control over her spouse because both believe it important for her to have the foods she craves in order to ensure a healthy child. It is needless to destroy dietary superstitions when they are not known to be harmful, and unwise, perhaps, to disturb other harmless beliefs when there is no scientific information to fill the gap left by their destruction.

Mankind apparently needs and will manufacture explanations for happenings.[21] When these explanations do not lead to harmful behavior and cannot be replaced by scientifically sound knowledge, it may be wise to let them stand unchallenged. When questions are asked, the physician bears the responsibility for replying with the best knowledge available and with recognition that the answer may be of considerable emotional import to the questioner. Discounting folk beliefs is justifiable only when such beliefs can be supplanted by sound information.

FETAL DEVELOPMENT AND BEHAVIOR

The environmental influences playing on the unborn child are important, but development itself, taking place at such tremendous speeds and with such exactitude during the period of gestation, presents data helpful in the understanding of the relation of the child to the world about him. The tissue embryology of this process is of less concern here than what Gesell has called "the embryology of behavior." [22] The gathering of data for this sort of study is extremely difficult. Some of the activities of the fetus are observable through the wall of the mother's abdomen. These data, useful as they are, cannot be as precise as direct observation when living fetuses are obtainable for study in the operating room. Such fetuses are usually dying when observed, but even so the study of them has demonstrated many interesting facts. These facts lead to the conclusion that in behavior, as well as structurally and physiologically, the intrauterine period is one of preparation for a broader type of existence. The workers in this field have been relatively few, and the work has been well summarized by Gesell. Minkowski,[23] Davenport Hooker,[24] and Gesell [22] have been the outstanding workers in the human field, with Coghill [25] contributing a necessary theoretic background. After fetuses are viable, continuous study of them is, of course, much easier; premature infants have become of unusual interest to health officers in recent years.

The first movement observable in the human fetus comes during the fourth week of gestation, when the heart begins to beat. It probably beats in short runs at first, then more regularly, until it establishes a rhythm that will last throughout life. By the time the embryo is 9.5 weeks old, its electrocardiogram shows the main features of the adult pattern; the heart has already reached a high state of development. Movement of the skeletal musculature begins about 8.5 weeks after conception. By this time body form is already clear, though the fetus is but an inch long. The first movements are of the trunk musculature: writhing, flexing, and extending of the axial muscles. Soon the extremities can be moved, first at the proximal joints, only later at the elbows and knees, and still later at the finger and toe joints. The first movements appear to be the expression of fundamental postural reflexes, reflexes that will be blended with others later and eventually with voluntary movements to make possible the highly developed motility of the adult.

This earliest behavior arises because of stimuli that are, so far as is known, due exclusively to growth potentials within the fetus. By 11 or

12 weeks, however, the fetus is able to respond to outside stimuli. A hair pressed against the cheek stimulates a movement of the head away from the stimulus as well as movements of the arms. There is a distinct withdrawal reaction if the sole of the foot is stimulated, and other parts of the surface of the body are also sensitive to touch. By 3 months, the basic behavior pattern of stimulus-response is laid down; on this anlage of action pattern will be built the individual, the pattern becoming more and more complicated as the possibilities for reception, for elaboration, and for action increase. The developing nervous system makes possible more kinds of reception and more ways of expression, and experience affects the kind of analysis of stimuli of which the nervous system is capable.

The digestive tract begins its function with the secretion of bile. Later, peristaltic movements are seen and digestion begins to take place. The movements of breathing begin long before the infant has air to breathe. Respiratory movements in human fetuses have not been well studied. In sheep embryos respiratory movement begins soon after the first month of intrauterine life, and the rhythmic pattern is established well before birth, beginning first with spasms, then brief runs of respiratory activity, becoming longer as the time for delivery approaches.[23] Respiratory movements have been recorded through the mother's abdomen in human fetuses approaching term. It would appear that the primary factor limiting the viability of the premature infant is the lack of development of the neuromuscular system. This makes the infant unable to sustain a respiratory rhythm long enough for life to be possible. Hiccuping has also been demonstrated in the unborn infant near term.

Fetal movements are strong enough to be felt by the mother after about 18 to 20 weeks of gestation. Activity increases in amount and power until near term, when there is likely to be a decrease, sometimes so marked that the mother fears the child may have died. The amount of fetal activity in unborn children varies extremely widely, as much as 1,000 per cent in the last 2 months of pregnancy.[3] Aside from the influences mentioned above, this variation probably indicates constitutional differences in the fetuses. Sontag has shown that there is a probable relationship between the weight of infants at birth and the amount of intrauterine activity, the less active fetuses furnishing the heavier infants. The significance of this fact is not entirely clear. It may be that this relationship indicates use of food for movement rather than for fat storage in these active fetuses, or it may be that a relationship exists between personality and body build and physical activity. Perhaps there are other factors influential in this feature of development. In any case, it is apparent that there are marked differences in the reactions of unborn infants and that some of these differences are due to environmental as well as constitutional factors.

Add to this sketch of the embryology of behavior changes in muscle tonus, the functioning of the endocrine system, of the hemapoietic organs, etc., and we see an intricate pattern of development eventuating in an individual able, with much help, to cope with the world without the protection of the mother's body. Birth is not the beginning of behavior; it merely marks the point at which the child has enough faculties developed to make independent survival possible. Developmental forces remain extremely important in the future of the child as he grows on to adulthood. The increasing range of reception of stimuli and the increasing ability to analyze and react make it possible for environmental factors, experience, to be more influential as development proceeds than it has been in the earlier period spent in the uterus.

PREMATURE INFANTS

In the premature or fetal infant nature is robbed of its opportunity to provide the reserves possessed by the full-term infant. This is obvious in the physical sphere where the lack of fat, the tender skin, and the poor heat regulation are very apparent. But the infant is immature from the point of view of behavior, too. Muscle tone is low; movements are feeble and of short duration. Feeding reflexes are incomplete and tire within a few minutes. The cry is feeble and short; sometimes all the movement necessary for the cry are made, but no sound results. Light, hearing, and touch sensitivity are present, but they soon tire and responses fail to appear to stimuli. The basic mode of behavior is inactivity, a base line from which the infant departs now and again feebly, only to return to it. This state is unlike real sleep in that it is frequently interrupted by incomplete movements of parts of the body. It is only after they reach the age at which they should have been born that one can say that these infants actually sleep or are awake. Earlier, they exist in a state that Gesell has called "torpor." In some infants the sleep-wakefulness distinction may be difficult to draw for some days or weeks after birth, even for experienced observers.[26]

It is remarkable how completely nurses who are in charge of premature infants agree that they have "personality" even in the earliest days of their extrauterine existence. It is difficult to define just what the factors are to which the nurses react, but it is clear that they have favorites in the nursery. There are also babies whose care they would like to avoid, and some who seem to arouse no emotional reaction at all. When one of this last group died, he was found to show a marked cerebral agenesis; he probably was less "human" in his appeal because of his incomplete brain. Probably some of these reactions of the nurse are related to such factors as the baby's ability to cling, his appetite, and how much care he must have. Nevertheless there appear to be more subtle features of the premature infant's behavior that influence the reactions as well. If personality differences exist in the premature infant, the same differences must be present in unborn infants of the same stage of development. The marked differences in amount of fetal movement also lend support to this view. In spite of the possibilities for the environment affecting the unborn child, these variations can be in large measure considered due to constitutional or genetic differences, except when capacities for development have been destroyed by disease, trauma, anoxia, or other accident.

The mental hygiene of the premature infant, of course, is secondary to the heroic measures necessary to keep him alive. The aim may be considered to be to reproduce the intrauterine environment as completely as possible—which must be very far from completely, since the child must eat and breathe and live surrounded by air instead of water. To achieve this aim, all stimuli should be kept muffled and exceedingly gentle. Light would have to be excluded almost completely and temperature held very constant to avoid stimulation. Some of these considerations have been necessary for the preservation of the life of the infant. Others, such as the matter of light and sound, appear to be less important, though further study may show that they are important from the point of view of the timing of experience.

The knowledge of the care of premature infants from the psychological viewpoint is very sketchy. It is certainly based more on analogy and hypothesis than on experimental data. The premature infant is building a personality under a distinctly abnormal environmental situation, however, and this fact would appear to be worthy of consideration along with the others involved in setting up the premature nursery. The persons in charge should have the benefit of knowledge of the developmental processes of the baby that they are protecting and attempting to lead into normal infancy. At the moment, knowing what facts are available and recognizing the responsibility to ensure that the necessary nursery procedures do not violate them appear to be the most that mental hygiene can suggest in the care of the premature infant. As time goes on, research and experiment will probably bring more knowledge, so that definite instruction on the psychological care of the premature infant can be given. The stimulation of contact with other personalities, which will be discussed later as very important in the life of the older infant, can hardly be important for prematures, since this would have been impossible for them to receive had they lived out their expected span within the uterus. With older infants, aseptic techniques that demand impersonal handling of the infant may interfere with personality development. This can hardly apply to the premature in his incubator, unless, as some have, one chooses to regard breathing and feeding as functions that require a social atmosphere for satisfactory accomplishment.[27]

The causes of premature delivery when it is spontaneous are not completely known, though obstetrical complications are frequently associated with the event. Infants occasionally must be delivered before term for obstetrical indications such as hypertension of pregnancy or eclampsia, placenta praevia and other causes of maternal bleeding. Recent research reaffirms that the premature is in far greater danger of suffering nervous system and other damage than a child born at term, not only because of fragility and underdevelopment at birth, but also because of the maternal and possible fetal conditions causing the premature delivery. Pasamanick and Lilienfeld have shown that epilepsy, mental deficiency, cerebral palsy, and certain other defects are a greatly increased risk in children of mothers who have obstetrical complications, regardless of time of delivery.[10] Harper, Rider, Knobloch, Pasamanick, et al. have shown the specifically increased risk for the premature infant.[28] The risks to the infant are usually directly proportional to his smallness. This, in turn, is probably proportional to the severity of the pathological condition causing the premature delivery, though there is still a great deal of research to be done before the various causative complexes will be completely understood. It is amply clear, however, that if prematurity could be prevented, and if infants could be protected from anoxia, infection, trauma, and toxins, a considerable number of children whose nervous systems are now damaged could be born with their genetic capacities intact. Rogers has shown that behavior disorders in school children are more frequent in those whose mothers have suffered complications before delivery.[29] With the facts now available, it appears that obstetric research and research in the care of the premature infant is imperative, not only to save lives, but to save the inborn capacities of infants from limitation because of tissue destruction.

The Psychological Care of the Premature and His Family. The premature infant must, for the protection of his life, be treated away from his mother for a considerable period, thus making impracticable the normal growth of the mother-child relationship. Mother love is frequently called an "instinct," but one gets the impression that more is involved. In general, people love those for whom they have to make sacrifices, and babies demand sacrifices. Many types of pressures—social mores, the expectancy of the family for her to act in a motherly way, her husband's pride in her motherhood, pity for the helpless infant—are involved in setting up the pattern of feeling and action we recognize as mother love. The pattern also appears to be the result of practice and learning; the mother reaches the feeling of motherly love and care through practicing motherly love and care. When a mother has a premature infant, this practice may be denied her.

Furthermore, a premature birth is abnormal. People frequently feel that what is abnormal is wrong, is evidence of sin. They tend to feel guilty about the unusual situation. Physicians and nurses have been trained to suspect syphilis in any unusual obstetrical event, even though this disease is far less important than it was fifteen or twenty years ago. In spite of educational efforts to the contrary, medical personnel may also harbor a feeling that there is some guilt or inadequacy involved on the part of the mother, and they may deliberately or unconsciously let her know that they feel so. Quite aside from the medical facts that appear to make them untenable scientifically, such attitudes are generally agreed to be harmful to patients and to stand in the way of setting up helpful relationships with them.[30]

Anxiety about the premature infant is to be expected simply on the basis that his existence is precarious. If the child is actually very small, no honest physician can be very reassuring to the parent even with the best and most modern of care at his command. The increased survival rates of prematures have brought both medical and, to an increasing extent, popular realization of the risk of the prematurely born infant having suffered nonlethal damage. In such cases he may be blind, be mentally defective, or show thinking difficulties later which may lead to behavior disorders. There is the risk not only of acute grief reaction in case of death, but of a long period of anxious waiting to find out what the child will be able to do. There may be in store the grief of caring for a blind or otherwise defective child for many years. The cost of the long hospitalization may be the cause of great anxiety and hardship for the family. These anxieties must be faced by the parents, and usually can be. It should, in most cases, be a matter of shared anxiety frankly recognized by physician, nurse, and parents. Such an attitude will make it easier for the nurse and physician to deal with the numerous telephone calls. They will keep in mind that the parents are not practiced in steeling themselves to death and defect as the medical profession is.

It should also be borne in mind that the parents' attitudes toward the situation are much more complicated than those of the persons attending the child medically. The parents may have the guilt feelings mentioned above, or, as frequently happens, members of the family may be letting the parents know by invidious comparisons how poorly they feel they have done with this job of producing a child. The young wife and her husband will need understanding from their medical friends through the anxious days or months—an understanding that may have to penetrate beyond what, on the surface, appears to be simply fear that the infant may not survive.

Because of the long separation necessitated by the hospitalization of the infant, some arrangement must be made so that the parents have opportunity to practice their parenthood as much as the situation will allow. Hospital technique may not allow them to hold the baby, but it will usually allow them to see him even when he is very small. As soon as he is large enough, they should be allowed to hold him and share in his care. Evidences of his development, such as heightened muscle tone, ability to feed from a bottle rather than by tube or feeder, or increased fat, should be pointed out. In so far as possible the parent should share the credit for his development with the nurse and physician. The fact that premature infants are reported, by nurses particularly, to have distinct personalities indicates a type of information to be shared with the parents. They are likely to gain much more in parental feeling for the child from reports of evidences of personality than they are from mere evidences of gain in weight. Obviously the physiological processes of feeding and breathing are much easier to report than the vague items of other personality function the premature can show. Yet it is the latter that will help the parents distinguish their child as an individual apart from the tanks and tubes and sparkling glass, the sterilizers, the caps and masks and gowns and the rigorous, impersonal routines of the premature nursery.

For quite a while before the baby can go home, the parent can come to the hospital to bathe and feed him. Even mothers with other small children can arrange to make a trip to the hospital once a day if they feel welcome there, although distances sometimes make this impossible. Nor should the parents be the only visitors; relatives need to see that this is a "good" child, too. By these means, the parents get some practice in the attitudes and duties of parenthood even though denied the responsibility that usually accompanies having a baby at home a few days after his birth.

Hospital practice is usually very elaborate. The rites that go with aseptic technique, necessary as they are in hospital, are utterly impracticable at home. What is more, they are unnecessary there when the child has reached a satisfactory weight and where nursery epidemics are not a threat. The parents should understand which techniques are necessary for this particular baby, and which are for the protection of the nursery, of the group of babies. If they do not understand, there will be guilt feelings aroused simply because the more elaborate techniques cannot be followed at home.

When a premature baby reaches a "normal" birth weight and can be discharged from hospital, he will be ready to be treated as a "normal" baby. The parents have been thinking of him as an unusual special baby, perhaps for months. If they continue thinking of him like this, he will be treated as "special" at home; this is conceded to be poor mental hygiene for most children. The parent needs to know from handling and caring for the child that he is no longer unusual but has now reached the age and development where he can fit into the world like any other baby. It is a matter of great surprise and happiness to parents to find this true even with infants who have been blinded by retrolental fibroplasia.[30] And parents are famous for being unable to detect mild defects in behavior or thinking which may in any case be undiagnosable at this point. There would appear to be no sound reason for treating the formerly premature infant in any special way once he has reached a weight to make leaving hospital safe. The setting up of the attitudes that will make this possible, as well as the teaching of the necessary techniques for the care of the infant—a feeling of competence here has tremendous anxiety-relieving potentiality—are challenging and satisfying functions for the public health nurse.

THE BIRTH PROCESS

The birth process has mental hygiene implications of two general types: (1), there may be psychological significance in the process itself, and the mother's attitude toward the experience may influence the future relationship of herself and the child; (2), accidents may occur at the time of birth which significantly alter the future relationship of the child with his environment.

Psychological Significance for the Child. The child is capable of responding to many stimuli by the time he is born. It is extremely difficult to know what his state of consciousness is like at birth and in the few weeks thereafter, but it seems doubtful that there can be much more than evanescent types of half-consciousness based extremely closely on the physiological state. One thinks in terms of analogy with the first feeble short runs of respiratory activity. Yet one cannot but be impressed with certain facts connected with the birth process. There is a temptation to read psychological significance into them. The birth cry, for example, seems to be the first evidence of the fear of being unable to get air that is present to some degree in most people. When one puts together this idea and the fact that evidences of anxiety always include some change in respiratory activity, it is almost unavoidable to mark this important event as having emotional significance to the child, even if he is in a state of something less than full consciousness. Rank [31] and others [32] have built this type of thinking into a theory of neurosis; this would appear to be hypothesizing capacity for thinking and feeling in the infant for which there is little or no evidence. Perhaps all these ruminations are simply those of the obstetrician who is anxious for fear the baby will not breathe. At any rate, the massive stimuli of pressure in the tight-fitting birth canal, the turning and twistings to be endured, and the air hunger tempt one to postulate that emotional responses may be present in the child and might have some lasting significance in personality structure.

The Mother's Attitude toward Childbirth. This attitude will tend to influence her later attitude toward the child. It may even determine whether or not there will be other children in the child's later environment. In addition, her attitudes will affect the course of the labor and her obstetric care and thus the length and severity of the child's exposure to the birth process. Grantly Dick Read [33] believes that tension and anxiety in the mother may directly affect the circular muscles of the cervix so that more time and pressure may be needed for dilatation. The mother's attitude will also affect the amount of sedation and analgesia she will need during labor and delivery; if this is very large, there is increased risk of fetal anoxia and consequent brain damage. These issues will be discussed more completely in connection with the psychobiology of the young adult period.

Birth Injuries and Other Accidents. Perhaps the most important birth accidents are those affecting the central nervous system. During the birth process a significant number of infants sustain hemorrhages into the cranial cavity.[34] In some, there appears to be little or no damage to the brain, and the hemorrhage is unimportant so far as the future is concerned. In others, the damage to the brain may be so severe that death results. Between these extremes lies a great variety of degrees and types of damage, from those resulting in mental deficiency of severe grade without motor involvement, to those resulting in severe motor impairment with little intellectual or personality defect. The psychological effects of mental or personality deficiency are apparent; the psychological effects of physical crippling are more subtle and more difficult to formulate clearly. The crippling changes the way the environment impinges upon the individual. Furthermore, the crippling limits the range of experiences the child may have; the hemiplegic child will never know the bliss of sitting in the highest crotch of a tree. The results of environmental molding of the personality will therefore be different in the crippled child.

Investigations in this field have dealt largely with the problem of crippled and sense-deprived children whose deficiencies have been brought on some time after birth by poliomyelitis, meningitis, or other cause. The birth injuries must be studied as a special type of this larger group. When the injury is contemporaneous with birth we do not deal with the problem of the child's contrasting his crippled state with a previously normal one. His only comparisons are with other children not so deprived. The significance of this factor has not been studied completely, although there is some evidence that the severity of personality deviations in cripples is correlated positively with the length of time the disability has existed.[35]

Studies conducted with standardized personality tests show little difference in frequency or severity of personality maladjustments between cripples and control groups. In other words, most cripples make satisfactory adjustments in so far as these tests can be relied upon to indicate maladjustment. Clinical studies of cases in which maladjustment is present show that the range of deviations tends to be the same for this group as for the general population, i.e., there is no standard symptom picture indicating that the patient is reacting to his crippling. The studies show reactions ranging from feelings of inferiority to aggressive dominance, from needing and seeking affection to withdrawal from all risks of affectional contact. Similarly, studies appear to agree that all sorts of physical crippling, of whatever etiology, can be lumped into a single category so far as effect on personality structure is concerned. These observations would appear to indicate that crippling is a factor of added strain on the personality structure and that the strain is of a relatively nonspecific sort. The personality, if it fails to withstand the strain, adjusts to it by means of reactions dependent upon the constitutional and experience factors inherent in the life pattern of the patient, the crippling being the precipitating factor in the appearance of the maladjustment. This view, while supported by many of the studies in the literature, is by no means accepted by everyone in the field. Others tend to stress the symbolic significance of various types of injuries and to feel that these special factors are important in determining the type of reaction following a crippling injury or disease.[36]

The effect of the birth of a crippled or deficient child on the parent-child relationship is generally agreed to be profound. One of the deep concerns of the pregnant woman is anxiety as to whether the baby will be "all right," and one of the first questions the newly delivered mother asks concerns the physical normality of her baby. Gardiner,[37] in a clinical psychiatric study of nine normal pregnant women, found anxiety concerning this issue a prominent feature in their psychology. Obviously so common a fear will have significance when it is realized at the birth of the child. The parents tend to overvalue the child and overprotect him as a compensation for their feelings of guilt about the disability. It has also been suggested that this overprotection is actually an overcompensation. The parent hates the child because of the disability, but this feeling is morally unacceptable and he forces himself into a protective and indulging attitude toward the child. He uses this activity as a mask, even from himself, of his real feelings of rejection. In either case, the child may become the object of oversolicitude, sometimes to the neglect of the other children. This was seen particularly clearly in a family observed over several years in the clinic.

T. D. was first seen at the age of 6 years 2 months, referred by the public health nurse because the child could neither walk or talk. The clinic pediatrician added the diagnoses of mental retardation and epilepsy. The mother had to be urged to attend the clinic; she feared T. would be institutionalized, and this she wished very much to avoid. The child was a serious financial burden to the widowed mother, since she vomited any sort of food except strained baby foods. These were so expensive that the mother's food allowance from the Aid to Dependent Children program was not sufficient. Since T. was completely incontinent, the expense of rubber sheeting, pads, etc., still further cut into the budget. Although the mother worried and cried about the problems, she strongly rejected suggestion that she hospitalize this child so that the extra financial drains would not interfere with the diet of the two normal children. Much of the mother's time and attention was absorbed by this child. A smaller brother shared a bed with T. and endured her daily convulsions, enuresis, and soiling. Arrangements were made to obtain special food and medicine allowances for the mother. Discussion as to the equal division of maternal care between the three children usually resulted in the statement that the other two were fond of T. and that they were not neglected. By the third visit to clinic, a year after the first, the mother had got a crib for T. so that the boy no longer had to sleep with her. When T. was seen at the age of 11 years 9 months the mother felt she was making "progress." In the years she had been observed she had learned to walk by holding onto objects; this was almost the full extent of her progress. At 12 years of age the following conditions obtained:

1. Idiocy—development still around 1-year level.
2. Convulsions vary from one a day to one a week. Mother has given no medication for more than a year, despite advice.
3. Vomits occasionally.

4. Soils and wets usually. Sometimes mother "catches" her, but she gives no warning.

5. Finger sucking. Finger shows firm contracture from long-continued sucking.

6. No longer mouths objects (previously a complaint by mother).

7. Constipation has disappeared (previously a complaint by mother).

8. Eats varied family diet now (see above for earlier complaint).

9. Has her own crib (see above for earlier complaint).

Conditions remained essentially unchanged until T. died at the age of 18. Her sister had graduated from high school, and a brother was attending school at the same educational level. Before her death T. had apparently enjoyed playing with her 11-month-old niece, who appeared to be about the same developmental age as herself.

The cause of death is not entirely clear. She had had blood in the urine on at least three occasions; this may have been menstrual blood or have indicated urinary-tract disease. After some months of feeding difficulty, she had refused everything but liquids, had contracted pneumonia, and had been hospitalized. She had recovered but had died at home approximately a month after release from hospital. The clinical notes show that for some years the probability of her death had been discussed with the mother and that the family took the loss of this child—which had preempted so much money, attention, and concern through the years—calmly, secure in the justified conviction that they had done the best they could under very difficult circumstances.

The devotion of the mother to this idiot, epileptic child was certainly completely unreasonable, and it resulted in the partial neglect of the normal children, though the mother's attitudes were such that this appeared minimal. The apparent cause for the mother's behavior was that she loved the child, but one wonders whether there were not other factors. One may have been the mother's devotion to a dead marital partner; she had lived with this man in a common-law marriage for 8 or 9 years before his death. There may be some significance in the fact that the mother had had syphilis, although the child was free of the disease. In any case, one is tempted to feel that the impulses for taking the long-continued punishment entailed by the care of such a child must have been more complicated than simple mother love. A situation of this sort occurring in a higher socioeconomic stratum was reported by the mother of a mongolian idiot. This child was eventually hospitalized. The impulses for keeping and caring for the child were obviously strong, but the mother was able to see the unhappiness the effort was causing and the threatened disorganization of her home. She did hospitalize the child, with results of relief from strain and a better home for her other, normal child.[38]

In these two instances, the crippling was very severe and in each it involved personality functions directly. When these functions are relatively intact, the problem is more subtle. Newell [39] reports the case of identical twins, one of whom was injured by poliomyelitis at the age of 2 so that her right arm and leg were crippled. She was neglected by both her parents and compared unfavorably with her healthy twin. She developed definite feelings of inferiority and persecution and was unable to use the assets of her personality effectively. The opposite reaction, that of oversolicitude, is apparent in the reaction of many parents. Frequently the parent expects the child to accomplish more in other fields because he is blocked in the physical field by crippling. In the present popular attention to the spastic child, the picture presented by the propagandists gives the impression that high intelligence is always to be expected of the spastic. This expectation is, of course, as unfounded as was the complete neglect of the intellectual factor when these children were treated as though they were all mentally deficient.

The public has tended to give generously to support efforts to help the crippled child, both through private foundations like the National Foundation for Infantile Paralysis and through governmental agencies such as the crippled children's program of the Children's Bureau. Such funds are used both for direct service and for research. Increasing attention is being given to research on the effect of crippling of various types of personality development and structure, a field of increasing importance. The large amount of money spent per child crippled by these illnesses, compared to the pittance spent per child crippled by mental deficiency, has frequently—and enviously—been pointed out by mental hygienists. Mental deficiency, although less spectacular, is frequently more damaging to the individual than orthopedic difficulty. But it does not show in appealing ways for use on campaign posters and has not yet aroused the public to such great generosity. Propaganda to generate sympathetic contributions for this group is more difficult to write. There has also been the discouraging tendency to relegate mental deficiency, as well as other mental illnesses, to hereditary etiology about which nothing can be done preventively or curatively. The patients tend to be neglected through a combination of prejudiced stigma and inadequate educational techniques, while research on causes languishes for lack of general interest and funds. Yet, a considerable but as yet indeterminable proportion, perhaps as high as 40 to 60 per cent, of cases of mental defect are preventable through improved obstetrics, the prevention of prematurity and the causes for it, and the optimum care for the premature infant to protect his brain from damage.

Several organizations, particularly the National Association for Mental Health and the Association for Retarded Children, are attempting to remedy the inadequate support for research in the fields mentioned. Their present campaigns must be themselves regarded as research enterprises to find ways of breaking through the attitudes of hopelessness toward the prevention of crippling by mental deficiency and the mental diseases. Public health has a major role in helping the public learn to face these tremendous medical problems, problems of medical care and of research, and to help obtain the funds, both private and public, to support service and investigation for their relief. There is every reason to feel that the expenditure of funds will be greatly rewarding in the relief of human suffering which extends through the lifetime of the afflicted and involves the families of the patient in grief and suffering for years.

SUMMARY

Behavior as well as structure develops during intrauterine life. The fetus is sensitive to many stimuli after the first few months of gestation. Different infants show different amounts of motility, differing degrees of sensitivity to stimuli. The fetal infant, the premature baby, has a "personality," difficult as that term is to define, which is primarily of constitutional origin. The care of the premature infant and his family has psychological aspects that have not been thoroughly worked out, but certain modes of action and attitude and certain practices may tend to protect the family group from unnecessary anxieties and other emotional stresses. The birth process is of significance to the mental hygienist in two respects. First, there may be psychological significance for the child itself, although this is at best hypothetical and based on analogy. The mother's attitude toward childbirth and her experience in it will influence the child-parent relationship. Secondly, the gestational and birth processes may result in injuries of various sorts to the child, leading to mental or physical crippling. This crippling will influence the child's relation to his home and social environment. In so far as these factors may be influenced through individual or group discussions in prenatal clinics, by improved maternal health services to cut down birth accidents, or by mental hygiene investigation and action with regard to crippled children, mental hygiene opportunities exist for the prevention of maladjustment having its roots in the situations surrounding the birth of the child.

REFERENCES

1. Ingalls, T. H.: "Mongolism," *Scient. Am.* 186:60–66 (1952).
2. Spitz, R.: "Emotional Growth in the First Year," *Child Study* 24:68–70 (1947).

3. Sontag, L. W.: "The Significance of Foetal Environmental Differences," *Am. J. Obst. & Gynec.* 42:996–1003 (1941).
4. Eastman, N. J.: Williams' *Obstetrics*, pp. 738–746, Appleton-Century-Crofts, Inc., New York, 1950.
5. Burke, B. S., S. S. Stevenson, J. Worcester, and H. C. Stuart: "Nutritional Studies during Pregnancy: V. Relation of Maternal Nutrition to Condition of Infant at Birth: Study of Siblings," *J. Nutrition* 38:453–467 (1949).
6. Goldsmith, G. A.: "Relationships between Nutrition and Pregnancy in Recent Surveys in Newfoundland," *Am. J. Pub. Health* 40:953–959 (1950).
7. Burke, B. S.: "Nutrition during Pregnancy," *Connecticut M. J.* 10:744–753 (1946).
8. Smith, C. A.: "Effects of Under-nutrition upon the New-born Infant in Holland (1944–1945)," *J. Pediat.* 30:229–243 (1947).
9. Anderson, G. V.: Personal communication, 1954.
10. Lilienfeld, A. M., and B. Pasamanick: "The Association of Maternal and Fetal Factors with the Development of Epilepsy. I. Abnormalities in the Prenatal and Paranatal Periods," *J.A.M.A.* 155:719–724 (1954).
11. Sontag, L. W., and T. W. Richards: *Fetal Heart Rate as a Behavior Indicator*, Monograph of the Society for Research in Child Development 3 (no. 4), 1938, National Research Council, Washington, D.C.
12. Sontag, L. W., and R. Wallace: "Study of Fetal Activity," *Am. J. Dis. Child.* 48:1050–1057 (1934).
13. Richards, T. W., and H. Newberry: "Studies in Fetal Behavior," *Child Development* 9:69–78 (1938).
14. Pettey, G. E.: "Congenital Morphinism with Report of Cases," *South. M. J.* 5:25–28 (1912).
15. Ober, R. E., J. M. Horton, and R. F. Femister. "Congenital Defects in a Year of Epidemic Rubella," *Am. J. Pub. Health* 47:1328–1333 (1947).
16. Wesselhoeft, C.: "Rubella (German Measles)," *New England J. Med.* 236:943–950, 979–988 (1947).
17. Gregg, N. McA.: "Congenital Cataract following German Measles in the Mother," *Tr. Ophth. Soc. Australia* 3:35–46 (1941).
18. Abolins, J. A.: "Rubeola och Graviditet," *Sätryck ur Nord. med.* 48:1369–1384 (1952).
19. Krugman, S., R. Ward, K. G. Jacobs, and M. Lazar: "Studies on Rubella Immunization, I. Demonstration of Rubella without Rash," *J.A.M.A.* 151:285–288 (1952).
20. Cooper, M. M.: Review article on pica in preparation, 1954.
21. Cantril, H.: *The "Why" of Man's Experience,* The Macmillan Company, New York, 1950.
22. Gesell, A.: *The Embryology of Behavior,* Harper & Brothers, New York, 1945.
23. Minkowski, M.: "Neurobiologische Studien am menschlichen Foetus," *Abderholdens Handbuch d. biologischen Arbeitsmethoden* 253:511–618 (1928).

24. Hooker, D.: *A Preliminary Atlas of Early Human Fetal Activity,* privately published, 1935.

25. Coghill, G. E.: *Anatomy and the Problem of Behavior,* Cambridge University Press, New York, 1929.

26. Escalona, S.: "Emotional Development in the First Year of Life," in Milton J. E. Senn (ed.) *Problems of Infancy and Childhood,* Josiah Macy, Jr., Foundation, New York, 1953.

27. Ribble, M. A.: *The Rights of Infants, Early Psychological Needs and Their Satisfaction,* Columbia University Press, New York, 1943.

28. Harper, P., R. Rider, H. Knobloch, and B. Pasamanick: Unpublished results of studies in progress, 1954.

29. Rogers, M. E.: "The Association of Maternal and Fetal Factors with the Development of Behavior Problems among Elementary School Children," Sc.D. thesis, School of Hygiene and Public Health, The Johns Hopkins University, Baltimore, 1954.

30. Lubchenco, L. O.: Unpublished manuscript on studies of infants with retrolental fibroplasia, 1953.

31. Rank, O.: *Das Trauma der Geburt,* Internationaler Psychoanalytischer Verlag, Leipzig, 1924.

32. Fodor, Nandor: *The Search for the Beloved,* Hermitage House, New York, 1949.

33. Read, G. D.: *Childbirth without Fear,* Harper & Brothers, New York, 1944.

34. "Round Table Discussion on Hemorrhage in the Newborn Infant," *J. Pediat.* 20:637–661 (1942).

35. Barker, R. G., B. A. Wright, and M. R. Gromick: *Adjustment to Physical Handicap and Illness: A Survey of the Social Psychology of Physique and Disability,* Social Science Research Council, Bulletin 55, 1946.

36. Kubie, L. S.: "Motivation and Rehabilitation," *Psychiatry* 8:69–78 (1945).

37. Gardiner, S.: Unpublished studies conducted in the Department of Obstetrics of the Johns Hopkins Hospital, 1940–1941.

38. Carey, G.: "Happiness as Deep as Tears," *Reader's Digest* 29:85–89 (1936).

39. Newell, H. W.: "Differences in Personalities in the Surviving Pair of Identical Triplets," *Am. J. Orthopsychiat.* 4:239–244 (1933).

CHAPTER ELEVEN

The Period of Infancy

The period of infancy may be defined as the time between birth and the beginning of walking. While vastly more complicated than the dark, relatively quiet uterus where the temperature is nearly constant, the environment of the infant is confined largely to one home and the people there. The child is, to use an American colloquialism, the "lap baby," unable to go anywhere unless carried by an adult. At the end of the period he becomes the "knee baby," able to stand on his own legs, but still markedly dependent upon the mother for emotional and physical support and care. Chronologically, the age at the end of this period is 10 to 15 months, though we have seen toddlers at 7 months and in one case, in which a long physical illness with chronic anemia had interfered with development, an otherwise normal child who did not walk until he was 24 months old. The age of walking, as the dividing event distinguishing infancy from the preschool period, is not accepted universally. Many students feel that infancy should be extended longer, usually using the chronological age of 2 years as the separation point.[1,2] The development of communication skills is the reason this age is chosen by most authors. Walking, however, depends primarily on neurological maturation, and is used because it is one of the last events almost exclusively neurologically determined.

GROWTH AND MOTOR PATTERNS

At the beginning of the period of infancy, the child grows with tremendous rapidity, but the rate falls precipitously during the course of the year.[3] Paralleling this rapid growth in weight and length there is an equally rapid development of behavior. At birth the head is wobbly. Movements of the extremities, although based on fundamental reflexes that gradually combine to make the synergistic motions of walking possible, are vague and appear useless and ill-directed. After 6 to 10 weeks the head is more stable. After a few more weeks it is so

173

steady that the plateau of this developmental curve is reached, and the steadiness of the head is no longer useful as a datum on which to judge development. A few weeks after birth the child begins to raise his head when lying face down, this activity developing continuously until he is able to crawl at 8 to 10 months. Development continues, with more weight being shifted to the feet. The child is able to stand by holding onto something even before the nervous system has developed sufficiently for him to be able to carry out the alternating movements and the balancing of walking, the developmental event that marks the end of the period of infancy as defined here. The ability to support the body in the sitting position begins to appear about 12 to 18 weeks, and the child can usually sit alone when he is around 8 months old.

The hands in earliest infancy are usually clenched. If they do relax, the slightest stimulation of the palm will cause them to clench again; the basic grasp reflex has not come under voluntary inhibition. Reaching purposefully for things other than the nipple does not appear until around 4 months, but reaching and grasping have become quite precise by the age of a year.[4]

Bowel and Bladder Function. At birth infants show reflex patterns indicating the incompleteness of the functioning of their nervous systems. One of the most important of these is the automatic action of bowel and bladder. Both empty when full, mobilizing the necessary muscles of the body to complete the reflex, including the tightening of the abdominal muscles and diaphragm in straining. In some infants the bowel evacuation soon becomes rhythmical, recurring at approximately the same time or times each day; other infants establish patterns in this field much later. In any event, the functions are reflexes and carry on without the possibility of control, since the neural connections are not yet in working condition. Control of the action of bowel and bladder is dependent on the nervous system being able to (1) bring to consciousness the fact that these organs are full and need emptying; (2) hold the discharge reflexes in abeyance. In all probability, the nervous system is not mature enough to carry out these functions, even in an imperfect way, until after the end of the prelocomotor period.[5]

How then is it that there are so many mothers who claim that their babies are "trained" at 4 months, and so many public health nurses even yet who advise mothers to start toilet training at 4 to 6 months? There appear to be several reasons, the first and most important being the characteristic property of the nervous system to discharge rhythmically. This characteristic will appear repeatedly in the discussions of almost every function of the human being; indeed, it appears as the first macroscopically observable movement of the fetus, the heartbeat, and in the fetal respiratory movements. The bowel and, to a lesser extent, the urinary bladder also have their rhythms, much slower but nevertheless predictable, at least in some children. What seems to happen in early "training" is that the child's nervous system responds regularly and the mother knows the time and sees to it that the child is on the potty at that time. Furthermore, the reflex of bowel evacuation includes restless squirming before the final peristaltic push, and the mother may observe this and be warned of what is coming. Mothers vary extremely widely in their abilities to "read" the predictive signs of incipient actions and desires of their infants, just as infants vary in the regularity of their various activities.[6] What apparently happens in successful early "training" is that the training is not of the child, but of the mother. She interprets the rhythm of the reflexes and the observable signs that the neural discharge is about to take place. The realization of the infant's need to void is in her consciousness rather than in the child's. One further factor can be recognized in these cases. This concerns the ability of the child to form conditioned reflexes that will control the bowel and bladder discharges to some extent. Just as the dog can be trained to salivate at the sound of a bell when over a period of time the bell is rung at the time of presentation of food, so the infant can be brought to have peristaltic waves of the large gut when the buttocks are in contact with a pot. This results only when the cortex becomes conditioned as a result of repeated "catching" by the mother of the child's own rhythmic discharges, the internal stimulus and the external stimulus becoming associated as a conditioned reflex.

Many parents seem to feel that a baby is but a small edition of an adult and that he *should* have control over the bowel and bladder. Since the child should have this control, they will see to it that he gets it, if it is humanly possible—which it is not. In teaching the marvelously rapid prenatal development it is often stressed that all the cells of the nervous system are present at birth. From this true statement it is inferred that all sorts of activity should be possible—it must be only a matter of training! What has not been stressed enough in popular education is that the fact that cells are present does not mean that they function. Their functioning does not depend solely on their presence in the nervous system, but rather upon what stage of development they are in and whether they are connected with the peripheral organ whose condition they will eventually transmit to consciousness and whose action other cells will eventually control.

There is little to condemn in very early toilet training, if it can be recognized as training of the mother and a partial conditioning of the child, without expecting consciously directed action on the part of the child. Success will probably occur only in children with reasonably dependable rhythmic discharges and only in those whose mothers are sympathetically attuned to understand the infant's signals and do not put responsibility on the infant. This combination of the right infant and the attuned mother does not by any means always happen, though education is believed to enhance the mother's sensitivity to the infant's signals. It is an unfortunate fact, however, that many parents tend to feel that the child does have some responsibility, particularly if the rhythm is irregular. Mrs. Jones across the street, whose children are grown and who has forgotten her difficulties, may tell stories that every one of her seven children was "clean" at 3 months. Then the mother begins to feel that her child *should* be clean, and irritation at her failure becomes projected as irritation at the child for his failure. Because this pattern is so common in parental thinking, it seems best to delay attempts at toilet training until after the period of infancy. Some authorities recommend waiting for a developmental age of 18 to 24 months, when the child will usually spontaneously begin his own toilet training, through imitation of adult patterns. The mother-child relationship is too frequently damaged by the useless attempts to make babies responsible. It is enough to have to wash the diapers without also having to be angry and frustrated by unsuccessful attempts to train the child before he learns to walk.

Crying. The aim of child care in infancy, when so many functions are dictated by the maturation of the nervous system, is to maintain an optimum environment for growth and development. The adult observer bears the responsibility for providing this, but his own watchfulness cannot foretell all the discomforts the child will have. The infant signals his discomfort by crying, indicating in this diffuse fashion that something is wrong. Thus the conclusion is reached that crying in infants is not the good thing it was once said to be. In most cases in early infancy it indicates a less-than-optimal condition that should be rectified.

Not many years ago, "spoiling" of infants was considered a serious matter. It is probably significant that this fear was most prevalent during the period when techniques for safe hospital delivery and infant care were of paramount importance. In the fear of bacteria, the needs of the human baby were subordinated to needs for asepsis and the desire for an efficient hospital type of management. During this period crying was considered good exercise; babies had a crying period every day normally even with the most adequate care, and if you paid attention to every cry, the child would soon cry for attention and not because of discomfort. This was the period of exceedingly exact feeding schedules; the baby appeared as a metabolizing machine responding only to physical stimuli by physical responses. There has followed a revulsion from this attitude, and the baby has begun to be recognized as a reacting human being, not a machine. One of the bases for this is, probably, the greater confidence we now have in aseptic techniques as well as the improved therapeutic weapons against bacterial infections. With the child's life more secure, it is more possible to think about whether he has his full measure of health. As already noted, it is possible to include the human element even in the exacting techniques of the care of premature infants.

For the first months of his life the infant will respond to a variety of stimuli such as loud sounds, a sudden jar, a short fall through space with a sudden, jerky extension of the body and limbs and usually also with crying.[7] This mass type of neurological discharge disappears about the age of 4 months; it has some usefulness as a developmental signpost. The child's response, including crying, indicates that it is an unpleasant experience; it might be considered as a sort of preconscious physiological "fear" reaction brought out by various types of threatening situations. Inasmuch as the child signals a "pain" response by crying, the situation may be interpreted as less than optimal for his growth and development. To avoid the reaction one would avoid the threatening situations and, positively, foster situations in which the infant is fully supported, particularly during the period before the head is entirely steady. After this reflex has disappeared and consciousness has developed so that he can recognize the play motive, games of tossing the baby obviously give him pleasure. He laughs and smiles during the play and may indicate that he wants more. Before the reflex has disappeared, however, full support of the body, such as cuddling in the arms against the breast, would appear to be indicated. Thus one can arrive at the conclusion that there is a neurological basis for a child's need for affectionate as well as efficient care, since one of the means of expressing affection for the child is to cuddle him.

Breast feeding makes the position of greatest maternal support for the infant mandatory on the mother, during feeding at least. To be sure, the physical position is not all that is important; the attitude of the mother as shown by muscle tension or strain is also a stimulus to the child and may interfere with his feeding, as is so beautifully described by Margaret Fries.[8] When the mother suffers tension and strain in feeding the child, what looks like an advantageous physical support in the nursing position is recognized by the child for what it is. The cause of this tension and strain may be pain of nursing, guilt feelings about having the child, excessive feelings of modesty, dislike of the child, or dislike of the home and husband. The child soon reflects these insecurities and tensions, a frequent reaction being digestive upsets. Part of this reaction may be due to changes in the mother's milk, both as to supply and quality, but there appears also to be a capacity in the infant to react to the emotional situation itself. In spite of the exceptional case in which the mother cannot relax and enjoy the close physical contact with the child during nursing, in general, nursing does assure the child of the close holding that is the antithesis of the frightening withdrawal of support that incites the Moro reflex. To the astute pediatrician in the well-baby clinic the exceptional case furnishes an opportunity for investigation, education, or treatment. Infants who show excessive crying because of apparent digestive discomfort generally live in a family situation characterized by marked emotional tensions.[9,6]

Mothers who cannot or do not nurse their babies not infrequently forget that, if they were nursing them, they would hold them closely in their arms. They reject or deny themselves the opportunity to hold the baby while feeding him, for fear that they will "spoil the baby." Such fears are likely to be most common in inexperienced mothers, advised by older women who foresee a spoiled first or only child and overstress the danger of spoiling in their advice to the impressionable girl. The following excerpt from the case record of a boy 2 months of age illustrates the situation:

Mother says she found breast feeding painful and put him on a formula as soon as she returned home from the hospital. He took both types of feeding well, but from the beginning has seemed to require a 3-hour feeding schedule, and the physician has advised her to follow this. Mother says she frequently props up his bottle beside him for feeding. She goes on to say that she never holds him very much as she is "afraid of spoiling him." This infant also is noted as crying a great deal. The advice in the case was recorded as follows: Discussed benefit to mother and child of holding him for feeding— the child's need for mothering while small.

The essential unity of mother and child has been recognized in changes in hospital practice, housing both in the same room. Maloney, Montgomery, and Trainham [10] describe the advantages of this system as follows:

The period of hospitalization of mother and newborn offers a great opportunity to give the new mother instruction in child care and to stimulate her interest in child development. It should also be a time to help her become familiar with her baby, to assist her in the establishment of breast feeding, and to reinforce her confidence in approaching her new responsibilities and enjoyment of her new opportunities.

Enough experimentation has been done as regards this practice to be sure that it is administratively feasible and that it is no strain on the mother in normal obstetric cases. Having the baby in her room certainly allays anxieties about him, since she can see him and can at once be effective in ministering to his needs.[11] Aldrich has shown that the causes for neonatal crying are better diagnosed by mothers who care for their children than by observers in a large nursery. The mothers reported 14.2 per cent of the crying as due to unknown causes, while the observers reported 35.1 per cent in this category.[12] Hunger was found to be the most frequent cause for crying in both instances. When the nursing care was increased from 0.7 hours per day per baby to 1.9 hours per day per baby, the crying decreased from 113.2 to 55 minutes per day per baby, or 51 per cent.[13] If we grant that the crying of the newborn indicates interference in some way with the optimum conditions for development, then it is obvious that the crying is not to the infant's benefit. With the infant in the mother's room, relief of discomfort can be much quicker than it can be in a large nursery with relatively few nurses and aides. Furthermore, rooming-in fosters the practicing of the forms and duties of motherhood. The baby shares in the glow of relief and gratitude that usually follows delivery. There is also the immediate possibility of the mother's making the association with the baby one of satisfaction for her, rather than the association of anxiety about the baby because she sees him only a few times a day and for short periods, the rest of the time wondering whether he is "all right."

Hunger and Feeding. The infant's ability to signal his physiological needs, that conditions are not optimal for his growth and development, is increasingly recognized. This is probably best illustrated in feeding, where it is true not only for the period of infancy but for later childhood as well. No doubt the 4-hour feeding schedule was adopted because most babies were hungry at 4-hour intervals. It is remarkable that the origin of the schedule should have been so completely lost sight of for a while. The schedule was, for a time, the master of the infant whose physiological needs originally gave rise to it. The baby has always been changed when in discomfort because of soiling or wetting, but when uncomfortable because he was hungry, he was made to await the scheduled feeding time.

The rhythm of hunger has a developmental history that is not complete at birth.[14,15] During the first 2 or 3 weeks hunger stimuli make themselves apparent at rather irregular intervals, but after this time the normal infant settles gradually into a schedule of his own. On the average, this schedule of the infant's own will indicate 4-hour feeding, but not every infant will have this rhythm, as illustrated by the case reported on page 178. The schedule is subject to variations dependent on the physical condition of the child and on the environmental situation. With increasing maturity, sleep also finds its physiological pattern and hunger disturbs less during the night. Eventually the infant conforms to the usual cultural pattern of a fixed number of meals a day as carried on by the family. The usual 6, 10, 2, 6, 10, 2 schedule can be shifted an hour or two either way, so that the feedings fall at times that fit the family schedule. Such changes, however, are frequently regarded as matters of great moment. We have seen families where the father rarely had the opportunity to see his child awake except on holidays, because he could not be about at the feeding times and the schedule loomed more important than his satisfaction and acquaintance with his child.*

Sleep. The maturational pattern of sleep has been demonstrated by Gesell.[16] Figure 3 shows a sample of this pattern, though it does not record the very irregular first 3 weeks. During the first weeks the normal infant sleeps about 19 hours a day. By the time he has learned to walk, this has dropped to but 13 or 14 hours. Like feeding schedules, which obviously control the timing of periods of wakefulness to a large degree, sleep schedules can be adapted to a certain extent to the convenience and needs of the family. Pointing this possibility out to an anxious set of parents determined to do the right thing for the baby may make the father's enjoyment of the baby and association with him quite feasible, whereas if schedules are adamantly fixed he would not have these opportunities. The baby is an addition to the family; neither he nor his schedule needs to be the absolute master of the family. The following case illustrates the types of adaptations that may be indicated.

U. O. is the youngest of four children. He was seen at the clinic when 4 months old, having come to well-baby clinic for prophylactic care. The family, including paternal relatives, numbered 13 and were congenial. All lived in a five-room house. The mother's only complaint about the child was that he seemed to cry now and then "to be held." The father is a baker who goes to work at 11 in the morning and arrives home at 8:30 in the evening. The children are all kept up so that he has the opportunity to play with them for a while, the family schedule being adjusted so that they make up for the lost sleep next morning. The record reads: "Sleep presents certain difficulties as the mother keeps all the children up until their father gets home about 8:30 P.M. so he can see them. He then plays with them and helps put them to bed. The

---

* Further discussion of the development of the feeding process will be found in the following chapter.

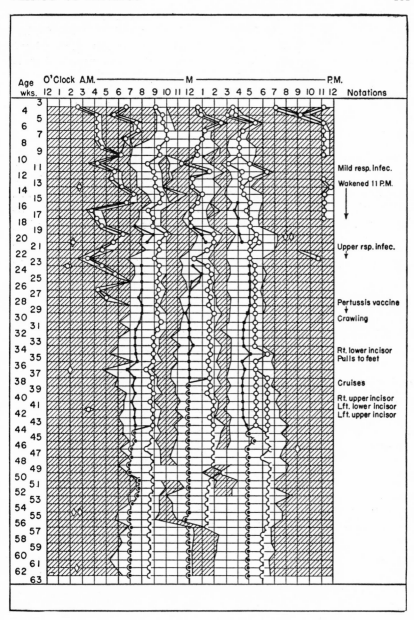

Fig. 3. Sleep (shaded), waking (white), bottle feeding (o), and solid food (•) of an infant, charted for 60 successive Thursdays. (*From Gesell and Ilg, Feeding Behavior of Infants.*)

baby loves this and cries for his father to take him as soon as he comes into the house, but then the mother has to rock him and walk the floor with him to put him to sleep. Usually sleeps in his parents' bed due to overcrowding." The advice given to the mother in this case was that the father might close his play with the baby by giving him the late feeding, arranging the rest of the schedule to fit this. The aim was to make sleep naturally follow the play and the feeding. It was also suggested that a crib of some sort be obtained for the baby, but the matter of floor space for it was a real problem in the crowded house.

Language. This function develops rapidly during infancy. In its study perhaps more than in those already discussed, we deal with an essentially human capacity, one that can be studied in other animals to only slight advantage. Hines [17] has made some interesting observations on the "language development" of macaques, however, and in her monograph records many startling observations on these animals which are eminently germane to the discussion of human development, both physical and emotional. The raw materials of speech are the auditory system and the vocal apparatus of the respiratory system. These, we have seen, are in a high state of development by the time of birth. During the first month of life the infant responds to noises and develops distinguishable cries to indicate his discomforts. This period is followed after a few months by responsiveness to tone of voice—with one tone the infant will smile; with another, pout. At first, the non-crying sounds the infant makes are the vowels *a*, in its various pronunciations, and *oo*, frequently associated with the laryngeal, gutteral, consonants. Later, the anterior consonants are attached before and aft to make more complete syllables. This capacity, together with responsiveness in the child to the parents' pleasure and encouragement, soon stabilizes certain combinations so that when the child is about three-quarters of the way through the epoch, "dada" and "mama" may be formed. By the end of the period a few words may be set well enough in patterns to be responded to with some regularity and dependability and may be useful in voicing the infant's demands.[18]

The rapidity of language development depends on several factors. Maturation is probably the most important in our culture where, in the normal family situation, the child is amply stimulated. This general subject will be discussed more fully in relation to the next epoch. Language development is usually more rapid in females than males and appears to be less rapid in children when demands are foreseen and met with oversolicitous speed than in children who need communication on the verbal level to get their wants satisfied. In the infant, as in the older child, however, communication is not the only satisfaction the child gets out of "talking." As early as the first few months the child begins to babble to himself, playing with language in a fashion that can be interpreted as nothing less than pleasure-giving. This tendency to obtain pleasure from the exercise of a maturing function will be seen repeatedly in child development; the understanding of it is frequently important in maintaining a sound and healthful child-parent relationship.

Social Development. The newborn infant shows little recognition of the fact that human beings are separate people with varying relationships to him. They appear to be no more than masses of light that stimulate the visual organs and have little other association. The infant may smile in the first few weeks of life, but this smile is more likely to come from digestive satisfaction than recognition of persons. Even after he appears to smile at people, it can be shown that he will smile at a hideous mask so long as it is moving, as well as at his mother.[19] The parents frequently do not discover this fact, and just as they often believe chance combinations of sounds the infant makes have the meaning of words, they cherish the belief that the baby smiles at them. Some have argued that this type of self-deception is actually a good thing in that it stimulates the parent to help the child to further development of speech and recognition. Real recognition probably does not take place earlier than 4 or 5 months, at which time the infant will smile at familiar and friendly people as distinguished from unfamiliar ones. Soon vocalizations are added to the smile; it becomes a laugh. The child learns to carry on jargon conversations, replying in the conversational form with those syllables available to him. This is playing with language with another person; it might be said to be the anlage of repartee in the adult. It is social activity. Such activity appears also in the bath where very early the child senses his contact with the person bathing him and kicks and splashes in a kind of pleasurable rudimentary game. He becomes aware of his own body, first examining his hands as they move, with an expression of Socratic wisdom and wonder. Later, toward the end of the year, he is able to direct his movements well and will repeat acts that are appreciated by those about him. His social activities during the year show progressive growth from awareness only in the sense of recognizing masses of light and shadow and noises, to interest in his own body and in things about him, to recognition of the attitudes of those about him, approval or disapproval, the familiar people distinguished from the unfamiliar. His response to change of position grows from one of the fear type to the point where he can enjoy frolicking games with others, he being played with rather than playing.

The child's crying at first appears mainly due to physical discomforts. It is difficult to say early in infancy when other types of crying intervene; many reports are subject to criticism because of the tendency of adults to assume that their thoughts and feelings are possible for the infant. Quite early, however, one gets the impression that the child cries because of frustration. If the nipple is removed from the baby's mouth before he has got his fill, he will cry.[8] At first this cry comes a short time after the bottle has been taken away; it seems that the cry is in response to "hunger pain." Later the cry comes more quickly, as though it were a cry of anger at the interruption of a pleasurable activity. Perhaps a conditioned reflex has been set up and the "hunger pain" is replaced by the removal of the nipple as the stimulus for the cry. At any rate, a change in emotional response from the simple physiological to the more complicated frustration pattern has taken place. In some cases the pattern of reaction is so predictable that it becomes a show-off game for the parents—the nipple is pulled out and the baby cries, time after time. Like the Moro reflex, this would appear to be a reflex that ought not be exercised, since the show-off pattern of frustration reactions may become fixed and appear as a problem at later ages. It would seem unwise to set up a conditioned response in this direction only to have it to regret when the child is more able to make his anger felt on the environment.

The acme of the infant's crying is reached when inhalation is withheld for a longer period than usual, the breath-holding spell. This pattern is sometimes seen in the very young infant, but usually is not present before the development of social consciousness as seen around the age of 6 or 8 months. Although this breath holding may result in the course of crying from any cause, such as severe pain or fright, it is most commonly seen in frustrating situations. The breath may be held so long that the infant becomes cyanotic and, in rare cases, he may actually lose consciousness or show marked changes of muscle tonus, "become limp." A typical situation is described in the following case:

B. S. was first seen in the clinic when she was 9 months old. She was the illegitimate child of a Negro girl, a member of a family where illegitimate pregnancy made a real difference. Intending to marry the father, the mother did not insist on contraceptive precautions. The marriage did not take place owing to a family quarrel, and after some hesitancy the pregnancy was accepted by the girl's family. The father continued his interest in the girl and contributed to the support of the child.

When about 3 months of age the child had her first breath-holding spell.

The mother reported: "The first time she did it I got very excited, and then I read about it in a book and next time she tried it I didn't do anything and she's gradually breaking herself." However, the child showed a severe temper reaction which lasted 30 minutes when her mother left her in the playroom. At the second visit (child aged 13 months) the mother said, "She doesn't try that so much any more. If she doesn't get what she wants, she screams. I make a little pallet on the floor and lay her there until she's through." The next visit at 22 months showed the child having clear-cut tantrums with the breath holding completely out of the picture. The mother was strapping her for the tantrums. This was advised against in favor of the more passive means of control used earlier. The following visit, age 2 years 3 months, showed tantrums less frequent and milder, but a year later they were slightly more severe but controlled easily by isolating the child in a chair until they were over. The mother was not disturbed about them. At the next visit, age 3 years 7 months, the mother felt B. had "about grown out of" the tantrums. Complaints about temper disappear completely from the record until the age of 6 when the mother remarked, "You can talk to her now." By 7 years 1 month the child's temper pattern had changed again; she was called "hardheaded," and the mother said she argued a good deal but did not show any motor outbursts.

The "hardheadedness" continued during preadolescence and particularly disturbed the child's grandmother, who reported that B. was "bossy" with companions and told them to go home if they didn't like what she wanted to do. The grandmother complained also that the child was a tomboy, having more interest in running games and skating than in playing with dolls. On the other hand, B. could prepare simple meals and showed interest and reliability in helping care for her younger siblings.

Her mother had married a man not B.'s father, but the father had continued to visit and to help pay for B.'s care. At 11 years 9 months the child was definitely showing puberty changes and the mother had prepared her for the onset of menstruation and given other sex information. Several times after B. began school, there were complaints that she finished her work too rapidly and then had to be punished for distracting others in the class. Once she was sent home with a note from the teacher which she feared to give her mother, skipping school for two days because she did not have the reply to it. This situation was resolved carefully by the mother, apparently maintaining the healthy child-parent relationship. In later interviews the child has had opportunity herself to discuss the techniques of leadership she can use, both the mental hygienist and the girl recognizing that she has attained a position of leadership in her group. At 10 years and 7 months the I.Q. was 106.

Breath holding is within the normal range of activity for infants in the first 18 months of life. Histories of normal children, taken during the age period when breath holding is occurring in some of the group, show that the phenomenon occurs in about 50 per cent of all children. The end of the period of susceptibility for breath-holding spells is widely variable, but the reaction pattern generally fades and changes when the walking skill is fairly well developed. The maturational determination of this change is indicated by the fact that it occurs later in retarded children than in those of normal intelligence.[20] Breathholding spells are common enough to appear frequently in histories of babies attending child health conferences if the mother is given the opportunity to tell about them. The spell is frequently a severe ordeal for the mother, particularly if cyanosis is deep or if loss of consciousness or the very rare convulsion supervenes. In older children, the spell may be accompanied by relaxation of the urinary sphincter.

Parents generally feel that the infant soon learns to try to control the people around him by the use of breath-holding spells. In at least a considerable proportion of cases, it is suspected that in this they practice the same kind of self-deception discussed earlier in connection with smiling and "talking." There the attribution of the ability led to a helpful response on the part of the parent; here it may lead to a punishing response, which may not be justified in the light of the infant's inability to profit by the experience. In any case, the breathholding spell induces considerable reaction in many families, and they will seek advice about the problem from the pediatrician or nurse.

For the most part, it is safe to say that breath-holding spells are not dangerous to the life of the child at any time. It may also be said that they tend to fade out of the infant's pattern of activity more rapidly if his physical needs are attended to calmly and without excitement, but his demands for domination of the household are recognized if they are such and acquiesced in only when they are justified in the eyes of the parent. The scurrying for cold water to dash in the infant's face to get him breathing again is unnecessary and probably only tends to reinforce the reaction for the future. What is advised here is not the complete neglect of the spell, but the realization that after the causes of physical pain or discomfort have been removed, the spell can be allowed to run its course without fear that the infant will be harmed by it. It is important to realize that breath holding is the acme of crying and is seen when the child is in pain as well as when he is frustrated in interpersonal situations.

Body Exploration. The infant's early interest in his hands has already been mentioned. This interest takes in the whole body later— pictures of infants playing with their toes and of puppies chasing their tails are legion. This would appear to be evidence that the child is becoming acquainted with the form of his body, its extent, its possibilities for reaching and grasping. If one observes a 3-month-old infant watching a toy tied above its crib, he appears to be trying to coordinate his movements to reach the toy long before he acquires the capacity to stretch out his arm in well-directed thrust and grasp. The hands come across the chest, the elbow "won't" straighten, the legs kick in what appears to be an overflow of innervation that cannot help the arms, which seem to be refusing to carry out the baby's determination to reach the toy. The photographers who use pictures of babies to caricature adult activities always try to catch the tongue protruding between the lips, as it does in some adults when they make determined efforts that require great concentration.[21] It is interesting to note that the child does not often object to this internal frustration with crying; again it appears that this exercise of a maturing function gives pleasure to the child rather than the frustration seen, for instance, in a 3-year-old trying to master a recalcitrant tricycle.

In the course of this learning of the body schema the infant discovers the genitals as the source of pleasurable sensations, and thereafter he is likely to handle them when opportunity offers, as when the diaper is changed or during bath time. In the male it is recognized that spontaneous erections take place very frequently.[22] It is in this sphere of exploration, manipulation, and probable pleasurable sensation from the genitals that one sees most clearly the tendency of parents to interpret the infant's activity in the light of their adult experience rather than for the simple pleasure-giving activity that it must be at this age. The following is a typical case showing these attitudes on the part of the mother:

U. I. was first seen in the clinic at the age of 7 months as a routine case, i.e., there were no complaints by mother, nurse, or pediatrician and the aim of the interview was prophylaxis. The baby was the first child of a Negro couple. The pregnancy was unexpected and unwanted. The mother "cried and took on" when she first learned of it but became reconciled to and, later, proud of the baby. She put herself under the best obstetrical care obtainable to her. She had a transfusion before delivery, but otherwise the pregnancy was not eventful. The baby was breast fed for 4 months, then put on a bottle because of failing maternal milk supply. No feeding difficulties except that orange juice was frequently rejected and was given irregularly. Motor development appeared somewhat slow; at 4 months he was able to hold the head steady and, though his mother reported he could sit alone at 7 months, test showed that he could not. The child sucked his thumb; this began at the time of weaning from the breast, when he seemed hungry. In the 4 weeks before the visit to the clinic the boy had begun to "feel himself." The mother thought it "a very nasty habit." She slapped his hands when he did this and called him a "bad boy."

He is a happy, placid baby, likes to play, particularly with his father who spends a good deal of time with him. He goes to people easily. The mother is a calm, rather easy-going woman who does not get angry, in contrast to her husband who does go into rages but is never violent. The mother is somewhat overprotective of the child. She says, "Hush now, Mamma won't let the bad doctors hurt the baby no more."

Advice on the various minor problems in the case included explanation of the genital manipulation in terms the mother could understand. The mother's tendency to look on it as "bad" was discussed in the hope that her feelings of "nastiness" might be modified. It was suggested that no direct attempt to control the activity be made, but that she might give the child a toy to play with to occupy his hands when the genitals were exposed. The sex adjustment of the parents was satisfactory to both partners.

In another male infant, first seen at 9 months, handling of the genitals was observed during the eighth month. The mother considered that this must be "stopped" and said "no, no" in a severe tone when it occurred. The baby made a game of it. The report reads, "He then grins at her knowingly and repeats the performance. Mother recently called the father on such an occasion, 'Come here and speak to your son.' The father scolded him and the child pouted but refrained from such handling while the father was in the room. The mother thinks he now does this to tease her." The treatment advised was to give the infant something to keep his hands occupied and not to make an issue of the genital manipulation since it would in all probability fade out shortly.

Such cases appear commonly in the child health clinic when the mother is allowed to make her complaints fully. The problem is not to "cure" something in the child but to interrupt the mother's projecting her own attitudes toward sex and masturbation upon the infant. She tends to judge his exploration and manipulation of the genitals as though it were of the same import that masturbation was to her during her struggle to deal with the activity, usually identifying infantile with adolescent masturbation. In some cases this complete idea may have to be the subject of discussions with the mother, but frequently the simple explanation and advice given above will suffice. If the disturbance in the mother cannot be quieted, more complete treatment procedures may be needed and the case is not one for prophylaxis within the child health station but one for treatment in a psychiatric clinic.

Rhythmic bouncing movements of infants and preschool children are occasionally seen. The form of the movements varies widely from individual to individual. Perhaps the earliest such repetitive behavior is head rolling, in which the infant rolls the head from side to side in the crib. We have a case in which the repetitive movement was hair pulling so that the child was almost bald over the top of the head. As soon as the child is able to crawl he may begin "bouncing" in his bed, resting on his knees and extended arms and dropping the buttocks against the legs, using the resiliency of the bedsprings in rising to hands and knees again. Sometimes the child will adjust his position so that each time his head moves forward it will strike the end of the crib; this is head banging. Such movements are rare enough to be considered outside the usual range of development, but common enough to justify inquiry as to their presence. They may be the result of a personality characteristic demanding sensual satisfaction of this type, but may be found that the infant is being exposed to a family where there is tension of some sort to which he is responding. The activity frequently is seen when the child is in a half-awake, half-asleep state as just before going to sleep or upon waking. In some cases, it occurs in the night when the child awakens or is partly awakened to void. In such cases, the activity will usually stop when the child is fully awakened. Pointless repetitive activities occur frequently in emotionally neglected children, usually in a setting of emotional apathy. Kinsey describes cases in which "bouncing" is a form of self-discovered masturbation leading to orgasm.[23] Such cases are rare and, except when the parents are unusually permissive, will probably require specialist consultation. This is not because the child's behavior is necessarily pathological but because the parents will require more complete ventilation and therapy than can generally be arranged for in a clinic situation.

Thumb sucking or finger sucking is, like manipulation of the genitals, a normal infant activity, although it may make its appearance considerably earlier. In the first few weeks of life the infant's movements are poorly directed, and the arms and legs are generally flexed. This being the case, the hands frequently are in contact with the face and stimulate the sucking reflex, just as the mother stimulates it by rubbing the cheek lightly when the infant goes to sleep at the breast. If thumb or finger gets in the mouth, at first its arrival there seems almost accidental. It is sucked on, forming a continuous stimulus to this reflex by its presence in the mouth. The use of the sucking reflex gives satisfaction to the infant the same way the exercise of any other developing function gives satisfaction, and the thumb sucking persists. As the motor coordination improves, the hand-to-mouth direction gets better and better so that the infant may be found sucking his thumb frequently. Thus the basis of thumb sucking would appear to be fundamental neurophysiological mechanisms present in every healthy infant.

Most parents object to thumb sucking. In many cases their attitude is undoubtedly related to sexual interpretations imposed, consciously or unconsciously, from adult experience. Physicians are apt to object to sucking on the basis of the introduction of harmful bacteria into the mouth and a supposed danger of dental abnormalities resulting from the practice. The fact remains that parents do object. In some cultural levels today, and even more frequently in the past, the need for sucking satisfaction was frankly catered to with a pacifier. The name "pacifier" indicated that the effect of quieting the squalling baby was paramount and that satisfying the child's needs was probably secondary. Preceding the mechanical age, when pacifiers are made of rubber and plastics, a sugar tit, made of a rag packed with grains of sugar, was used.

The idea that the infant needs to suck a certain time or amount, and that this amount of sucking is not completely correlated with appetite, was developed by David Levy.[24] This idea is also expressed by some proponets of breast feeding who feel that the greater effort involved in sucking the breast over sucking the rubber nipple tends to leave the infant more satisfied.[14] On the other hand, no evidence has been presented to show that such is the case. In our own experience, of 95 cases in which thumb sucking was considered a problem severe enough to be listed as such in the records, there was no indication that thumb suckers are more frequent among bottle-fed infants than among breast-fed ones.[25] Sears reports a group of children raised by cup feeding from birth and others weaned at various ages and by various methods, from sudden to very gradual. His conclusions are that frustration reactions to weaning are dependent upon the amount of practice the child has had in sucking as well as on a postulated sucking drive that must be satisfied.[26] In any case, it is obvious that the need for sucking is different quantitatively in different infants. Some cannot be satisfied by sucking the thumb or fingers, while others will put aside hunger for a considerable period by the use of thumb sucking. This difference is not an isolated trait, but is a part of the constitutional differences in personality. For example, a pair of twins was seen one of whom made his wants known by lusty crying when he was hungry; the other placidly sucked his thumb while awaiting his turn at the breast. Thumb or finger sucking is usually associated with hunger and, later, with teething, but it soon acquires an emotional significance as a consolation device. These emotional overtones will be discussed more fully in connection with the preschool period, during which the habit frequently disappears.

Many means for the prevention of thumb sucking have been used and are still being used to some extent with infants. The use of a cuff restricting flexion at the elbow is one of these, and frequently a sock or mitten over the hand will change the sensation of the thumb or finger in the mouth sufficiently so that the baby gets no satisfaction from the sucking. There is no experimental evidence as to whether these preventive devices are good or bad. Generally speaking, they are condemned by psychiatrists as frustrations that may warp character in later years, but may be used by the pediatrician who has more respect for the immediate satisfaction of the infant's parents and is not concerned about future problems until they are met. The attitude we have adhered to is one of respect for the almost universal distaste parents show toward thumb sucking, tending, however, to let the mother "do something about it" in a way that diverts the child rather than centering his attention on the habit in infancy. At the same time we have attempted to teach respect for the neuromuscular mechanism underlying the sucking and to help the mother realize that it is, for the most part, an evanescent activity that will not become a serious difficulty in the otherwise normal child. This attitude would appear to be justifiable until more experimental data on the emotional effect of thumb sucking and of attempts to stop it are available.

THE STIMULATION OF DEVELOPMENT

The development of the fetus within the uterus progresses satisfactorily unless interfered with by genetic incapacity or by disease or disorder in the mother. Development in the infant, however, will not progress unless it is actively aided, not only physiologically but psychologically as well. The infant deprived of the stimulation of association with adults who have a direct interest in his growth into a personality, as well as his growth into an adult-sized person, does not develop properly. When denial of emotionally toned relationships is severe, the infant fails in physical as well as psychological development and remains an infant or goes on to die, not primarily of disease, but because of lack of suitable stimulation. There are physiological homologues for this psychological phenomenon. Brattgord has shown that the retina cannot develop certain substances necessary for vision unless it is stimulated by light, and that the capacity for developing these substances will be lost if the stimulus of light is too long delayed.[27]

Maternal Care. The failure of infants to thrive in the absence of proper emotional stimulation was first apparent in children hospitalized on impersonally operated pediatric services.[28] In such wards, children would recover from the acute illness which led to the hospitalization, only to show progressive deterioration of general health with low hemoglobin values in the blood, chronic diarrhea, loss of weight, and a peculiar lack of vitality. This syndrome, known as marasmus, might lead to death if the child remained in hospital, but he usually recovered quickly if sent home to be cared for in a richer emotional atmosphere.

Building on this knowledge and other data, it has been found that the child will not develop either physically or in total behavior unless he receives stimuli in certain emotional settings.[29] There is also evidence to indicate that later personality deviations are associated with less severe emotional neglect in infancy. These are generally in the direction of inability to experience close personal affectional ties to others, and they may lead to delinquent behavior. Bowlby in his *Maternal Care and Mental Health* has summarized these studies most usefully, adding his own data bearing on the problem.[30]

There appears to be little doubt that the personality of the child can be permanently damaged by emotional neglect during its early years. It is not clear at what age such neglect is most damaging, how long it can continue without leaving ineradicable changes in personality, or when, if ever, vulnerability to such neglect ceases. Bowlby feels that the first 6 months of life may not be too vulnerable to damage, and this concept gains some support from investigations by Levy which tend to show that the infant is unable to relate one clinic visit to another until after the age of 9 months.[31] At the present level of knowledge, it appears that neglect of stimulation by contact with adults interested in the child will be maximally harmful during the second half of the first year and until the period when language is well established, perhaps 5 years of age. Further research is necessary better to define these limits. Pasamanick has shown that institutionalized children may show the effects of lowered stimulation before 12 months of age.[32]

Studies of animals support the conclusion that there are patterns of behavior that never can be learned unless they are acquired at a particular time in the developmental sequence.[33] There are "critical periods" during which these patterns must be integrated into the animal's general behavior, and if they are not then acquired, the capacity to learn them is permanently lost. This is homologous to the inability to develop vision without the stimulus of light. There is every reason to believe that this principle accounts for the failure of the infant, if denied proper emotional stimulation at critical periods of his development, to learn patterns of reaction necessary to the growth and development of the mature personality, and for the later failure of therapy to correct such personality deficiencies.[34]

For parents of the average infant in the average home, this line of thought and the experimental data need not be terrifying, though it is clear that it justifies concern that the child rather than the schedule will be more important in infant care, and that any mechanical contrivance that intercepts the direct contact between child and parent should be suspect. The implications are more disturbing when the child must be hospitalized or cared for away from his own home. Pediatric services have been altered to a large extent to maintain the emotional stimulation of the child. Hospitalization is kept as short as possible, and more services are encouraging a parent to stay with the child.[35] Chronic cases are kept in bed only as absolutely necessary, and toys and playrooms are as much a part of the medical armamentarium as syringes and sterilizing rooms. Nurses are encouraged to play and talk with their charges and to become emotionally attached to them.

Some infants are separated from their parents for other reasons— maternal or paternal ill health such as tuberculosis or mental disease, desertion, illegitimacy, etc. Frequently such children are institutionalized. In institutions, impersonal management is an extreme risk. The staff has many children to attend to and usually cannot hope to match the 1:1 ratio of mother and child. Precautions against epidemics necessarily contribute to the isolation of the individual child. The staff sees children come and go and hesitates to become attached to each, knowing that this can only make for a greater emotional wrench when the child does leave. The recognition of these circumstances has led to helpful reforms in institutions, but the risks remain. The present tendency is to avoid institutionalization whenever possible. When parent substitutes are needed they are obtained as foster parents so that the child will continue to receive optimum attention emotionally. Many social agencies in the United States have closed their institutions completely, a wise reform that is spreading to other parts of the world.

Maternal Care and Love. The word "love" has deliberately not been used in describing the kind of care needed by the infant and young child, to avoid what might appear to be sentimentality, obscuring the fundamental life-preserving quality of this emotional stimulation. Bowlby describes this as "maternal care" rather than "love." "Love" is avoided also because it implies a reciprocal feeling to some extent; in earliest infancy there is little possibility of response, and in childhood the response will be immature. In public education it is at times useful to tie these concepts to the word "love," but oversentimentality should be avoided. It is not momentary anger or an hour's neglect by a busy mother that must be feared, but rather emotional coldness. Many writers have pointed out that in some classes in the American culture, "love" has taken on a meaning of fatuous romanticism. Such an attitude degrades the word, robbing it of the strength of its loyalty and duty meanings. It is love in the deeper sense of devotion and service as well as mere enjoyment that is implied by Bowlby's "maternal care." It is probably wise to make this clear if "love" is used in public education concerning the child's need for emotional stimulation from the environment.

SUMMARY

The period of infancy is the "lap baby" period. The child enters the epoch at birth equipped with some capabilities for action and reaction very highly developed. On the other hand, although the cells of the central nervous system are all present at birth, many functions are not possible since the integrative connections of the cells are not functional. In the motor sphere, the child develops from random mass movements to well-directed reaching and grasping, from reflex-determined kicks and writhings to the synergistic movements of walking. Socially, he develops from a being unable to respond to people except as masses of light or darkness, to one who can distinguish familiar figures, carry on jargon conversations, and even use a few words. From crying only because of a few physical discomforts and smiling because of internal digestive satisfactions, he reaches emotional reactivity including pleasure of various degrees and obvious fear and anger at frustration. From complete impossibility of controlling his sphincters, he approaches the time when sensations of fullness and need to evacuate can be recognized. This capacity cannot be dependably functional even at the end of the period. Sleep and feeding have moved from almost chaotic periodicity at birth to definite physiological rhythms which may be already, however, subject to disruption by emotional storms. The sucking reflex may have taken on the function of a consolation device in infants with personalities needing this sort of physical sensory satisfaction.

The period is seen as a dynamic epoch of development in which the child has adapted himself to the social and emotional milieu of his home to a remarkable extent. In dealing with activities that are frequently regarded as problems by parents, an attitude has been advised that respects cultural patterns of thought and action toward them, takes into account the possible unconscious factors dictating the parents' attitudes, and recognizes the common tendency to "do something about it," directing the "doing something" into channels that will accrue to the child's benefit rather than his detriment.

The methods suggested have been used successfully in a child health station. Dealing with the parents' concern—usually the mother's—about the child's total activity, rather than only those functions regarded as "physical," makes the child health station a much more potent factor in preserving the health of the child as well as enhancing the satisfaction and happiness of the home the child came from. This is the aim of mental hygiene in public health.

REFERENCES

1. Spock, B.: *The Commonsense Book of Baby and Child Care,* Pocket Books, Inc., New York, 1946.
2. U.S. Children's Bureau: *Your Child from One to Six,* Government Printing Office, Washington, D.C., 1945.
3. Wetzel, N. G.: "On the Motion of Growth, XVI, Clinical Aspects of Human Growth and Metabolism with Special References to Infancy and Preschool Life," *J. Pediat.* 4:465–493 (1934).
4. Grinker, R. R.. and P. C. Bucy: *Neurology,* 4th ed., Charles C Thomas, Springfield, Ill., 1949.
5. Gesell, A.: *Infancy and Human Growth,* The Macmillan Company, New York, 1928.
6. Senn, M. J. E. (ed.): *"Problems of Infancy and Childhood,"* Transactions of the Sixth Conference, Josiah Macy, Jr., Foundation, New York, 1953.
7. Holt, L. E., and R. McIntosh: Holt's *Pediatrics,* 12th ed., Appleton-Century-Crofts, Inc., New York, 1953.
8. Fries, M.: "Factors in Character Development, Neuroses, Psychoses and Delinquency," *Am. J. Orthopsychiat.* 7:142–181 (1937).
9. Wessel, M. A., J. C. Cobb, E. B. Jackson, G. S. Harris, and A. C. Dotweiler: *Paroxysmal Fussing in Infancy, Sometimes Called Colic, with Particular Reference to Its Relation to Family Tension and Allergy, J. Pediat.* 14:421–425, 1954.
10. Maloney, J. C., J. C. Montgomery and G. Trainham: "The Newborn, His Family and the Modern Hospital," *Mod. Hosp.* 67:43–46, 1946.
11. Thoms, H.: *Training for Childbirth: A Program of Natural Childbirth with Rooming-in,* McGraw-Hill Book Company, Inc., New York, 1950.
12. Aldrich, C. A.: "Neonatal Crying: A Study of Its Incidence, Causes, and Control," *Hospitals* 20:68–75 (1946).
13. Aldrich, C. A., C. Sung, and C. Knop: "The Crying of Newly Born Babies. II, The Individual Phase," *J. Pediat.* 27:89–96 (1945); "III, The Early Period at Home," *J. Pediat.* 27:428–435 (1945).
14. Simsarian, F. B., and P. A. McLendon: "Feeding Behavior of an Infant during the First Twelve Weeks of Life on a Self-demand Schedule," *J. Pediat.* 20:93–103 (1942).
15. Simsarian, F. B., and P. A. McLendon: "Further Records of the Self-demand Schedule in Infant Feeding," *J. Pediat.* 27:109–114 (1945).
16. Gesell, A.: *Embryology of Behavior,* Harper & Brothers, New York, 1945.
17. Hines, M.: *The Development and Regression of Reflexes, Postures and Progression in the Young Macaque,* Contributions to Embryology, no. 96, The Carnegie Institution of Washington, Publication 541, pp. 153–209, Dec. 31, 1942.
18. McCarthy, D. A.: *The Language Development of the Preschool Child,* University of Minnesota Press, Minneapolis, 1930.

19. Spitz, R. A.: "The Smiling Response: A Contribution to the Ontogenesis of Social Relations," *Genet. Psychol. Monogr.* 34:57–125 (1946).

20. Bridge, E. M., S. Livingston, and C. Tietze: "Breath Holding Spells," *J. Pediat.* 23:539–601 (1943).

21. Golden, F. L.: *Fellow Citizens*, Hill, New York, 1950.

22. Halverson, H. M.: "Genital and Sphincter Behavior of the Male Infant," *J. Genet. Psychol.* 56:95–126 (1940).

23. Kinsey, A. C., W. B. Pomeroy, C. E. Martin, and P. H. Gebhard: *Sexual Behavior in the Human Female*, W. B. Saunders Company, Philadelphia, 1953.

24. Levy, D. M.: "Finger Sucking and Accessory Movements in Early Infancy," *Am. J. Psychiat.* 7:881–918 (1928).

25. Hewitt, R. T.: Unpublished study, School of Hygiene and Public Health, The Johns Hopkins University, Baltimore, 1951.

26. Sears, R. R., and G. W. Wise: "Relation of Cup Feeding in Infancy to Thumbsucking and the Oral Drive," *Am. J. Orthopsychiat.* 20:123–138 (1950).

27. Hydén, H.: "Histological Factors in Behavior Changes," address delivered at the opening ceremonies of the Maryland Psychiatric Institute, Nov. 18, 1952, to be published.

28. Chapin, H. D.: "A Plan of Dealing with Atrophic Infants and Children," *Arch. Pediat.* 25:491–496 (1908).

29. Spitz, R.: "Hospitalism; An Inquiry into the Genesis of Psychiatric Conditions in Early Childhood," in *Psychoanalytic Study of the Child*, vol. I, International Universities Press, Inc., New York, 1945.

30. Bowlby, J.: *Maternal Care and Mental Health,* World Health Organization, Geneva, 1951.

31. Levy, D. M.: "Observations of Attitudes and Behavior in Child Health Center; Sample Studies of Maternal Feelings, Dependency, Resistant Behavior, and Inoculation Fears," *Am. J. Pub. Health* 41:182–190 (1951).

32. Pasamanick, B.: "A Comparative Study of the Behavioral Development of Negro Infants," *J. Gen. Psychol.* 69:3–44 (1946).

33. Scott, J. P., E. Frederickson, and J. L. Fuller: "Experimental Exploration of the Critical Period Hypothesis," *Personality* 1:162–183 (1951).

34. Goldfarb, W.: "Variations in Adolescent Adjustment of Institutionally Reared Children," *Am. J. Orthopsychiat.* 17:449–457 (1947).

35. Spence, J. C.: "The Care of Children in Hospitals," *Brit. M. J.,* Jan. 25, 1947. Reprinted by Federal Security Agency, Children's Bureau, Washington, D.C., 1948.

CHAPTER TWELVE

The Preschool Period

The child enters the preschool period when he ceases to be the "lap baby" and becomes the "knee baby." Later, he becomes the "yard baby," the yard gradually enlarging to include the immediate neighborhood. This social area is rather suddenly extended, both geographically and in number of interpersonal relationships, when the child enters school. The beginning of the preschool period is marked by the child's ability to walk, primarily a matter of neurological import; the end of the period is defined in terms of a cultural institution, the formal education of the child. The function marking the start of the period is common to animals and man; the change marking the end can happen only in a highly organized society of human beings. The difference in these landmarks is suggestive of the type of change that takes place in the individual during this phase of development. Infancy includes a growing "humanness" in ability to communicate, to perform complicated tasks, and to respond specifically to emotional situations, as well as motor development. But during the preschool period the events that mark the development of the child are far more in the sphere of intellectual accomplishment and emotional relationships. Whereas in infancy, concepts about behavior could often be in terms of the structure of the nervous system making that behavior possible, during the preschool period we deal with much more complicated functions of the nervous system. It becomes impossible to follow the course of neurological development in accounting for behavior. Although there can be no doubt that physical growth enters into the picture at every change in and new capacity for behavior, the amount and kind of stimulation for behavior become increasingly important. Few parents fail to recognize the uselessness of attempting to train the child to walk, but all know that speech requires specific learning and training. Every healthy baby will suck at birth, but not every child will automatically learn to talk or read. To master these latter accomplishments requires stimulation. The capacity may be there, but accomplishment appears only if the need for it is felt through stimula-

197

tion by the environment. In other words, there is a change away from primarily instinctual animal behavior not dependent on the outside world, to more "human" emotion- and thought-determined behavior dependent upon the environment for its appearance. The two types of determination of behavior are both present throughout development, but the importance of the two in the functioning of the personality changes remarkably as behavior becomes more complicated, as it responds to the stimulation of the demands of the culture as well as the demands of its own internal economy.

It must be pointed out again that the use of epochs of development, such as infancy and the preschool period, is artificial and arbitrary. Growth is a continuum, a smooth curve to which we do necessary vio-

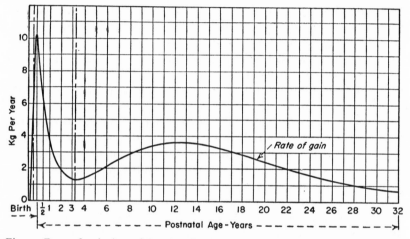

Fig. 4. Rate of gain in weight of males from early fetal to adult life. At birth, rate of gain is about seven times as rapid as it is at 3 years. [*Redrawn from Norman C. Wetzel, "On the Motion of Growth," XVI, J. Pediat.* 4:465-493 (1934).]

lence in studying parts of it rather than the whole at once. Many subjects introduced in the study of infancy must be taken up again in later periods, though not all. As we have seen, once the head is steady this factor is no longer useful in study. Speech, however, must be a matter of concern throughout life, and we shall discuss it in each period from infancy, where it began with the birth cry, until old age, when it appears to deteriorate less rapidly than some other human functions.

Walking begins around the chronological age of 12 to 15 months and school begins, in the cultures with which we are concerned, around the age of 6 years. Roughly the years between these ages are the years of the preschool period.

The rate of growth, most rapid at birth, falls precipitously during the first year and reaches its low during the third year in the average child. The rate at its low point is less than one-seventh of what it was at birth. After this low, the rate again gradually rises so that by the tenth year it is between two and three times what it was at the lowest point. These variations in rate of growth are of tremendous importance in the understanding of feeding and other behavior in children. The curve of rate of growth by age is shown in Fig. 4.

CULTURAL AND ENVIRONMENTAL VARIATION

Within the uterus the environment is similar for all children. In early infancy, the child is more a receiving than a reacting organism; the differences in the environment are probably imperceptible to the infant less than 6 months old. Feeding and cleansing are the principal functions around which life goes on. In later infancy and the preschool period, however, the environment is neither so uniform as before, nor is the child incapable of reacting to it and adapting to it. Inasmuch as there are different kinds of homes, different personality reactions may be expected.

With each human being unique, each home will also be unique. Such a situation presents great difficulties for scientific studies seeking generalized biological laws. In spite of the difficulties, some progress has been made. Anthropologists tend to find variations in distribution of certain personality traits in different cultures.[1] For example, in Japan there appears to be a capacity to make radical changes in patterns of behavior under certain situations. The daughter-in-law is able to suppress her dominating tendencies, not always without difficulty, until the mother-in-law dies. Then she at once assumes a dominant role, in some cases in marked contrast to her apparent previous personality. Similarly the child, who is frequently much indulged and has little responsibility put on him, suddenly puts off his childish ways about the age of 10 and becomes mannerly and responsible.[2] After defeat in World War II a large majority of the people were able to assume a new role toward the winners. The situation of defeat was recognized, and the generous conquerors were welcomed, frequently to the amazement of Americans who do not have the cultural background that enables them to abandon old roles and take on new ones so easily.[3] The American may regard this as evidence of insincerity, duplicity, or immorality, for he values consistency highly; the Japanese sees the matter quite differently. Similar findings come from studies of other cultures as well.[4]

Within the culture of the United States (and to varying extent, Western European and similar cultures) there are some rather consistent differences in environment which regularly affect personality structure relatively specifically. In the United States there are the large groups of immigrants, who have usually had a lower economic status for a few generations and who have rather specific problems of adaptation. Children in adolescence particularly seem to come under stress in such groups, struggling to respect their parents in the face of recognizing their inability or, worse, unwillingness to give up the old and live by the new rules. There are the various economic classes and the varying drives to move up in the scale. Some authors feel the lower classes socioeconomically are less avid in trying to raise their status than the higher. Factors of this character will be brought in as they are needed to understand personality formation.

FEEDING PROBLEMS

With the exception of temper outbursts, difficulty in feeding is the most common complaint mothers make about their infant and preschool children. Of 188 normal children between the ages of birth and 5 years studied in well-baby clinics in the Eastern Health District of Baltimore, 67 were complained about on this score.[5] This experience is duplicated with children considered sick enough to be brought to the pediatrician in practice. Foord reports the incidence of complaint of feeding difficulty as high as 80 per cent among parents of first-grade children in a public school serving a middle-class neighborhood.[6]

Aldrich and Aldrich believe the feeding problem to be a distinctly modern one, which followed upon the introduction of vitamins as a part of infant feeding.[7] When parents began to consider a particular food all-important to the child and to insist that he take it, then trouble began. This is probably too easy an answer, since parents have always been faced with the problem of the introduction of new foods. There is little evidence that children's personalities have changed in recent years to such an extent that they now tend to reject new foods, whereas in the past they welcomed the different feel on the tongue of cereal from milk. Furthermore, the fact that there is a marked diminution in the need for food which parallels the decrease in rate of growth appears to be one of the basic causes for complaints of feeding difficulty.

The introduction of solid foods, occurring in our culture usually before the sixth month, is frequently the source of rifts in the child-parent relationship. The child appears deliberately to spit out what is put into his mouth. There is a neurological reason for this reaction. The anterior part of the tongue and the lips set up a reflex to empty the mouth, whereas posteriorly in the mouth cavity and pharynx the reflex is to swallow. The mother who places a little food just inside the mouth finds it extruded, not swallowed, just as the child pushes the toy he mouths about the anterior part of the mouth cavity with his tongue and lips. Placed on the back of the tongue, the food will be swallowed. Aldrich and Aldrich consider the first reflex protective; [7] the second is obviously necessary to life. The pattern of frustration and ill will that can be set up between mother and child in the period of introduction of solid food may affect the relationship between the two for a long time, as well as interfere with their satisfaction in each other in the immediate situation. The knowledge that food will be swallowed if placed far back on the tongue—where the end of the nipple lies in nursing—may avoid a struggle giving unhappiness to both parent and child. Recently these facts have been recognized by commercial designers of spoons for babies. Longer, narrow shapes are replacing the blunt, shallow, broad earlier patterns.

Figure 4 showed the fall of the rate of growth to be rapid during the first two years, reaching its low point about the beginning of the third. Clinical experience shows a high rate of feeding difficulties persisting into the period well beyond that involved in the introduction of solid food. The problem becomes less important numerically only after the low point has been passed. The mother, used to seeing the infant avidly awaiting his bottle and crying lustily if he does not get it, is puzzled when her child begins to show little appetite. When he was not hungry before, he was always sick. A surprising number of mothers convince themselves, when this slackening of appetite appears, that their children actually are ill, even though the children play well and are not thin. It is almost axiomatic in clinic work that the child whose mother insists that "he doesn't eat a thing" is observed to be well nourished.

The point is often made that the great increase in physical activity of the child after he learns to walk must require a great deal of food as the energy supply, and that this should balance the decrease in demand that occurs by reason of the decrease in rate of growth. Actually, the energy required for the chemical transformation of food into bone, muscle, and other organs is a great deal more than that required for the conversion of food into body movement. The net result is a decreased need for food, even though physical movement increases.

The extent to which the parent-child relationship can be damaged and the smooth running of the home be disrupted by feeding difficulties is remarkable. If the child has any aggressive personality traits, he proceeds to exercise the power bestowed upon him to dominate the family. He realizes that his lack of appetite is disturbing and that he can control the family by refusing to eat. The mother, faced with a frustrating situation but at the same time with one that arouses deep anxiety, vacillates between anxiety and irritation at the child, perhaps bowing to his domination with fawning efforts to get him to eat. In one such situation, the family, of Catholic faith and with a picture of the Christ on the wall of the dining room, dispatched a member to the next room to speak as though the voice came from the picture, telling the child to eat. A story read from a book in payment for eating the spinach, another for a teasponful of meat, etc., are other means used.

If the child does not have aggressive personality traits, he may eat the food but vomit it later or at once, a more passive way of reacting to the family pressure, though vomiting may also soon become a means of obtaining family control. The method is more devious and perhaps less healthy than the more direct refusal to eat or the use of the bargaining outlined above. Once the pattern of emotional turmoil is attached to the eating situation, direct physiological reactions to emotional stimuli set in, further complicating the problem by tending toward a vicious circle of the physiological reaction aggravating the emotional stress.

The following is a typical case of feeding difficulty:

G. D., a severely disturbed child from many points of view, was first seen when he was 4 years old. He is the son of a father who comes from a stable and financially secure Italian family. The father is the oldest child of his family and feels he did not get the advantages his younger brothers and sisters had because when he was young the family was not so well off. He feels continuously thwarted that he cannot get ahead financially as has his father. He hates his plodding job because it is out of line with his ambitions. The mother had an Irish immigrant home and was raised by grandparents who she feels made her "too particular" so that she "can't stand noise, dirt, or confusion." She has a temper and throws things at her husband in their frequent arguments. Usually these are about money, but the sex adjustment is also a source of concern. The husband is jealous, but has a strong sexual urge which finds expression in nightly intercourse plus demands three or four times a day when he is home. He is both proud of his sexual prowess and has sought medical treatment because he felt it excessive. He twits his wife that she cannot satisfy him and jokes about the possibility of getting other women; this hurts her feelings even though he has not carried out the suggestion so far as she knows.

The boy is an only child, much wanted and prized before his birth, the more because two miscarriages preceded the successful pregnancy. During the pregnancy the mother was concerned, fearing abortion, but worried also because of high blood pressure which led to her being put on a salt-free diet.

He was breast fed for 7 months, with cereal added at 3 months and vegetables at 5. Bottle feeding continued until 13 months, and there was no difficulty weaning. He never showed much liking for meat, but otherwise all foods were taken well. Around the age of 1 year, his appetite began to fall off, causing great concern to the family. He ate some of everything, but too little in the estimation of the parents. Outside the home, at a restaurant or someone's home, he ate well. The father felt his "thinness," which actually is not marked at all, as a reflection on his, the father's, ability to feed him, and he compares the boy unfavorably with a cousin who is chubby and is considered the model of health by the paternal relatives. He gets excited about the boy's eating at mealtimes, and has been known to leave the table shouting, "Oh, God, why does this have to happen to me?" Feeding between meals is no problem, though the boy gets an ice-cream cone, usually, in the afternoon. He drinks a quart of milk a day gladly.

The mother began toilet training early, at 2.5 months, but was not disturbed by her failure then, beginning again when the child could sit on the "toidy seat" by himself. By the time he was 20 months old he was completely trained. There was no breath holding in infancy, but about the time he began to walk he began to have tantrums characterized, when full-blown, by beating with his fists, biting, kicking, and screaming. These tantrums were usually set off by denials from people; the example the mother gave was anger because his arthritic old grandmother would not get down on the floor and play with him. These tantrums were managed by the mother by isolating the boy in another room on a chair. Sometimes several hours elapsed between the tantrum and the punishment, since the parents were "mortified" and quieted the outburst as rapidly as possible, waiting until there was no company to administer the punishment. The parents themselves did not always agree on handling the boy at these times, so that the mother sometimes left the room until the tantrum was over. The nights following severe tantrums or punishments were likely to be marked by mild nightmares in which the child cried and had to be comforted. The boy bit his nails. They were very short at the time he was seen. The difficulty with relatives other than his parents noted above appeared in his resistance to their "smothering" attempts to show him affection. He was jealous of his parents' fondness for each other and protested if he saw them, for example, dancing together. For some time the mother had noted a tendency for him to answer "no" to whatever she asked him, and, in general, to resist any sort of direction.

He was an only child who had little contact with other children. Once when he was frightened by thunder, his mother reassured him by telling him that he had a guardian angel. He promptly turned the angel into an imaginary playmate with whom he played for hours. Later there were two of these angels, plus an imaginary baby brother, a girl called Michaelina, nicknamed Mickey, and a boy named Jimmy. These diverted him for considerable periods, but he has said to his mother, "Mom, I'm tired of playing with those make-believers!"

Fears were not very deep-rooted but did appear. Thunder and sirens alarmed him. An aunt attempted to scare him with the bogeyman, but the mother corrected this to such an extent that he could play at being the bogeyman, putting a paper sack on his head and making appropriate noises. His ability for imaginative play was noted in the clinic. He asked if a little house was for "play people." He acted out a story about three ducks, a father, a mother, and a baby. The mother duck and the baby slept in the house, the father outside. Then the baby killed the mother and broke her in pieces, after which the father duck came in and was welcome.

The numerous behavior problems were considered to be due primarily to the child's being subject to conflicting loyalties to both his parents, who too often seemed to be going in opposite directions. The father's thwarted ambitions and his conflicts about them made the very common pattern of comparisons with different children more severe in this family than it is ordinarily. It was felt that the situation could be solved most rapidly if the child were got into nursery school, the object being to give him playmates and to enlarge his experience in a group of contemporaries and under more objective leadership in order to balance the home environment. Some suggestions were made concerning symptom management; it was advised that the automatic "no" response be handled by giving the child alternative methods of getting things done and letting him choose which he would use. The question of punishment was discussed to the end that when punishment was necessary it be given at the time of the act to be punished. Thus, if he had a tantrum at his grandmother's, it might be best to take him home at once or punish him there, rather than punish him hours later. These were the only two problems of the eleven listed in the record which were selected for immediate symptomatic treatment. The necessary treatment with regard to the family situation was begun in the very fact that the mother was provided with a person to whom she could unburden herself and tell her story.

The nursery school experiment did not work out well. The child attended two days, then was kept home two because of rain (the family fears colds). After this he did not want to return. His father was disappointed that the nursery school, in a crowded part of the city, did not have a broad grassy play space and decreed that the child should not return. The mother now blames the father for the continuation of the child's problems, a convenient way out for her. This was the situation at the second visit, one month after the first.

The next visit, 6 months later, when the child was 4 years 7 months old, again showed no improvement; in fact, the situation was even more acute. The mother was 7 months pregnant and the danger that G. would be rejected in favor of the new baby seemed very likely to be realized. The feeding problem was worse, the meals now climaxed with vomiting when the conflicts got bad. This earned the father's sympathy. At the conference, which the father attended with the mother, the boy refused to let the parents leave him. He clung to his mother while his father "reasoned" with him, finally threatening not to take him for a long-promised train ride. This threat he later said he had no intention of carrying out. Finally, the boy was carried out to the playroom where he vomited. When his demand that the father be notified was not acceded to and his vomiting was taken care of with few remarks, he quickly turned to playing and seemed happy. The pattern of threats not intended to be carried out was familiar to the child. His grandmother told him he would not get any Christmas presents if he were bad, to which he replied that he had got some the year before when he was no better. Then she said that was because Santa had forgiven him because he was sick. The boy replied that he could be sick again!

The discussion of the case this time included the father, who was led to tell of his struggles to get ahead and congratulated on his success thus far. The handling of the boy at this interview was used as an example of what must be done when necessity demands action and decision after explanation, rather than indecisive "reasoning." The fact that security in the child may depend on the parents' knowing what is best and being able to act consistently on their conclusion was brought out. The father, after 6 months, felt the nursery school was now necessary. In the course of the three interviews, the mother had got a little clearer grasp of her husband's personality and was not as hurt by his sexual boasting. Though there was still disagreement between the parents, the father was now willing to ask for help and accept suggestions.

Following this interview, this boy was not seen again for 2 years, though the mother reported his progress and her inability to keep clinic appointments by telephone conferences and letters. At the next visit the boy was 6 years 4 months old and in the first grade. He had successfully completed nursery school and kindergarten. Many of the problems were no longer acute, and the mother was much less concerned about them. In feeding, for example, she said the boy got enough to eat because he was free to raid the icebox, the only restriction being that he clean up after himself. He always sat with the family at meals, but was allowed to take large or small helpings as his appetite directed. Tantrums were rare and consisted of argument without the mass-reaction physical outlet so apparent earlier. The baby was accepted without much demonstration by the boy; he liked him but was not demonstrative about it. The boy still stuck close to his mother and seduced her into giving him a good deal of attention in dressing him, though he can do most things for himself. He was less dependent on the imaginary playmates than he had been, though "Jimmy" and "Mickey" still appeared occasionally in his play.

He was obviously still not at ease in his relation to his parents. At the time of the visit he sided with his mother against his father, saying to his father, "Listen to mother. She is the smart one in this family. You're just a dumb Italian." This was obviously the most important issue in the case. The mother's relation with the father had improved a little in that there were fewer violent fights, but the boy's lack of respect for his father probably mimicked the mother's attitude, at least her attitude when angry. It was advised that the boy be protected from arguments so far as possible and that special efforts be made to help him learn the fields in which his father was due respect by encouraging companionship between them and showing appreciation of the father's ambition and hard work. The adjustment between the parents had improved but still left something to be desired.

The next visit, though occasional telephone contact intervened, came when G. was 8 years old. He was well nourished and seemed mature for his chronological age. His mother complained, but with humor, that he was noisy, demanding and kept the house in an uproar from the time he came home from school until he went to bed. She had told him that if in his boisterous play he gets hurt she would not take care of him but would send him to hospital. When it was suggested that the child might feel she genuinely wanted to get rid of him, she laughingly remarked, "My God, he knows that," but the ring was a pleasant one, not one of cold rejection. The two brothers got on well, the little one mimicking G. The mild talking and mumbling in sleep had disappeared. G. got on well with friends, but occasionally withdrew from them, probably when they rejected his somewhat dominating leadership. A little nail biting persisted.

It is clear that feeding problems may be the issue about which the emotional tensions present in the family may find expression. No parent can treat a child exactly the same each time he does some particular act. Splashing mud on his clothing is not so great a fault at the end of the day, when the suit is ready for the laundry anyway, as it is when the child is freshly dressed to go to a party. In the first case, the incident may be enjoyed by the parent as well as the child; in the second, the parent is likely to punish—and the child is likely to be confused. A group of parents' ideas are involved which the child is not able to grasp and understand. So it is in the eating problems. Items not directly related to the food refusal get bound up in the situation. Suppose a grandmother is dying of cancer of the stomach; the child's refusal to eat brings up all the sentiments that the failing grandmother's illness has induced—perhaps even guilt over the mother's only partly conscious and strongly repressed wish that the old lady would die. Or perhaps the husband has had an unsatisfactory luncheon conference with a finicky or unmannerly eater; the sentiments of that situation will be added to the child's refusal to eat. These adult concerns and countless others are imposed on a child who has no appetite. What is fundamentally a relatively simple biologic phenomenon becomes an emotionally charged battleground. It is the transfer of this emotional charge from the real-life situation that aroused it to the eating or other situation involving persons and things not originally involved that is the "bad mental hygiene." The prophylactic problem so far as the child-parent relationship is concerned is to keep feeding problem as feeding problem, not contaminated with emotional sets originating in other connections.

Prophylaxis of Feeding Problems. In the child health station, where these problems are complained of so commonly and where they may be anticipated, the mother can be warned that appetite will begin to diminish toward the end of the first year and continue to be small for a year or two. An explanation of the slowing of the rate of growth through these years can be given in simple terms, so that she understands why the child does not eat and so that she does not feel that she is in some way responsible for the decrease in appetite. With some humor, she can understand the common finding that it is usually a well-nourished child who seems to be the worst feeding problem according to the mother's complaints. Such explanation and instruction, preceding the period of dwindling appetite, will allow the mother to see in it not aggravating behavior on the part of the child but evidence of normal and expected development. The situation is also one that increases the mother's confidence in the clinic. If feeding difficulties are already present, this sort of information imparted by the physician immediately after he has examined the child, or by the nurse at the physician's direction, can be most effective in aborting the problem, in separating the child's eating from the emotional loads from other sources that may have been attached to it. By means of such an early approach, the unraveling of complicated situations may be made unnecessary. In some rare cases, when the situation is definitely pathological, psychiatric treatment may have to be sought for members of the family—usually not for the child.

Confidence in the child's own self-direction through his internally stimulated impulses, discussed in connection with infant feeding, is not misplaced during the preschool period. Davis [8] has demonstrated that children will maintain their nutrition excellently if allowed to select as they wish from a variety of foods. Her experiment began with infants of 8 to 10 months and ran well into the preschool period. There is experimental evidence in support of the reassurance which is a part of the treatment of feeding problems that, if left alone and not hounded, the child will eat what he needs. Spock sums the matter up as follows: "It is important for her [the mother] to know that her child's instincts are sound to start with, that his appetite will vary, that he will probably pick a well-balanced diet in the long run if he isn't given too many prejudices." [9]

Motor development is intimately interconnected with feeding problems, particularly in the first few years of handling solid food. In the period of infancy we observed the development from the almost random movements of the newborn to precision of reaching and grasping and the synergy of walking. In the preschool period this development continues. In reaching and grasping, the child needs a concept of his body that includes only the body itself, but in feeding the body is extended beyond its actual tissues since tools are used. This extension of body concept requires much practice as well as development of the nervous system, which is itself partly dependent for growth on stimulation by practice. The experienced driver of an automobile handles his car as an extension of himself; he knows where the fenders are as well as he knows where the end of his nose is. But he did not always know this; it had to be learned. The baby is not as fortunate. He has to learn where the tines of the fork or the bowl of the spoon are at a time when his nervous system is as yet not fully functionally developed. He will miss his mouth, push food off his plate, give up and resort to the use of his hands. As in the case with talking, the child enjoys the exercise of developing new functions and resents being interfered with in their exercise. He does not have the adult standards of neatness in eating or the fund of associations that may induce nausea in the mother when she sees the cooked cereal in a mess all about the baby's plate and on the floor. In such a situation aggravation is likely to arise from the mother's assumption that the baby is deliberately violating a set of standards like her own—and enjoying it. The mother also realizes there will be a larger pile of laundry for her to wash. Unchecked by the knowledge that the child does not have the physical equipment to do better, and seen without appreciation that the child is enjoying the extended control he has over his environment now that he can feed himself, this situation may tend to interfere with the emotional satisfactions both mother and child need in their relationship with each other.

MOTOR DEVELOPMENT

Development of the neuromuscular system provides the basis for a vast array of new activities. Many of these are difficult to standardize as belonging to a particular place in the developmental sequence. The ability to tie a bowknot, in a culture using string-tie shoes at least, has been standardized for use in intelligence tests. It appears around the age of 7. Usually tying shoes precedes the ability to tie the knot in the test situation by some months. Another such point is the way in which the child climbs a flight of stairs. About the age of 3, he ceases to hitch himself from one step to the next, bringing both feet to rest on each step, and is able to use the alternate step progression in the adult pattern. Shortly before this accomplishment appears, a grasp of form is evidenced; the child will now place the rectangular block in the rectangular hole, the triangle in the triangle, etc. This is evidence that sensory impulses are modifying and directing a motor system that is becoming increasingly subject to adaptation to incoming sensory stimuli, modified and integrated by the central nervous system.

Shortly after the child learns to walk, he will begin to climb, usually first on steps, later using chairs and boxes. Here, again, is seen the enjoyment the child gets from the exercise of a developing function, the joy of conquering not only the obstacle in front of him but also the remaining deficiencies of a nervous system which still leaves him unable to do everything he can imagine. Occasionally, the child will be aggravated by the refusal of his body to serve him; it is not unusual to see a 3-year-old throw away the blocks that won't stay on top of the tower he is building, or kick the tricycle that won't respond to his efforts to make it go. The climbing urge is combined with an urge to investigate, a combination that sometimes spells havoc to bric-a-brac.

The child health station, anxious to preserve and foster the adventurous spirit and motor satisfactions of the child while at the same time preserving a strong and appreciative mother-child relationship, has an opportunity to discuss these features of personality development with the mother before the problems of broken vases and scratched furniture come up. The mother who can see developmental progress of her preschooler in the shattered glass top of the coffee table on which he has been found sitting is less likely to explode in anger and resentment at having her finest wedding present broken and scratched. She will be warned to pack away the finest decorations for a few years or put them definitely out of reach. She will be advised that the cookie cutters and pans in the lower kitchen cabinets will be as good stimuli for the child as the china figurine on the mantel. She may achieve the appreciation of a mother who refused to have her coffee table refinished when her children had grown out of this period. That mother said that each chip and scratch had a history of which she was somehow proud and which aroused a wave of pleasant nostalgia and love for her boys.

This does not mean that children should not be taught that there are qualitative differences between objects. A nursery school will frequently have, in addition to the toys to be played with, a number that are to be looked at but not touched. These are present in the school specifically to teach the distinction between what is to be handled and what is to be appreciated otherwise. It is expected that in learning the distinction the child will have a try at handling the "to-look-at" toys and that the lesson will have to be repeated many times. In the home, it is well, however, to have the things "to look at" of low enough value so that during the period of mistakes and unlearned or partly learned lessons not too much is lost. Again, one must recall that the child's associations with the words "valuable vase" will be quite different from the mother's, who multiplies her appreciation of it by knowing its history and the sacrifices made by the family to own it.

During this period just following the onset of walking, the child is more accomplished at using big muscles than small ones; the muscle control appears to continue to develop in its original pattern, from the proximal to the peripheral muscles. Somersaults will be managed before the fork is properly held in the fingers. For this reason, toys for children of this age should not be too small. Blocks a foot long and 4 inches wide and deep are better than smaller ones. A pile built with them is bigger and seems to give more satisfaction. If they are hollow they will, of course, be lighter and more adapted to the child's strength. Boxes such as orange crates—nails countersunk and splinters smoothed, of course— give the child a chance to build something on which he can then climb and from which he can reach. More elaborate blocks in the form of steps are useful and give stimulus to the exercise of the big muscles of the extremities. A little later, a tree with low branches is an irresistible invitation to climb, and where a tree is not available a jungle-gym of pipes is a good substitute.

Big toys and the climbing operations of children may well give rise to anxiety on the part of the mother concerning smashed fingers and broken bones. Here, as in the management of feeding difficulties, there can be some confidence in the child's own protective devices. In general, the child's own store of fearfulness will keep him out of too dangerous adventures. Such reassurances can be honestly given to the overanxious mother. It can be pointed out that splinters, scratches, and bruises are common to any enjoyed physical activity, from building a wall of orange crates to playing football as a young adult. The price of the enjoyment of physical exercise must be paid at any stage of development.

Many children in the preschool period have tremendous energy. The profusion and variability of their physical activity is staggering to the average adult. A well-trained college football player once set out to mimic the activity of a 15-month-old boy and found that the boy soon had him crying for surcease.[10] The span of attention is likely to be short. Activities change, and no sooner has a mother gone back to the job she interrupted to satisfy the child's last demands than some new request is made. The tricycle ride is interrupted to chase a piece of paper blown by the wind, and the tricycle remains where it was, squeezed out of attention and memory by the new interest. The collection of blocks, dragged outside with such happy plans to build a garage, seems only to be well scattered before the child climbs the apple tree to see if the robins are hatched yet. Then he proceeds to go for a ride, steering the tricycle around the now-forgotten blocks almost without seeing them. The great fun that older infants and young preschool children have playing peekaboo is probably accounted for on the basis of this short attention span, which makes disappearances far more real to the child than to the adult. As the end of the preschool period approaches, longer periods of concentration will become apparent. Coloring books may occupy attention for half an hour or longer, and dolls may be completely dressed before the activity changes to something else. Completed tasks are the exception rather than the rule during the preschool period, however.

The active, adventurous child has thus far been pictured as typical, but there are wide variations in the fund of energy, even in normal children unrestricted and not overly restrained. Fries and others have shown that variations in amount of activity may be noted in very young infants, before postnatal environmental differences can have had much effect.[11] These differences in pressure toward action, frequently called differences in temperament, are apparent throughout life. That the active, adventurous type should be presented first is perhaps natural in a book written in the culture of the United States. The shy, retiring, relatively inactive child is likely to be looked upon as pathological in some way in this culture, but there is little direct evidence that these traits are actually indicative of greater risk of future mental disease.

FEAR AND ANXIETY

The control of adventurousness by fear varies widely. In many cases it seems clear that the urge to rough-and-tumble freedom has been suppressed by repeated restrictions imposed by a fearful mother. Such mothers tend to value the physical safety of the child too much and overprotect him as a consequence, so that he is robbed of much of the pleasure of exercising his developing functions. Davis [12] and others [13] have shown that such restrictive child-raising methods are more characteristic of the middle and upper economic classes than of the lower. The latter authors feel that the differences account for slower development of motor coordination in children of the higher economic groups.

Some children are encouraged toward adventure by one parent, usually the father, while the other may be restraining by frequent warnings of physical danger. The child may well be confused at the breach in family solidarity and find himself allied with one parent against the other, a situation contributing to stress in the parent-child relation. The films "The Feeling of Rejection" [14] and "Preface to a Life" [15] both deal with problems in this area.*

* See film list, p. 423.

Fearfulness itself is a development of the preschool period which, as we have just seen, may be overaccentuated so as to become a restraint on the freedom of action, physical and psychological, of the child. In general, fear is an unpleasant emotion, carrying with it uncomfortable sensations of the heart beating, excessive sweating, feelings of tension in the chest and upper abdomen, trembling, and other responses of the central and autonomic nervous systems. Stark fear is seen in nightmares in children of preschool age. In many cases, these phenomena can be traced to fearsome activities of the day before—a fire, a fall from a tricycle, etc. But sometimes the dream is more fanciful and seems to draw its emotional force from more vague sources which, even at this age, have to be symbolized in the dream. The child appears unable to face directly the unrest and tension in the home, the fear of dislike by either parent, the feeling of rejection by one or the other parent, or any of the other things that disturb the amiability of the home. An occasional nightmare may be explained on the basis of the first group of causes if the history is quite clear. But in a continuous series of nightmares extending over a period of time, the well-baby clinic pediatrician will have to take the time to look for deeper sources of the child's unrest. This sort of investigation is not considered a part of the pediatrician's job in most clinics, but to keep the baby "well" it may be necessary to adjust the happiness of the home. In the following case the child's terrors occurred in the state of half-sleep rather than in deep sleep, but the source of the difficulty lies in the strained family relations.

T. R. was 4 years 3 months old when first seen in the clinic at the mother's request. The mother said, "She seems to be an unhappy child, and we don't want her to be unhappy." The evidences of the unhappiness were nightmares and daytime fantasies about a wolf which she feared would attack her. She actually "saw" this wolf one night just before going to sleep, and her fright had aroused the sympathy of her parents, particularly her father, so that he read to her for hours. She got too little sleep, often not falling off until midnight or later. She was hypersensitive to reprimands from her father and was intensely jealous of two little boys who rode to nursery school with her in his car. She rather separated herself from other children, playing mainly with these same two boys, trying to dominate them, and rejoicing openly when they fell and hurt themselves.

The father was an insurance salesman with the genial, assured, and buoyant personality that might be expected of such a person, but with an undercurrent of tension that appeared as hypochondriacal complaining. It was the kind of personality that looks so well put together but not infrequently slips into alcoholism in trying to relieve the tension. The mother worked in her husband's office. She said she had a reputation for being a calm, resourceful person and agreed that she looked like one, but she said she actually went to pieces in crises and tried to put off decisions as long as possible. The child was intelligent and had developed rapidly; she could tie her shoes at the age of 3 and showed other evidences of precocious development.

The principal problems were the fear and the sleep difficulty. The sensitivity to the father's reprimands and jealousy of the boys indicated that she was ill at ease in her relation to the father and in the family situation. The mother easily saw this and made the adaptations suggested, which consisted of taking an attitude of patience while the child struggled through the relation with her father. The job was made easier for the child by his stopping taking the other children to school. A child is not really ready to share affection easily until 5 or 6 as a rule. The mother picked the child up from the nursery school at 3 rather than 5 in the afternoon, and they companionably did the housework in the hours before supper. A bedtime routine was set up to make going to sleep a logical "next step" in an ordinary program rather than a great achievement. When the routine was over, the lights went out and the child was expected to go to sleep. Surprisingly to the parents she did just that. Seven months later the mother reported "big improvement." The wolf was gone, and the child occasionally asked to go to bed before the set time. The mother reported saying to her husband, "My Lord, was it this easy and we've been going through all this agony?" A little adjustment in the father's attitude was suggested; he had been treating the child like a little adult and as a sort of special guest rather than as a member of the family. The third visit, a year after the first, showed no sleep difficulties, the wolf still gone and the child happy though she seemed to get into too many fights. A new baby was expected, and the mother said she was getting a puppy for T. so she would understand how much care the new baby would need and therefore be less jealous of it when it came. It is to be noted that this was a spontaneous move on the part of the mother and not suggested by the clinic.

The total time spent in treating this case up to this time was about 2 hours for the mental hygienist and the same for an assistant to record and judge the child's behavior while away from the mother.

The little sister arrived, T. helping to pick out the baby clothes before the event. In the preceding months, there had been some increase in temper outbursts, the child occasionally striking the mother. The mother explained that getting angry was quite all right but that it could not go on to hurting people. T. tended at this period to get into fights at school, usually taking the side of the "underdog" or mistreated smaller child. At the end of the year her kindergarten teacher commented that T. did not participate freely in classes and did not volunteer very often. The child explained that she was so frequently overlooked when she raised her hand she just quit raising it. During kindergarten it became evident that the child was generally precocious (Stanford-Binet I.Q. 141) and that she had talent in art. Her father took some of her work for appraisal by a children's art teacher and was told that there was some talent, particularly in depicting action. In addition this experienced teacher remarked spontaneously that T.'s works were those of a happy child. At this point it was noted that the child turned to either parent with requests and no longer seemed overly concerned about relationships with her father. Once she was observed trembling when in danger of being late to school. Asked about this by her still somewhat oversolicitous father, she remarked quite matter-of-factly that she was tense because she might be tardy.

At the age of 6 years 9 months, all was going well except that the mother noted a tendency to choose one friend exclusively. This pattern recurred throughout the rest of the history to the age of 11 years, 8 months, though the friends changed, usually under the force of external circumstances such as changing schools and, once, skipping a grade. The latter was at the principal's suggestion that T. was obviously not sufficiently challenged by the work offered. The friends were frequently out-of-the-ordinary people. One was a brilliant but erratic boy in her class who was generally disliked. Although it was reported to the mother that the boy's parents were separated and his father homosexual, she did not interfere in the friendship except to see to it that the children were at her home rather than the boy's. T. simply explained that she liked the boy and felt he was not really understood by others. On another occasion, her best friend for months was a retarded girl 2½ years older than she. This girl used poor grammar, which disturbed the mother, but she again did not interfere. On another occasion, T. picked two unpopular children to work with her at a year-long art project and, according to the teacher, contributed to increased status and self-confidence for both.

There are many other episodes in this history, including two successive years under unhappy and unsuccessful teachers, painful years for parents and the child. The artistic talent has received wide recognition and the child's work is permanently placed in three exhibitions of childhood art, one abroad. After several years of very tomboyish activity and neglect of personal neatness, she has recently begun to take careful care of her person, though still not of her clothes. She has menstruated once and then skipped 5 months. She had been prepared for this and showed no concern about it. Once she remonstrated with her mother for giving sex education too early to her younger sister.

Although this child's precocity was recognized at the first visit to the clinic, there was then no knowledge of the now obvious artistic talent, or of the talent for handling people—unless the use of the nightmares for controlling the father may be taken as the first evidence thereof.

The capacity to feel anxiety develops from the kind of mass action seen in the Moro reflex until it reaches the adult level of distinguishing between the rational fear of external violence or emotional rejection and the anxious but unfounded worries about things on the other side of the bridge not yet crossed. In this development there may be terrors such as those just described, or waking fears, as of dogs or other animals, of darkness, and of many other things. It has been amply demonstrated that these are not "innate" fears, that they are learned from people in the environment, and that, in general, they are built on a base of general tension and uncertainty as to status in the family. Not all fear seen in preschool children is unpleasant fear, however; some of it appears to be quite pleasurable to the child. It is frequently used as a means to get adult attention on a very direct basis. The feeling of anxiety is a developing function. Often the child seems to get the same kind of joy out of exercising this function that he gets out of exercising speech. For example, two 5-year-old girls playing together postulated a wolf behind the garage. They would dash out to peek around the corner and scurry back, giggling with glee. They seemed to be exercising their ability to feel fear and getting a great deal of pleasure out of it. The little sister of one of them, aged 3, took up the game in a different way. She invented a wolf in the basement and said she was afraid to go down there to play. She was quite satisfied when her mother, recognizing the stimulus and the request for attention implied, suggested that she go down and pet the wolf. She went down to her play. Such exercises of the fear reaction can hardly be considered pathological. Their recognition for what they are can form the basis for honest reassurances of the worried parent, provided, of course, that the diagnosis is based on an understanding of the situation and is not an offhand device to get on to the next case.

LANGUAGE DEVELOPMENT

Language development in the preschool epoch begins with a child already accomplished in saying many syllables, to a few of which he has attached some sort of significance for communicative purposes. With this as the foundation, development takes place with great rapidity during the period from 18 months to 5 years, after which the developmental curve levels off to a more gradual rise. Initially, nouns are very common; the names of things are learned most rapidly. Soon verbs and modifying words and connectives are added. The speed with which language function is expanded depends, of course, on developmental age, but there are other factors as well. McCarthy shows that development is more rapid in children of professional people than in the children of laborers, even when differences in mental age are controlled.[16] This means that the stimulation of hearing language with complete, structured sentences and broad vocabulary is effective in molding the child's language development at this age, as it certainly is later in school and college. Direct imitation is of great importance early in speech development when the child formulates for himself the sounds that he hears made by others about him. This frequently precedes the realization of the meaning of the syllables.

There is no doubt that the child enjoys language and uses it as a plaything as well as a means of communication. Indeed, the communicative function of language seems almost a fortunate accidental side effect at times. Infant babbling, the prattle of the early preschooler, the satisfaction of repetition in the older preschooler, the talk that seems to be for nothing but talk's sake of the preadolescent, all indicate that communication is not the only use the child has of language.

Adult language is often very stereotyped in tonal qualities. In learning it the child selects from the various sounds he can make until he is left, eventually, with the restricted group of sounds employed in his own mother tongue. The capacity for learning new sounds tends to be lost. A child learns Chinese as easily as he learns English, but if he tries to learn Chinese after his syllabication has been restricted by the habitual use of English, he has the greatest difficulty in learning the numerous intonations and *ng* sounds. The hard *ch* of the German *ich* is as easy to learn as the hard *g* sound (though guttural consonants are of later development than labial ones), but a college German student who is previously unfamiliar with the language has the greatest difficulty learning to make and use it. Much of the child's language play is early confined to the syllables used as language about him, even when the child or groups of children develop individual languages of their own.[17]

Within the range of syllables of the language spoken in the environment there is still room for a great deal of play, changing the initial and ultimate consonants and altering the vowels. Sometimes this is to find a word that expresses a feeling in sound. Who shall deny that *sqush* expresses better than "crush" what happens when one stamps on a juicy caterpillar? Early, and later as well, however, the changing of words for fun may not be attempting to express anything but pleasure. Such changes may arrive at words embarrassing to the parent. The child notices the embarrassment and concern at once and tries the word over again. If he continues to "get a rise" out of the parent, he may well continue to use the device to keep front stage in the family. A boy 3 years 2 months of age was reported by his mother to use a "four-letter Elizabethan word meaning fornication" in this way. The mother was a tremendous nagger of the boy and he equally adept at aggravating her. This was a new way, and a very satisfactory one, of doing it. The child who is not fixed in patterns of rebellion will find it sufficient to have reached the limit of parental tolerance, and the adjuration that this word or phrase is not used in the family is sufficient to satisfy the child. The offending word then drops out of the vocabulary. Usually, if comment can be restrained, no comment at all on the part of the parent is even more successful.

Rhythm in language appears very early, in the babbling of the infant. As soon as language becomes at all intelligible, the parents begin to teach, and the child to learn, nursery rhymes. This can be looked upon as an expression of the untaught wisdom of the race or culture and can only be criticized, either in form or content, by purists who have not learned to respect the wisdom that has accumulated over thousands of years. These would substitute for this wisdom impudent hypotheses gained by ascribing to children the same meaning and associations for words that adults have. Nursery rhymes fill the need for repetitious exercise of the language function; they also furnish a ready means of "exploding" tensions in words, tensions that might otherwise rise to pressures which would require some less desirable type of release. Rhythmic speech may be made a part of larger rhythms. The bedtime story with its repetitious uses of words and rhythms is an excellent device for setting up the pattern of going to sleep. "You brush your teeth and go to the toilet and read a story and say your prayer and go to sleep." It can swing along so that sleep is an almost inevitable result at the end.

The content of nursery rhymes and fairy tales has aroused much concern. The same concern is shown about Bible stories. It is true that there are fearsome things in many of them. Jack and Jill fall, Daniel goes into the lions' den, Hansel and Gretel are abandoned in the woods by cruel parents. The child's ability to know the meaning of cruelty and horror is certainly not the same as that of the adult; these stories are not, somehow, given any personal reference. This is probably related to Piaget's discovery that language, to the preschool child, is not always a means of communication, nor is it a matter of expression of any logical type of thinking.[18] Sequence, cause and effect, and similar rules of logic are not indigenous in language usage.[19]

Nouns, the names of things, are first used as such. Later they take on the force of verbs, and "milk" means not a white liquid, but "give me milk," although the whole sentence does not appear for months after the "one-word sentence" has been effective in getting needs satisfied. Language and reasoning are developed according to a pattern; part of this pattern is that the words gradually—but only gradually—take on the meaning that is dictated by the culture in which the child grows.

The importance of the content of nursery rhymes has been discounted by saying that the words used are not of the same consequence to the child that they are to the adult, and that entertainment by rhythmic language is one of their principal functions quite apart from their content. It must also be said that their content fits into the thinking pattern of the child. They contain violence and danger because these sentiments are acceptable to the child; they are characteristic of the preschool child's extremist trends in emotion and action. A small child is rarely a little happy or a little sad, a little kind or a little cruel, a little angry or a little hurt. An angry child is likely to show a mass-action temper tantrum and when it is over to appear, and be, completely happy again. It is only when he approaches the end of the preschool period that he begins to show some modulation of emotional expression.[20] Thus, in his language, the child tends to go to extremes. Some years ago *The New Yorker* published the verbatim musings of a little boy while taking his bath.[21] He was talking about his parents. The poem—for it had a rhythm that was unmistakable—closed with these words:

> He will not speak to nobody because he doesn't have to.
> And when they come to look for him, they will not find him
> Because he will not be there.
> He will put spikes in their eyes and put them in the garbage,
> And put the cover on.
> He will not go out in the fresh air or eat his vegetables,
> Or make wee-wee for them, and he will get thin as a marble.
> He will not do nothing at all.
> He will just sit in the noonday sun.*

Shocking, but normal and typical of the kind of "testing the limits" emotionally that the preschool child tends to do. What the words mean is another question; at times they mean what they say, but they may be nothing more than play with emotion and language, giving the child the satisfaction of exercising developing functions.

Speech disorders of various types are seen early in language development. Some arise and disappear so rapidly that they never arouse enough anxiety in parents for them to appear in interviews as complaints. It may be recalled in the history taking that for a short while the child stuttered, or that he talked baby talk longer than usual, but little anxiety about the difficulty is expressed by the parent. The development of language does not appear to follow a smooth curve of increasing ability; there seem to be spurts and plateaus in the addition of words to the vocabulary. In times of excitement, the language function seems not to work fast enough to satisfy the child's almost explosive need to express himself. In such situations some stuttering may be noted. This often appears when the child is trying "to get a word in edgewise" in a going conversation. He gets so tense with the restrained excitement that speech begins with a few false tries. The difference be-

---

* Reprinted by permission. Copyright, 1939, The New Yorker Magazine, Inc.

tween these instances and those in which stuttering develops and persists is not entirely clear. There is an increasing amount of opinion that stuttering, like most other behavior deviations, is easier to cure the earlier treatment is undertaken.[22] This places the burden of case finding on physicians generally and on clinic physicians and the public health nurses so far as the health department is concerned. When stuttering persists, it probably represents a sustained suppression of tension related to more serious conflicts than simple competition to be heard. Mimicry may account for the fact that stuttering tends to run in families, since the nervous system has a proclivity for falling into patterns of malfunction of this sort. It has also been suggested that hereditary factors, having to do with the malfunction of speech areas of the brain, are involved. In any case, prolonged stuttering will require expert psychiatric, psychological, and pedagogical care, and the public health function will be one of referral to the properly manned clinic for such cases. In some cases, these clinics will themselves be the responsibility of the health department.[23]

Baby talk is often fostered by parents, much less often in our present culture than in an earlier and more sentimental period. In such a situation mimicry makes baby talk "normal"; it becomes a special language for the child to use. As Spock points out, if persisted in too long it will interfere with the child's social adjustment.[9] Baby talk that appears in the preschool child intermittently is extremely interesting because its etiology is frequently very clear. When a new baby arrives to displace the youngest child from his position in the family, baby talk often appears, particularly in the evening when the child is tired and wants "mothering." This pattern of "regression" in language is not the only function that slips back to an earlier level of functioning; the crying may change to an infantile type, and locomotion slip back to the walking and running on the toes, a pattern common in toddlers. The prenatal clinic is an excellent place to discuss such matters with the expectant multipara.

There is, in the child health station, opportunity to anticipate the parents' concern about language usage in the child. The engineer father whose logical thinking is his pride will be less aggravated by the child's vagaries of language usage if he realizes that he is seeing a stage of an orderly development rather than a symptom of future violent murder—or, worse, of a woman's type of intuitive thinking rather than a manly logic. The scandalized mother whose child has arrived at some of the Anglo-Saxon words that are not used in polite society will be able to avoid overevaluating their significance for the child if she realizes how the words arrived and why they satisfy. This would appear to be a part of the work of keeping babies and their families well and to be within the scope of the health officer's concern.

FANTASY AND TRUTHFULNESS

In the case on page 205 the child's use of fantasy-born companions was noted. In this respect, as in others, this case is extreme, but it illustrates a capacity of children. This child needed companionship, and he made it for himself. When he reached nursery school, the fantasy companions were less important and tended to disappear. They may be very disturbing to parents. In a sincerely and rigidly moral family, the chief complaint about a child (age 4 years) was that he told "lies." It was the habit of the father to hold the boy on his lap in the evening while reading his paper. He would explain the pictures as they leafed through. The time was during the Russo-Finnish war, and there were some pictures of bombed houses with children looking at them. The next day, the boy was heard telling his playmates that he was building some nice brick houses for the little Finnish children. These "lies," of which the parents became more tolerant when their function was clarified in several interviews, changed content as the boy grew older. In one interview they concerned the number and size of fish caught when the father took him fishing. The family gradually has learned to ask the boy whether he is talking about real or make-believe things and, with some effort, has learned to hesitate to make moral judgments about the make-believe stories. They have never recaptured enough of their childhood freedom to appreciate the fun of the fantasies.

"Truth" means little to the child, and the unrealistic fantasy, particularly when it serves a purpose, seems as true as the factual incident. Few children accept blame for things, and even the most obvious guilt is passed on to someone else. This is particularly true in a household where there is competition between the children, and this means almost every family where there is more than one child. Responsibility for acts and words is an attribute that human beings develop with help. Some appear to fail to develop it even with help. To regard its incomplete development in the child from a moralistic viewpoint is to show disrespect for the process of development. To allow the child to go uncorrected is to neglect the educational job that falls on every parent. What seems better is to recognize that there is reality and there is make-believe, but the two spheres are not the same. It is useless for the parent to ask who broke the dish when it is obvious that only one child could have been the culprit. It is better, and more likely to get an accurate response, to ask how the accident happened, not raising the question of guilt at all. To accuse and get a denial, which must then be dealt with, gives an opportunity for a useless rift between parent and child. Out of such a rift, the child may reach the conclusion that he cannot be secure with a parent who will accept a denial of the obvious as a subject requiring attention and discussion. That the parent makes wrong conclusions at times, and may punish for misdoings not actually done by the child, is a price that has to be paid in this sort of approach. The parent, of course, does not need to defend a mistaken position, unless he is driven by some conflict in himself which then becomes the issue of therapy. He, too, can apologize and admit his error. This breeds less insecurity in the child than a discussion of the obvious. The physician may be able to turn the rigid moralistic parent who sees a liar in his child into an appreciative parent who can see development of responsibility as a goal and see it in the light of pleasant memories of his own fantasies. If so, he has made possible a smoother-running home with greater emotional health.

The fantasy life of the child in fear, in make-believe companionship, and in shifting of responsibility does not complete the picture. Fantasies of himself in adult situations are signs that his growth has a goal. The boy loves to do things his father does. He plays with trains, trucks, and airplanes. The girl fantasies herself in a mother's position and plays at dolls and cooking. Dress-ups are a part of this sort of fantasy and are often a part of the recreational pattern of the home. Dress-ups are much more fun if they are or can be imagined to be flowing evening dresses rather than sports clothes, for example, and if there can be a "show" with dancing. Such complete play patterns are likely to occur late in the preschool epoch and continue into the school period. Their appreciation by the parents furnishes satisfaction to the child and tends to make it unnecessary for him to engage in show-off activity of less desirable types.

FAMILY STATUS OF THE CHILD

One of the continuous developmental tasks a child is faced with is finding his place in the family constellation. The only child has this problem in sharing the love of his parents and will frequently show jealousy reactions. In the case quoted above, this was evidenced by the boy's protests when the parents danced together. Such incidents and the emotional reactions of anger accompanying them seem to settle into patterns very rapidly so that the child's behavior is almost pre-dictable; if the parents embrace, the child will attempt to come between, and if the embrace is teasingly continued, there will be a more violent emotional outburst. There is something ludicrous about the high degree of predictability so that, in some cases, the parents use the reaction in a "show-off" way. Similar predictable reactions will appear when one child is cared for or fondled in another's presence, a pattern of behavior observable in animals other than humans as well. Fostering negative emotional reactions by teasing and showing off may habituate the child to such behavior so that eventually the reaction may be more difficult to resolve.

In larger families, this problem of status in the household, while it has its elements of competition for the parents' affection, is also a matter of competition for playthings and clothing. The attitude toward possession shows a pattern of maturation from the early preschooler, who seems to want his possessions only when someone else also wants them, to the later period when he wants them as his own even if no one else is interested at all. We shall see in a later period of development that doing something with an article is of little consequence; the private possession is sacred simply because it is a private possession. The early need to possess things, to exercise authority over their use, and to choose whether or not to share them is a right of the child that parents are particularly likely to look upon as selfish and intolerable, especially if the doll or toy is snatched from a little visitor at the first tentative move to play. The owner sweeps down like a hawk and grabs the toy. One mother says soothingly that the toy belongs to the child of the other and the visitor should not have taken it. The other mother is giving her preschooler a lecture on sharing things, while suffused with embarrassment and apologizing between phrases for the child's "selfish" actions. But it is through such experiences that the child gains his knowledge of his place in the family and protects that place from the invasion of others. These reactions, therefore, must be respected as learning experiences. They probably have deep biological roots and have been related by many to such phenomena as pecking order in chickens and territorialism in birds, as well as analogous—perhaps homologous—behavior in mammals, especially the primates. It is no small matter to bring such forces under the control of a social order; it requires effort in teaching and learning.

Struggles to find one's place in the family are frequently acute in "middle" children and are not confined to the preschool period. Oldest and youngest children occupy the ends of the series, and those positions are somehow valued peculiarly in many cultures. Feeling these differences, the middle child may make special efforts to draw attention to himself, finding, in some instances, that the only way or the most successful way is by troublesome behavior. The behavior is then an irritant to the parent and may lead to a vicious-circle development, which may escape diagnosis by the parent but be readily understood when brought to attention in interviews in which such problems are invited for discussion. Such situations are common enough that they might be the subject of discussions with multiparas in the prenatal period. Reactions of this type may well be more important in the happiness and emotional health of the home than a routine check for pus in the urine, but searching for the pus cells is almost certain to be done whereas it is a rare clinic that is concerned with this sort of situation in anticipation of its occurrence.

Another phase of the child's realization of his place as an individual has been called the "period of negativism." Very commonly the child goes through a time when "no" seems to be an almost automatic response to nearly any question—even those usually responded to, so far as action is concerned, by an enthusiastic "yes." This phase is said to occur somewhat earlier in females than in males.[24] It may be related to the somewhat more rapid development of language in the female, although the period of negativism is certainly more than simply an evidence of the child's learning the meaning of the word "no." Kanner calls negativism a "natural and physiological" period occuring during the third and fourth year of life.[25] The direct challenge of the authority of the parent frequently leads to a jaw-set "you will or else" on the part of the parent, and it must be admitted that occasionally the "or else" treatment may be inevitable. However, some rephrasing of questions helps. For instance, "Let's go to bed" may bring out a positive "no." In this situation, the question may be "Do you want to walk upstairs or go piggyback?" The child chooses and gets upstairs—when he doesn't say "I don't want to go up at all," and this doesn't always happen. It also helps if moves are not made suddenly. A call 5 minutes before it is necessary for the child to come in, asking him to be ready then, dissipates some of the resistance that rises when an immediate action is demanded. These things help in "handling" the child at this period, but Kanner's "insisting with gentle firmness on the more important matters of daily routine"[25] while disregarding the "petty and irrelevant 'I won't' and 'no, no, no,' replies" is none the less necessary. Here, again, it seems wise to point out that if the parent allows long discussion of and argument about the petty and irrelevant, delaying an obviously necessary decision, the child may well feel less secure than if the parent acts "with firmness in the right." The child can hardly be secure with a parent who does not know what is best.

REPETITIOUS BEHAVIOR

Many preschool children become habituated to some sort of repetitive bodily activity which they seem to use as a consolation device. The body affords areas, frequently later associated with the physical satisfactions of love-making, which give pleasurable sensations when stroked or rubbed. The tongue and lips, the genitals, the buttocks, the umbilicus are such areas. When the preschool child is thwarted—as he must be at times, however gently—he needs consolation. The parents can supply the physical contact that seems essential for this comforting in many children, but in others this does not seem enough, even though generously given. If for any reason the parent cannot meet the needs of the child for cuddling embrace, actual bodily contact, the child may seek this comfort from within his own body. This need for physical contact in comforting the child decreases through the preschool period. The 2-year-old may have to be picked up and allowed to cry it out on the mother's shoulder. The same child at 4 may be comforted with words called across the room.[26] It is interesting to note that many of the consolation devices to be described also tend to disappear late in the preschool period, unless the child finds himself in a situation of need to retain immature patterns of reaction. Although the need for physical comforting is seen in almost all children to some extent, individual children vary widely in their need for it. One sees children who would appear on the basis of parental rejection and coolness to need to satisfy their craving for love by sensations of their own bodies, yet do not. On the other hand, one sees children who are showered with genuine love and are cuddled a great deal but who still appear to need something more. Such differences demand further research as to explanation.

Thumb sucking is the most common of these consolation devices. This "habit," which may involve the fingers instead of the thumb, is usually seen when the child finds himself unable to cope with the outside world and retires to satisfactions to be gained alone. Thumb sucking, in infancy a part of the hunger pattern and related to a need to exercise a fundamental physiological pattern of movement, now becomes a means of emotional satisfaction through physical sensation. When recovering from a bruise, when reacting to scolding, when forced to do something in spite of negativistic refusal, when nothing seems worth doing at the moment, when tired and sleepy, when lonely, or when excluded from a group, the child retires to suck his thumb. Sometimes, though rarely, the child uses the thumb sucking aggressively to get the parents' attention and, thereby, recognition of his status in the family. The reaction is most common in the early preschool period. Levy [27] reports that at 24 months, 14 per cent of children are thumb suckers; at 48 months, 21 per cent. The pattern generally fades out in the early school years, until it remains to be seen only at bedtime or when the child is sick.

Parents tend to deplore thumb sucking, even the best-informed parents who are anxious to live up to the most modern thinking of psychiatrists. Kanner, reviewing the literature, believes the concern about thumb sucking is of relatively recent origin and is dependent upon Freud's interpretation of the act as having sexual significance, the orthodontists' concern about its causing malocclusion, the concern of persons interested in communicable diseases that infection would be introduced by the habit, and, finally, the psychologists who condemned it because it interfered with socialization.[28] There can be little doubt that the present almost universal distaste is related to the more or less conscious realization that in some way the act is related to the adult use of the body for sensual pleasure in the sexual act. Thus, while it may be now stated that physically and psychologically there is extremely little evidence that thumb sucking in itself is detrimental, to make the statement is almost inevitably to waste words and damage the relationship between parent and physician, for the statement usually cannot be believed by the parent. To discuss the complicated psychology of why the statement cannot be believed by the individual parent would certainly be beyond what can reasonably be expected of the pediatrician in the child health station. In practice then, the physician usually recognizes the parents' prejudice tacitly. Instead of attacking by denial of the assumed "badness" of the "habit," he reassures that it will disappear toward the end of the preschool period. He advises that to call attention to it tends to keep it before the child, perhaps to use as an attention-getting device. In attempting to modify the habit, the suggestion of play using both hands or the assignment of a task that substitutes activity for boredom is more successful. In this way, both the parent and child are diverted from the thumb sucking, and the parent is given an innocuous and actually helpful path for the expression of the energy that the distaste for the habit has left unsatisfied.

The danger of malformation of the dental arch by thumb sucking, while it probably does occur very rarely,[29,30] is not of so great consequence as is the acute unrest that may arise in the family about the habit itself. When one recalls the buck-toothed people he is acquainted with and checks on their thumb-sucking history and heredity, he is much more likely to find the latter than the former of importance in making the front teeth stick out. Reassurance on this point can be given without hesitation. So far as the thumb is concerned, there are no data indicating that permanent deformity ever occurs and clinical experience in a child health station has not uncovered any, except in the extremely pathological situation in the case recorded on page 167.

Like the other consolation devices to be discussed, thumb sucking in itself probably has no significance as a damaging psychological factor. But it may well have symptomatic significance, calling attention to tension within the home. It behooves the physician to look for this, define it and the sources of it as clearly as possible, and then decide whether the symptomatic approach suggested above is appropriate for the case in question. It may be better to suggest adjustments in the attitude toward the child in the home so that this habit is needed less by the child. Or, and this conclusion should be fairly rare if the physician has studied the case, it may be necessary to indicate that expert help is needed. The physician in the child health station too often "unloads" such cases with the statement that he has no time for them. Too frequently this means that he hesitates to study a case because it touches sensitive prejudices in himself. In coming to the easy conclusion that he "hasn't time," he denies himself a type of case study that is fascinating and rewarding in results, and he fails to do his full job as a physician, the treating of the whole person. As every pediatrician knows, this means treating the whole family in problems involving the child's behavior.

Thumb sucking may occur alone or in combination with stimulation of other areas of the body. Frequently one sees the child sucking its thumb and having the other hand inside the panties rubbing the buttock, or the free hand may be playing with or pulling at the umbilicus, rubbing the genitals, or pulling at an ear. It is strange, but the nipples appear not to be involved in these accessory movements. These movements all seem to have the same significance that the thumb sucking does and may be treated in the same way. Some of them, particularly the handling of the umbilicus and the genitals, may occur separately, but the significance of them is probably no different. The parental dislike of these patterns may be even greater than for thumb sucking, however, and this must be recognized in planning therapy. The principle outlined above, of diverting both parent and child from the activity in question, has advantages for the child and for the home.

In some cases, patterns of movement other than rubbing or sucking are used to subserve the same function. The wide range of repetitive actions mentioned in connection with infancy runs into the preschool period for varying lengths of time, but the habits disappear earlier than thumb sucking. It is sometimes extremely difficult to find any stresses playing upon the child, and one is brought to the conclusion that one is dealing with behavior that does not have psychopathological significance. These sorts of activity have not been related to personality traits in adults, though this would appear to be a fruitful field for research. Kinsey reports cases in which rocking in the early preschool period leads to orgasm and is a form of masturbation.[31]

The repetitive device may be sensory rather than motor. The child may have a liking for fur or wool and prefer to have a certain fabric touching some particular area of skin on the body. In some cases, this pattern is more elaborate or becomes elaborated, so that a particular toy is demanded consistently over a period of months, the child refusing to go to sleep unless the ritual implement is at hand. The frequency of the use of such materials in the general population has not been studied, but in an upper-middle-class nursery school, two-thirds of the children brought some materials of this sort for use during naps.

The comfort and security the child derives from such habits is plainly seen. The therapy appears to be to attempt to build up sources of comfort and security in the parents or parent substitutes until the child is able eventually to make interpersonal relationships that are more rewarding to him than the resources of his own sensory nervous system. It must be admitted that, even for the skilled psychiatrist, evaluation of therapy is extremely difficult, since to a large extent such habitual tendencies are time-bound. When they do stop, it is hard to tell whether therapy or the natural maturation of the personality has caused the happy result. Many of the reactions described above take place in a hypnogogic state, the half-awake, half-asleep period that occurs both on going to sleep and on awakening. In this sense there is relationship with the sort of night terrors described in the case on page 212.

The behavior patterns just described have been grouped as consolation devices, but they are also used as a means of release of tension. This is true particularly of the motor patterns of rocking or bouncing. Nail biting is more likely to appear as a tension-relieving device. It is not likely to be a severe problem in the preschool years, though it is not infrequent. In 55 normal children between the ages of 12 and 23 months, but one case was found. Between the ages of 48 and 59 months, 4 were discovered in 28. Wechsler estimates that the habit is present in perhaps 40 per cent of children who reach the sixth grade [32] (approximate age, 12). Lip biting and similar repetitive acts appear to have similar significance. Kanner [23] believes that the habit is likely to appear in situations involving interpersonal strain, such as meeting new people.[25] Management of nail biting is similar to that for the other repetitive acts—an accurate estimate of the importance of the habit as a symptom, and then handling the situation surrounding the child so as to lower the pressures upon him. Management of the habit itself is best accomplished in the preschool years by diverting the child into other activities.

TOILET TRAINING

Toilet training was discussed in the section on the period of infancy; the conclusion was that that period was not one in which the child could be expected to have any real understanding of the aims of the training. By 18 to 24 months, however, the child itself will begin to show a good deal of curiosity about the toilet and will, if the home is not one where a fetish is made of the privacy of the toilet, want to take a try at this more adult type of activity. This is the signal for the beginning of toilet training if it is to be most quickly effectual. The child usually gives some warning of the impending bowel movement. This warning is much easier to note than that preceding urination and this, along with its occurring more regularly and less frequently, may well account for the fact that bowel training is ordinarily successful earlier than urinary. It is also a factor, no doubt, that soiled pants are more bothersome and less comfortable to the child than wet ones. Of 188 "normal" children whose histories were taken in the Eastern Health District of Baltimore, the cessation of soiling occurred as shown in Table 2.

TABLE 2.   Status of Bowel Control by Age *

Months	Per cent usually soiling	Per cent occasionally soiling	Per cent never soiling
0–5	100	0	0
6–11	61.9	23.8	14.3
12–17	36.7	33.3	30.0
18–23	28.0	24.0	48.0
24–29	4.0	12.0	84.0
30–35	0	5.6	94.0
36 +	0	0	100.0

* Unpublished analyses by C. Tietze.

In the interpretation of such figures, it must be kept in mind that the mothers may tend to report more favorably than the facts justify, and also that in some of these cases the data were collected after the soiling had stopped. In the latter situation, the ages at which developmental events take place tend to be falsified in reporting roughly in proportion to the length of time that has passed since the event has actually taken place. Usually this is an unconscious warping of the facts in the direction of the age at which the event "should" take place according to the prevailing folklore in the community. The estimated mean age for "never soiling" in this group is 19.8 months. Although no numerical data can be presented to support the conclusion, it is the clinical impression that the cases in which training was begun after the age of, say, 15 months were trained in a shorter time and with less aggravation on the part of all concerned than those in whom training was begun before the age of 1 year.

Adults generally tend to regard defecation as a rather unpleasant sort of behavior. Some of the reasons for this are obvious; the odor is unpleasant, and the consistency of feces makes cleansing difficult. There are probably less conscious factors which also contribute, perhaps related to the ancient recognition of the relationship between feces and some epidemic diseases, a folk concept heavily reinforced by modern public health propaganda. It has also been suggested that both the elimination processes have unpleasant emotional connotations because of puritanical sexual notions, both being anatomically associated with the genital area. The child has no basis in experience for regarding the act or the product as unpleasant. To him there is probably no differentiation at all between feces and any other sticky, malleable mud in which he would play, except that feces, being a product of himself, may have an added value for him. Thus the child may on occasion play in his feces, smearing himself, his clothing, his crib, and occasionally the walls as well. Such activity has received rather more stress as an important factor in character formation than its frequency justifies. In studies of normal children this behavior has been complained of very rarely. Management is simply to clean the child up with as little show of distaste as possible and make arrangements to make the play less available in the future. Clay or mud and water play will satisfy the child's needs in this direction in most instances.

Folk medicine lays great store on the child's bowels being kept "open." Repeatedly, mothers report that the child gets cathartics if he does not have a movement every day. Even if he does, he frequently gets a "cleaning out" every week. Some mothers are not satisfied unless there are two movements a day. There is a tendency for pediatricians to reinforce this sort of thinking. Although they will neglect to ask about the presence of such gaudy symptoms as a destructive temper tantrum, they never fail to ask about the color, consistency, and frequency of the stools. In families where bowel movements are taken as matter-of-fact occurrences, there is surprisingly little trouble with constipation. Here, as in eating habits, a great deal of confidence can be placed upon the child's inherent ability to take care of his physiological needs. If medication is necessary, it is best given by mouth rather than by enema or suppository. It is doubtful if training to stool by the use of suppositories is ever justifiable.[9] Constipation is frequently completely relieved when the pressure to move the bowels daily and to submit the movement for inspection is relieved. The child relinquishes its weapon for organizing parental concern by resistance to moving the bowels when this weapon no longer accomplishes its end. In some cases, the mother, because of a need to engulf the child as an individual and to refuse him freedom as a person, will not be able to make the change from overclose supervision to a more nonchalant attitude. In such cases the proper place to apply treatment is obviously the mother. It then behooves the pediatrician to make the etiological diagnosis and to treat the child's disease by the psychological relief of the mother and by her education. The need is not to treat the patient as a person in this case, but to treat the family as a biological unit, the ill-health of any member of which may eventuate in symptoms in any other member. It is remarkable how quickly some of these patterns of behavior will disappear when the pressures are taken off the child through education of the mother. Greater respect for the child as an individual and as an organism that will function normally if given a chance will usually result in satisfactory function.[33]

Prolonged soiling may be due simply to developmental retardation. In such cases, the retardation will be recognized and training will be delayed until the child reaches the developmental level necessary. Relapse into soiling, after a period of control, is usually typical of assertion of independence by the child. Relapses and prolonged soiling in "normal" children may appear when the child is displaced or prevented from ever attaining his rightful place in the family and has to use what means are available to him to regain or gain his status. Thus relapses may occur in the "yard baby" when there is a new "lap baby" in the family. They may occur in a well child when a sibling gets sick and gets special attention for a period. Getting the parents' attention by aggravating them is better in the child's eyes than being unable to get their attention at all. Here, too, the problem is first one of diagnosis of the etiological strain within the family, and then one of correction. This may amount to nothing more than the suggestion that the mother or father make special efforts to satisfy this child's need for attention and love.

In the matter of bowel training, the aim is to build a set of habits as early as possible, within the child's capabilities—habits that are conducive to the physical health of the child and to smooth adaptation to the culture in which he is to grow. The eventual aim is to make it possible for the child to regard the function of the digestive tract as demanding a minimum of attention yet giving certain unobtrusive satisfactions.

Psychoanalytic psychology teaches that there is an association between forcing the child's bowel training and the setting up of behavior patterns characterized by stubbornness and negativism and also excessive orderliness and miserliness. There is no statistical evidence for this association, though many clinical histories can be brought forward in its support. The succession of levels of erotic significance in this psychology is oral, then anal, and finally genital. The theory states that those persons "arrested" in development at the anal level show the character traits described above. However useful these concepts may be in psychoanalytic therapy, they remain to be proved at the level of controlled observation of normal individuals.[34,35,36]

Urinary training is generally somewhat more difficult to achieve in children than bowel training. The frequency and irregularity with which urination takes place has already been mentioned as one reason for this. In the Eastern Health District it was found that the average age at which mothers reported their children as "never wet" in the daytime was 30.5 months, or almost a year after the time they cease soiling. Actually, mothers do not usually include "accidents" such as those in which the child comes in wet because he got too interested in his play to recognize the need to void. In circumstances such as this, wetting may occur as late as the fifth or sixth year and still be well within the range of normal. In such cases, daytime wetting may indicate an excellent ability for the child to lose himself in play with others, a trait of social value in his personality. Like soiling, urinary incontinence in the daytime may be used by the child as an attention-getting device or as an indicator that he is trying to compete for love with a younger child who is not yet dry. Urinary-control problems rarely precipitate the severe clashes between child and parent that are found when the problem is bowel control. It may be that, since bowel irregularities are less common, they are noticed more and brought to attention more forcibly just because they are uncommon and stand out in the mother's thinking. It may also be that the function of the gastrointestinal tract can be so easily "tinkered with" by means of drugs. The mother expects more of the child in the control of the gut which yields to external control by the drugs, expecting less control of the urinary system which is better protected from her machinations. There are probably also reasons having to do with the symbolism surrounding the two functions. In any case, daytime wetting is rarely the threat to smooth parent-child relationship that soiling is. The fact that soiled diapers and clothing are more unpleasant to wash than merely wet ones is important.

Nighttime dryness is usually achieved shortly after daytime urinary control. Table 3 shows the experience with 188 "normal" children in the Eastern Health District of Baltimore.

Enuresis is defined by Kanner, probably too narrowly, as incontinence of urine, not due to physical pathology, beyond the age of 3.[28] If the average age at which children achieve day and night dryness is 31.5 months, it hardly seems that 4.5 months will include all the scattered cases of normals making up the far end of the distribution curve. In our group, it will be seen that almost 20 per cent of the cases did not achieve control until beyond the age of 3. Inasmuch as any time fixed must be relatively arbitrary, it would be better that, if an age must be

TABLE 3. Status of Nighttime Urinary Control by Age *

Completed months	Per cent usually wet	Per cent occasionally wet	Per cent never wet
0–5	100	0	0
6–11	90	5	5
12–17	63	27	10
18–23	44	28	28
24–35	21	28	51
36–48	4	14	82
48 +	0	6	94

* Unpublished analyses by C. Tietze.

determined after which enuresis is to be called symptomatic, it be placed high enough so that no more than a small percentage of "normal" children are excluded from the "normal" group. Spock [9] inclines toward placing the age after which some concern might be felt by the physician and parent at 4 or 5, an age more nearly in line with our findings.

The "cause" of enuresis has been the subject of much speculation. It is generally agreed that local or neurological pathology accounts for only a very small proportion of the children brought to attention by their parents because of this complaint. It is also well recognized that enuresis tends to "run in families." It has been judged hereditary by some authorities. On the other hand, Kanner makes the cogent point that families in which enuresis is prevalent rather expect the appearance of it and are not particularly active in discouraging it. He also points out that enuresis is, in his experience, more common in homes of low standards of cleanliness than in better homes from the point of view of housekeeping. Some have felt that enuresis is important as a sign of constitutional deficiency in the child, evidence of a neuropathic constitution.[37] Kanner has pointed out that the symptom rarely stands alone but is part of a galaxy of behavior traits that point to a child who is ill at least in his relations with the world. Most workers will frankly admit, however, that they have seen cases in which healthy persons without discoverable physical deformity, disease, or evidence of psychological strain wet the bed for no discoverable reason.

A safe and reasonable attitude toward enuresis would appear to be that this behavior is a peculiarly sensitive indicator of emotional tensions in some children. Sometimes, as in the competitive situation mentioned above, the stress may be easily apparent and correctible. In others, the situation may be much more complicated and delicate, involving perhaps a feeling of insecurity in the child because he recognizes a rift between his parents or feels the strain of an abnormally constituted home. As an indicator of strain, the symptom might be compared to the benzedrine test for occult blood in the stools; it is an exquisitely sensitive indicator, but one must be careful not to misinterpret a positive test as meaning serious pathology when something innocuous may be giving rise to the reaction.

In the child health station, mothers frequently express concern about enuresis if given the opportunity. In the absence of evidences of emotional strain and after finding out about the emotional and cultural situation in which the child lives, the physician may be able to suggest reassuringly that the range of normal for bed wetting extends to 5 or 6 years. He may suggest cutting down on fluids at supper and thereafter —it is surprising how frequently children are needlessly allowed to fill up on water just before going to bed. He may inquire as to what hour the bed wetting takes place and suggest getting the child up a little before this time. It may be found that the parents are placing too much stress on the bed wetting in a child who overreacts to the pressure. In such a case the advice may be to abandon efforts for a period and then start over more gently. In a child near the end of the preschool period, passing on some responsibility to the child himself is often helpful. This can be done by giving the child an alarm clock and a flashlight and rewarding him with a gold star for dry nights. This latter technique is frequently effective in gaining the child's cooperation in the attempt to control the wetting. As is the case with almost all the problems of development and emotional relationships discussed, there is no single method of "cure" other than by studying the case to find the significant factors and then attempting to modify those which will bring relief to the child and family.

Usually there are two aims in attempting to stop nocturnal enuresis; one is to get a dry bed, the other is to so adjust the functioning of the child that he is not placed under strains that precipitate enuresis. The aim before the age of 4 or 5 will usually be the former, and for this the conscious cooperation of the child may not be required at all. It is quite possible to get a child out of bed, toileted, and back to bed without awakening him beyond a still definitely hypnogogic state which is not in the least a part of the next day's memory. If the procedure is gently accomplished, it is hard to see how any trauma can result. The problem is quite different when enuresis persists into the school years. This is rare, and the school physician may need the assistance of the psychiatrist in handling it. In such cases, of course, much more is involved than having a dry bed. If the child must be gotten up, he will have to be completely awake and conscious of the purpose.

HEALTH-DEPARTMENT RESPONSIBILITY

The preschool years are ones of fascinating and extremely rapid development, physical, behavioral, and emotional. The wordless, barely walking infant becomes the chattering, roaming, adventurous, curious, and gaudily emotional child. Such precipitous, pell-mell type of expansion of personality functions cannot take place without an occasional thwarting and blocking, with the consequent release of tension in ways that are normal but not always desirable. If the physician can recognize that the facts of emotional development yield to preventive management as easily as do the facts of physical disease, and if he can come to feel the same sort of consideration for the mother's concern for the emotional health of her child as he shows for her concern for his physical health, then child health stations will come nearer to reaching the ideal of guarding the health of the whole child. This can be done by working through and with the child's parents. It is only much later that the child reaches independence from his family and is a unit in himself. The severing of the umbilical cord is only a physical separation. The child is still a part of his mother and father and, to a lesser extent, of the other members of the family, drawing his sustenance, both physical and emotional, only through them. Although his future personality will show the influence of his culture and his social class, during the preschool period these influences will not reach him directly, but through his parents. It is the physician's responsibility that the relationship between parents and child be such that the enormous development that takes place is furnished optimal stimulation and optimal control in so far as is within the power of his instruction and treatment.

The clinical opportunity for accomplishing this aim so far as the health department is directly concerned lies in the well-baby clinic or child health station. Such clinics serve only a small part of the population, however; most well-child supervision is done by general practitioners and a lesser amount by pediatricians.[38] Some of these will be serving in health-department clinics and will be available through that contact for educational efforts on the part of the health department. Others may be reached through postgraduate training programs arranged in cooperation with the local medical societies. In any case, the health department has a responsibility for helping to raise the level of well-child care so that it takes the whole child into consideration as a growing personality, not just as a metabolizing machine.

Community Agencies. There are agencies in many communities to which the health officer may look for assistance in this branch of his responsibility. One of these is the Child Study Association of America. This national organization establishes small discussion groups, usually of mothers with children of about the same age, and furnishes material and leaders for the purpose of enlarging the area of understanding between mothers and their children. The organization also arranges larger community meetings for lectures on various aspects of child care. It prints educational pamphlets and books, many of which are excellent in their presentation of the issues of child care which give rise to anxiety in the parents. The alert health officer will find in this organization personnel and experience and material that can help fill the need.* In an increasing number of cities public adult educational programs are including discussion classes for parents based largely on this pattern. In some instances, the Red Cross, mental health associations, and other community agencies will furnish programs of this type also.

In the case reported on pages 202 to 206, a part of the management included enrolling of child in a nursery school. The nursery school consists of a group of children, usually between 2 and 5 in age, under the direction of a teacher trained to understand the preschool child. Nursery schools are to be distinguished from institutions whose only aim is to care for children while their mothers are at work. The nursery school is not primarily to free mothers for work—or pleasure—but to educate the child and his mother. The child is taught successful and comfortable living in groups. The mother learns to understand the development, particularly the social and emotional development, of her child. Because it makes them available to groups rather than to individuals, the nursery school can offer a wide selection of toys designed to develop the child according to his needs. It offers the opportunity for expression in painting and the plastic arts which allows the

* Child Study Association of America, 221 West 57th Street, New York, N.Y.

constructive release of tensions in creative work rather than their destructive release in tantrums, food refusal, or other symptoms. It offers cultural opportunities in music that are difficult to give in the individual home.

These educational aims of the nursery school have not been primary in the support they have received from tax funds. The maintenance of their standards has not always been easy because of this. In the United States, during the depression of the thirties, nursery schools were Works Progress Administration projects, set up primarily to employ teachers who were out of jobs. When the depression was over, there was a period of difficult times followed by another period of Federal subsidy. This time, the primary aim of the support was to release homebound mothers for the labor force. Again nursery-school standards had to be protected so that while filling the nation's immediate need their educational standards were not sacrificed. With the end of the war, all Federal subsidy was withdrawn and the number of nursery schools shrank rapidly, since the schools are expensive to run because of the program of health, nutritional, and educational services they offer. The people in crowded areas of cities, where play materials and play space are most needed, cannot support adequate nursery schools without subsidy. Where it has been possible to maintain the schools, this subsidy has come from churches, individuals, and philanthropic organizations. Some schools are maintained as laboratories by universities offering training to teachers, nurses, physicians, and psychologists. Cooperative nursery schools, in which mothers act as part-time teachers under the supervision of a professionally trained teacher, are being developed, both as a means of lowering the cost of nursery schools and to increase their educational effectiveness.[39]

There is a perceptible movement to include nursery schools in the public educational system. This has been the case for years in England, where it is done on a national basis.[40] In the United States a few areas are experimenting with this means of meeting the educational needs of the preschool child. The aim of this education is not the imparting of facts. It is rather to offer the opportunity to the child for well-rounded development, physical, intellectual, and emotional. The child's functions do not develop to their highest unless fully stimulated. The nursery school offers a means of furnishing this stimulus to a larger share of the population.[41]

Although the usual nursery school does not include the aim of treatment of behavior disorders, the schools do offer potent means for giving a child whose developmental pattern has gone awry a chance to regain his normalcy free of the pressures that were etiologically important.

Most nursery schools are parent-education schools as well. While the child has surcease from the mother and vice versa, the school, through its education of the mother, can relieve some of the chronic but active strains. Under the social pressure of the group in a nursery school, feeding and nap problems disappear readily unless very deep-seated. The mother who sees a clean plate without any fuss made about it in nursery school is better able to get an objective view of her child's reactions to the family's forcing than if she had not seen the change. The lonely, overprotected, too-dominated child expands and becomes joyful, freed of his unnatural suppressions. The mother has the opportunity to see the capabilities which he could not show previously. The health officer may have a valuable helper in the nursery school in managing minor behavior and developmental problems in his clientele. At the same time, he has some responsibility in keeping up the standards of these schools.

The health officer usually is responsible for licensing nursery schools. Regulations provide that minimal requirements of space, light, ventilation, and drainage shall be met by the schools. Obviously there must be rules determining in what sort of building any institution serving the public can meet. Very few communities have done more than dictate the minimal physical requirements for the plant. Few have given the health department any other responsibility, although departments of education are being made responsible for educational standards.[42] The health department is asked to furnish some service to nursery schools at times, particularly if the school operates under public auspices. The children are usually given a physical inspection each day when they arrive at school, before they are allowed in the rooms used by the group. The inspection may be done by a public health nurse or by the head teacher who has been instructed in what to look for by an experienced nurse. If the teacher takes this responsibility, she operates under the nurse's supervision.

Nursery schools are frequently criticized as health hazards and for other reasons. Usually the latter include that they are a symptom of the disintegration of the home and that they are expensive to run. These objections will not be discussed here, though the author feels the advantage is in favor of the schools. The health hazard usually mentioned is the danger of epidemics being spread within the schools. It is certainly reasonable to raise the question.[43] The British experience during the war indicated that there was an excess of respiratory diseases in children attending nursery schools over those not attending.[44] In the nursery schools of Baltimore the disease rates were low, and although epidemic diseases were discovered, they did not tend to spread dangerously through the school population. In these schools carefully instructed teachers make the morning inspections. The danger of spread of infection must be admitted; it is offset to some extent by the health training the school offers. Vitamins A, D, and C are usually regularly administered. Diets in well-run schools are carefully planned to provide the other nutritional essentials. Tooth brushing and hand washing are group activities that gain associations as pleasant routines and do not become the irritatingly irksome tasks they may be when they involve parent-child arguments each time they are done. It must be admitted that these health habits ought to have happy associations in the home as well as in the school; parent education by the school sees to it that this is accomplished so far as possible.

The health officer will find in the nursery school teacher an ally in health education, both for the physical and emotional health of the preschool child. He may find her a resource for teaching the fundamentals of the emotional health of the preschool child to his nurses and to his pediatricians in well-baby clinics. He will, in carrying out the usual licensing regulations, see to it that schools are not set up under conditions involving health and safety hazards. He will endeavor to see to it that a qualified public agency supervises the schools of the community educationally as he does from the health standpoint.

SUMMARY

The preschool period is one of extremely rapid physical, intellectual, emotional, and social growth. None of these will reach its highest fruition unless it takes place in healthful, appreciative, and stimulating surroundings. The problem of public health is to educate its clientele and to offer needed services if they are not otherwise available, so that the socially and personally valuable potentialities reach maximum development. This aim is so broad that it cannot be reached if any narrow definition of health that neglects any part of human living is used as a basis for work. Health must be defined to include something more than a sound body; it must be in terms of a healthful person, with his body sound and capable of full use in living an intellectually satisfying and emotionally stable life.

REFERENCES

1. Scott, J. P. (ed.): *Conference on the Effects of Early Experience on Mental Health, Sept.* 6–9, 1951, Roscoe B. Jackson Memorial Laboratory, Bar Harbor, Me.

2. Personal observations clarified by discussion with many Japanese colleagues and with Dr. Ardath W. Burks, Director of Research Affairs, and the staff

of the University of Michigan Center for Japanese Studies, Okayama City, Japan, 1953.

3. Maloney, J. C.: *Understanding the Japanese Mind,* Philosophical Library, Inc., New York, 1954.

4. Murdoch, G. P., and J. W. M. Whiting: "Cultural Determination of Parental Attitudes: The Relationship between Social Structure, Particularly Family Structure and Parental Behavior," in M. J. E. Senn (ed.), *Problems of Infancy and Childhood,* Josiah Macy, Jr., Foundation, New York, 1951.

5. Tietze, C.: Unpublished analyses of material of the Mental Hygiene Study, Eastern Health District, Baltimore, Md.

6. Foord, A.: Personal communication, 1953.

7. Aldrich, C. A., and M. M. Aldrich: *Feeding Our Old-fashioned Children,* The Macmillan Company, New York, 1941.

8. Davis, C.: "Self-selection of Diet by Newly Weaned Infants," *Am. J. Dis. Child.* 36:651–679 (1928).

9. Spock, B.: *The Commonsense Book of Baby and Child Care,* Duell, Sloan and Pearce, Inc., New York, 1945.

10. "Baby Wears Out 205 Pound Athlete," *Look Magazine* 11:(6) 24–27 (1947).

11. Fries, M. D.: "Some Basic Differences in the New Born Infant during the Lying-In Period" (film), obtainable through New York University Film Library, New York.

12. Davis, A., and R. J. Havighurst: "Social Class and Color Differences in Child Rearing," *Am. Sociol. Rev.* 11:698–710 (1946).

13. Williams, J. R., and R. B. Scott: "Growth and Development of Negro Infants: IV. Motor Development and Its Relationship to Child Rearing Practices in Two Groups of Negro Infants," *Child Development* 24:103–113 (1953).

14. "Feeling of Rejection" (film), National Film Board of Canada, 620 Fifth Avenue, New York, 1949.

15. "Preface to a Life" (film), Mental Health Film Board, Inc., 166 E. 38th St., New York.

16. McCarthy, D. A.: *The Language Development of the Preschool Child,* University of Minnesota Press, Minneapolis, 1930.

17. Merry, F. K., and R. V. Merry: *The First Two Decades of Life,* Harper & Brothers, New York, 1950.

18. Piaget, J.: *The Language and Thought of the Child,* Harcourt, Brace and Company, Inc., New York, 1926.

19. Cameron, N.: *Reasoning Regression and Communication in Schizophrenia,* Psychological Monographs 50(1), whole no. 221 (1938).

20. Bridges, K. M. B.: "A Study of Social Development in Early Infancy," *Child Development* 4:33–49 (1933).

21. *The New Yorker Magazine* 15:11 (1939).

22. Glasner, P. J.: "Personality Characteristics and Emotional Problems in Stutterers under the Age of Five," *J. Speech & Hearing Disorders* 14:135–138 (1949).

23. Maryland State Department of Health, Division of Crippled Children and Heart Disease Control: *Maryland's Crippled Children's Program: Plan and*

Description, July 1, 1952, *to June* 30, 1954 (mimeographed). See also E. Davens, "The Maryland Crippled Children's Program," *Councillor* 18:(4) 7–11 (1953).

24. Levy, D. M., and S. H. Tulchin: "The Resistance of Infants and Children during Mental Tests," *J. Exper. Psychol.* 6:304–322 (1923).

25. Kanner, L.: *Child Psychiatry*, 1st ed., Charles C Thomas, Publisher, Springfield, Ill., 1935.

26. Escalona, S.: "Emotional Development in the First Year of Life," in M. J. E. Senn (ed.), *Problems of Infancy and Childhood,* The Josiah Macy, Jr., Foundation, New York, 1953.

27. Levy, D. M.: "Fingersucking and Accessory Movements in Early Infancy," *Am. J. Psychiat.* 7:881–918 (1928).

28. Kanner, L.: *Child Psychiatry*, 2d ed., Charles C Thomas, Publisher, Springfield, Ill., 1948.

29. Lewis, S. J.: "Thumbsucking, A Cause of Malocclusion in the Deciduous Teeth," *J. Am. Dent. A.* 17:1060–1073 (1930).

30. Mitchell, H.: "Thumbsucking: A Practical Appraisal from Mental Hygiene and Orthodontic Points of View," *Canad. M. A. J.* 44:612–617 (1941).

31. Kinsey, A. C., W. B. Pomeroy, C. E. Martin, and P. H. Gebhard: *Sexual Behavior in the Human Female,* W. B. Saunders Company, Philadelphia, 1953.

32. Wechsler, D.: "The Incidence and Significance of Nail Biting in Children," *Psychoanalyt. Rev.* 18:201–209 (1931).

33. Lemkau, P. V., and M. M. Cooper: "Mental Hygiene Problems in a Well Baby Clinic," *Ment. Hyg.* 31:449–456 (1947).

34. Sewell, W. H.: "Infant Training and the Personality of the Child," *Am. J. Sociol.* 58:150–159 (1952).

35. Orlansky, H.: "Infant Care and Personality," *Psychol. Bull.* 46:1–48 (1949).

36. Sears, R. R.: *Survey of Objective Studies of Psychoanalytic Concepts,* Social Science Research Council, New York, 1943.

37. Michaels, J. P., and S. E. Goodman: "Incidence and Intercorrelation of Enuresis and Other Neuropathic Traits in So-called Normal Children," *Am. J. Orthopsychiat.* 4:79–106. 1935.

38. American Academy of Pediatrics: *Report of the Committee for the Study of Child Health Services,* The Commonwealth Fund, New York, 1949.

39. Whiteside-Taylor, K.: *Parent Cooperative Nursery Schools,* Columbia University Press, New York, 1954.

40. Wheller, O. A., and I. G. Earl: *Nursery School Education and the Reorganization of the Infant School,* University of London Press, London, 1930.

41. Blatz, W. E., D. Millichamp, and M. Fletcher: *Nursery Education, Theory and Practice,* William Morrow & Company, Inc., N.Y., 1936.

42. Maryland Legislature, Senate Bill 34, chap. 489, 1947.

43. Williams, H. C. M.: "Nursery Schools: Medical Aspects," *Practitioner* 153:309–316 (1944).

44. McLaughlin, M. E.: "Physical Health of Children Attending Day Nurseries," *British M. J.*, 1:591–594, 631–634 (1947).

The School Period

It seems obvious that the epoch following the preschool period should be called "the school period," yet the name carries with it certain difficulties, particularly because school attendance continues into adolescence and beyond. Gesell has used the simple device of calling this period "from 5 to 10," but this was dictated by the nature of his material rather than by any consideration of definition.[1] On the basis that sexual drives tend to be rather less powerful during these years than earlier or later, Freud designated them the "latent" period.[2] The period has also been called simply "childhood," though there would appear to be no reason for exempting the preschool period from inclusion under that title. In any case, the term "the school period" has been chosen to represent this epoch because it connotes the emergence of the child from the home into a larger sociological sphere. The "yard baby" now becomes the school child.

The delimiting of the period presents little difficulty at the lower age since, by law, the child starts school at 6. School-starting ages vary little the world over in cultures having formalized education at all. None have come to attention in which the legal age is less than 5 or more than 7. This limit brings out exceptionally clearly the differences between biological fact and the cultural practices based upon it. To be sure, the beginning of schooling has become a little vague through the introduction of nursery school and kindergarten. Nevertheless, in the American culture the child starts school at 6; the law says so. Obviously, this law is possible only because the average child is ready for school at 6, but this natural maturational factor that makes the law reasonable is almost lost sight of, once the cultural institution is set up. From the point of view of the growth pattern, the school-age period begins about the time the rate of growth begins to increase, about 5 or 6. There is a gradual rise in the rate of growth through this period, culminating in the adolescent growth spurt.

The event marking the end of the school period is the beginning of the appearance of the secondary sex characteristics. This is not a very satisfactory type of limit in that it makes the period shorter for girls than for boys and because different individuals will come to the end of it at widely different ages. In girls these ages will be, roughly, from 9 to 13; in boys, from 10 to 14, with a considerable number of cases lying outside these ranges. In some cultures, religious rites have determined the age of onset of adolescence as exactly as our laws dictate when a child shall begin school. Such a dictate is subject to the same criticism as that made of the school-starting law; it can apply only to the average and neglects the wide range of chronological ages of which that average is made up. In determining the end of the school period, we are reduced to examining the facts in the case of each person, an irksome but more exact method so far as the individual is concerned. A better illustration cannot be found of the fact that the sum total of development is a continuum, even though events in it have more or less definite beginnings and endings. As Gesell tersely put it, "growth is motion." [1]

The scatter of developmental levels around the average attained by the 6-year-old child presents problems for educational systems. Some children will not be ready to meet the demands of school life at that age, while others will have been ready to start for more than a year. Because most school systems admit children but once a year, some children entering may actually be not yet 6 upon starting while others may be almost 7. If a developmentally retarded child happens to have his birthday at an unfortunate time of year, he may be admitted to school very much too early for him, whereas a child with accelerated development may be equally unfortunate in getting started overly late. These are problems that are, for the most part, poorly handled—in North American cultures, at least. It is not until the child begins school that developmental comparisons are made, except in cases where retardation or acceleration is extreme. Some attempts have been made to classify children before they begin school, but too often chronological age is the determining factor rather than the state of the child's readiness to accomplish the tasks set by school attendance. Adjusting school-starting age to the child's ability offers a significant opportunity to promote mental health. In many cultures there is tremendous pressure for doing certain tasks at the "right" time, which leads to a feeling of "disgrace" in the family if such events are delayed because of immaturity. At present, in the North American culture at least, all except the most patently pathological children start school at 6, and the school must adjust itself to the child's development. On the other hand, school authorities reflect cultural patterns of rigidity in bureaucratically refusing to admit developmentally mature children who are under the required chronological age.

DEVELOPMENTAL ACCOMPLISHMENTS

The child who leaves home for school is already an accomplished person. There is still some of the violent all-or-none quality about emotional reactions that found its acme in temper tantrums, but these are now toned down somewhat. Eating, while still not a polished performance, is less likely to be a problem than earlier. Buttons have been mastered, but the selection of clothing and getting it put away is still an accomplishment for the future. Bouncing a ball can be done fairly well, but throwing effectively must still appear. Romping play is well managed, but organized games with team loyalties remain to be developed. Small-muscle control has improved sufficiently so that the fingering of musical instruments becomes teachable even for many children with no special talent. Speech as a plaything and as a means of understanding and giving orders is adequate; as a medium for the exchange of ideas it is only on the threshold of development. Bowel and bladder management, though still incapable of avoiding occasional "accidents," has reached a relatively high degree of social control. The body, which was two-thirds trunk and one-third legs at birth, is, at the end of the preschool period, half trunk and head and half legs. The chubby infant has changed to the lean and lithe school child. The infant who smiled only when he felt good on the inside after feeding has changed to a child who is highly responsive to emotional situations and both recognizes humor and exhibits it himself.

SEXUAL DEVELOPMENT

The body forms of the male and female child are not markedly different during the school period. In both the growth takes place proportionately more rapidly in the legs and arms than in the trunk, and in both the pelvis grows more rapidly than the shoulder girdle. This similarity of body form is reflected in the relative ability of the two sexes in games requiring skill. Although each sex is somewhat more skillful at games generally reserved for it in our culture, studies show that both boys and girls increase in skill at most sports at approximately the same rate.[3] Campbell found that at the ages 5 to 8 there was little sex differentiation in play, that girls or boys were selected for teams according to their skill alone, and not by sex.[4] It is only as the changes of puberty begin to make their appearance that the sexes fall apart in activity, body form, and skills. Boys and girls when together enjoy the same sort of activity, but separately their interests are different. How much, if any, of this difference is sex-determined is difficult to say. To a large extent, the culture dictates that boys will play with cars and trains and, later, erector sets and that girls will play more with dolls, cookstoves, and ironing boards. As was pointed out in connection with the age of starting school, however, it is wise to remember that the culture itself is simply an expression of the wants and needs of the individuals in that culture and that the differences that exist may be basically sexually determined. Gesell records many differences between boys and girls. His studies show that girls tend to ask more penetrating sex questions than boys, that they tend to enjoy school more, that they are easier to train as regards taking care of clothing. These findings confirm conclusions that have become so well known as folklore that they are the basis of conversation whenever parents talk of children. Gesell points out that boys seem more intense and sustained in their interests than girls are in theirs.[1] The boy will be preoccupied with the same construction job over a considerable period, while the girl tends in the same time to be playing a game involving many different types of activity. This tendency is more apparent late in the school period than early; the boy may be content with the multiple subgames of playing house at 6, while at 8 he will be about his slingshot or work at his wagon and only that, the girl still playing the more varied type of game. Perhaps this is the budding expression of the capacity of the male to hold routine jobs while his wife can manage the multiple duties involved in housekeeping. It may have something to do with the fact that so many males in proportion to females become virtuosi, in spite of the fact that more females are able to perform musically. In any case, Gesell's observation has implications in the parental appreciation of growing boys and girls.

The interest of the sexes in each other is not so marked as it was in the preschool period. The question of external anatomical differences has usually been settled by question or by personal investigation during the preschool period. It will more rarely be the subject of play between the sexes at this epoch than it was in the one before. Boys tend to talk in sex terms a good deal, mimicking their elders in this respect, and are likely to have learned the whole of the colloquial sex vocabulary fairly early, frequently without knowing the meaning of the expletives they use. They may use these terms at home, not realizing that they are taboo in polite society, and the parents will be presented with the opportunity to teach a more acceptable set of words. The boy may tell jokes which to his rather larval sense of humor are funny in their own right, but to the adult are funny because of the sexual *double-entendre*.

While heterosexual experimentation even to the extent of attempted intercourse is not rare and must probably be considered within the range of normal, however much effort there may be to prevent it, experimentation in groups of boys is more frequent. Contests as to who can urinate the farthest or the highest are common. They may become sessions of mutual or group masturbation. Frequently in such groups, the older members will be pubescent and the school-ager will be an initiate trying to act like the big boys. It is surprisingly rare for adults to recognize the fact that this sort of activity occurs commonly and must even be called a part of the normal male sexual development. When through accident the group is discovered, the community is likely to become alarmed. The man too frequently forgets how he acted as a child, revealing his unconscious memory only in markedly overreacting to such a situation.

The introduction of the school-age boy to sex play may also be by older persons, usually male adults. This sort of occurrence is probably no more rare than the attacks by older men on school-age girls. They cause much less furor in communities because they are less frequently found out and also because they do not touch the taboos of our culture quite as much. Adult male homosexuals may induce young boys to act as their partners. Here the community furor is greater, and justly so. There is probably a certain opportunism in the establishment of homosexual patterns of sex outlet, and it is necessary to discourage the exposure of any child to this risk.

During the school-age period, experiences in the sexual sphere are not likely to arouse very intense emotional reactions in the child. He may be puzzled by them and may ask about them if he has the opportunity, but in most cases he does not appear to become emotionally disorganized because of them. It is the period when sex is talked about most and, perhaps, lived least, in the sense of feeling. For just this reason, however, it affords a good opportunity for sex education, particularly formal sex education. Gesell says,

> The period from 5 to 10 years is not a dormant or a latent sexual period. It is a period of progressive organization; unremitting elaborations of the self and sex attitudes are laying the foundation for the more acute development of puberty. The guidance during this precritical period should consist in progressive orientation. Information must be skillfully imparted and also skillfully withheld—some facts should be given in advance as a buffer against misinformation.[1]

Ramsey [5] showed that sex information in boys at age 10 is already rather far advanced. He found that 69.1 per cent of his sample of 291 urban Midwestern boys knew of the mother origin of babies, 57.5 per cent knew about intercourse, 43.2 per cent had learned about masturbation, and almost a quarter of the group knew about prostitution by this age. By far the greater part of this knowledge came from male companions, according to the boys. Ramsey agrees with most similar studies in his finding that parents provide their children with very little of their sex education. It is generally agreed that street talk is not the best way to achieve sex knowledge, and it is usually assumed that this knowledge is best gotten in the home. The changing of the culture to the extent necessary for the home to be really effective in sex education has discouraged many workers. They look to the schools to perform the task, preferably not directly in classes so named, but indirectly through courses in science and literature. Such courses include something of sociology and biology, and in the hands of well-trained teachers of sound personality, they afford excellent opportunities for imparting sex knowledge. Because sex at the ages under discussion is a matter of knowledge more than of feeling, formal teaching of the biologic facts is not too difficult for the good teacher. A 9-year-old girl, for example, came home from school intensely interested in the fact that the opossum has three sets of babies at the same time: one riding the mother's back, one in the pouch nursing, one still unborn. This girl obviously was accumulating a fund of knowledge that would be available to her a few years later, when she needed it to understand human sex functioning.

SOCIAL DEVELOPMENT

Friendship Patterns. From what has been said already about the sex development of the school-ager, something can be gathered about the types of friendships children form at these ages. Language in the preschool period was used mainly for entertainment and for the transmission of orders, only occasionally for the exchange of ideas. During the school ages, the collection of information is important and language develops as a tool to give and get facts. There is a good deal of pride about "what I know" and great appetite to learn more.

Friendships are built in mutual interests and mutual projects, doing things. Friendships in boys are built about mutual ambitions to excel, perhaps in some sport or in projects to make something. These projects are often ludicrously too big. The 8-year-olds who spot a tree trunk and see in their imagination a dugout canoe complete with sails are really hurt when mother asks to postpone her help on the sails until the boat is finished. Ridicule by elders is particularly cutting; the child's sense of humor rarely includes the ability to laugh at his own foibles. An insecure parent can effectively trammel the imagination of a child by ridiculing his overambitious ideas. They had best be allowed to become failures unobtrusively if they are doomed to failure, or else made into successes by providing help at critical points. In both sexes there is the urge to make things. The increasing motor control makes possible the completion of surprisingly difficult projects at times. Mutual interest in reading may also be the basis for friendships, more frequently in girls than boys.

Especially in the later school period "gang" activity appears, particularly in boys.[6] The preadolescent "gang" is likely to have a hide-out somewhere in a shed or cellar not likely to be desecrated by the presence of adults. Much constructive planning and work requiring a high degree of cooperation may enter into the planning and building of such places, and if materials are not or cannot be gotten otherwise, they may be taken without permission. The hide-out is used to store tools, to cook food, and to hold more or less organized meetings. Frequently the gang indulges in much violent fantasy about fighting other gangs, and the clubroom may be an arsenal for weapons, at this age likely to be stones and well-hardened mud balls rather than the more dangerous weapons of older gangs. The fantasied wars occasionally take place, but assaultive injury rarely results. Generally the fantasy takes the place of actual fights.

The significance of gang organization in the development of the child is recognized but is difficult to measure. Certainly the school-aged gang gives opportunities to test social and cultural skills with a group of social peers; this would appear to be a developmental task of the school period that is accomplished partly through gang organizational patterns. It seems clear also that the juvenile gang does have direct relationships with later gang organization which may be destructive.[7] It also appears that, while gang activity occurs in all classes, it is most common in the lower socioeconomic groups where organized recreational activities are not readily available, where there is often a grudge against society to be worked off, and where crowded living space forces many children to play together in inadequate area.[8]

Although with the beginning of school life the social contacts of the child expand tremendously, the family should remain the home base and the relationships with the parents the ones the child most depends upon. Friendships, school teachers, even communities may change, but ideally, the parents remain always available for love and always approachable. The child varies in attitude toward them. Early in the period, when the all-or-none type of emotional reaction is still frequent, the child may become extremely angry at his parents. He may momentarily hate the parents and say so. He is not aware of social niceties, and he may tell the unexpected guest to go home. At this period the child at times seems to prefer almost any home to his own; it is as though he were trying to determine whether his was as good as the rest, to determine whether others' standards were as hard to fit into as those in his own home. Later, there is less direct reaction and more genuine evaluation. Differences in family ways are subjects of criticism or of questions: "Why does Mary Jane get a quarter for a good grade when I don't?" "Why do I have to go to bed at 8:30 when Josephine gets to stay up until 9:30?" It is a rare parent who does not answer such questions with "because I say so," now and again, particularly if more accurate but less blunt explanations have proved unacceptable. But the child is trying to learn the whys and wherefores and is entitled to his explanation at 8 or 9, whether or not he accepts it at the time. The blunt response too early in the conversation may dull the child's wish to learn; sullen and insincere acquiescence without respect for the parent is a high price to pay for relief from the questions. It is also a high price for the child to pay in the sacrifice of his curiosity to unexplained authority. The child's attitudes toward the parents will be variable; as is so frequently pointed out in sciences dealing with people, the only constant is that there will be change. Generalizations have been made [1] indicating that at some periods children rather regularly turn to one parent or the other as they develop through this period. It is suspected that individual variations, in children as well as in mothers and fathers, make the generalizations questionable. It would appear that the best attitude for the parents would be to preserve their own love for each other and a mutual willingness to sacrifice not only physical comforts but privacy of mind to meet their children's needs.

This attitude toward the school child is not always easy for the parents to achieve. At times the parent can never please the child and can get no pleasure from him. Usually such a condition is more indicative of unhappiness, of psychopathology, in the parent than in the child. A healthy mother who herself had a reasonably normal childhood does not become nauseated at a 6-year-old's "accident," or at the fact that the 8-year-old has to be made to take a bath. If the 7-year-old wets the bed, the mother may be concerned at the stain on the mattress and the increased laundry, but she is not disgusted with the child to the extent that she cannot give him sympathy in his embarrassment. The parent may be aggravated by the noises of shouting and fussing that go on when school children play, but with the annoyance there will be appreciation of the child. The father may resent the fact that his tools are misplaced, but he will appreciate the toy his son made with the tools. The parent whose own emotional reactions make appreciation of the child impossible, whose irritable moods and outbursts of anger are expressions of deep dislike and are not tempered by humor, is a sick parent who needs help. Such help is at times within the range of psychiatric treatment that can be given by the public health officer, practicing physician, or nurse. The following case illustrates how this sort of situation may be managed:

When 8.5 years old, K. W. was brought to the clinic by his disturbed and resentful mother, on advice of the school nurse. The mother complained of his temper, that he used "awful language," was disorderly, and was inattentive in school. She had always been much concerned about constipation. She had never allowed the boy to flush the toilet; she had to examine the stool. He was prophylactically "cleaned out" once a week and was given enemas for "poor movements," for headaches, and for "grouchy moods." Toilet training had begun at 3 months and continued up to 4 years. The boy had been afraid of the toilet until he was 6 and had continued to use a pot until that age.

Delivery had been premature and difficult and the child's development slow. Although K. had never said what he was afraid of, he always hid his head under the covers when going to sleep.

The father was said to be calm and quiet, while the mother described herself as a "nervous jitterbug." By this she meant that she was obsessed about the need for complete cleanliness and orderliness. She was easily hurt and had little self-confidence. She had grown up in a family of three girls, with a meek, submissive mother and a very strict father. She said that she was "completely ignorant" of sex when she was married. She had always been frigid.

K. had a sister, aged 3.5. She was "good" in contrast to his "badness." When they quarreled, he was always blamed. Often when both were enjoying some activity, he was punished for "picking on" her.

The mother was assured of the boy's normality—that all 8-year-olds are noisy, dirty, and careless to a considerable extent. She was also advised that his intestinal tract would function without enemas, cathartics, and general concern and that responsibility for this should be his. It was suggested that he be given increasing responsibility for dressing himself, getting to school on time, etc. The need for impartiality in treating the children's misbehavior was stressed. The mother was reassured that the case was not at an emergency level of severity as she had feared.

At the second visit, spiteful temper reactions were reported, to which the mother had responded with spiteful punishments. She had made K. write, "I must not be spiteful and mark the rug with my heels," 100 times. It was suggested that making him clean the rug would have been more constructive, and the mother said that she had thought of this but feared he would not do a good enough job. The mother's artistic pride in her immaculate house was discussed with her. The alternate satisfaction of building sound personality structures in her children was held out to her. She grasped this concept and showed real interest in it.

As time went on, there was steady improvement in mother and child. She became able to disregard his bowel functioning except for occasional casual questions. She now distributed blame for quarrels between the children more equally. Nightmares disappeared, but temper outbursts were still observed. The mother reported that she had found a plastic Sacred Heart of Jesus pitted by a bayonet which an uncle had given the boy as a souvenir. K. admitted having done the deed in an angry moment. Being a sincerely religious Catholic, his mother felt badly about it, but instead of being shocked and punishing K. severely, she now realized that he needed some outlet for his anger, which she resolved to supply with a dart board. She was able to describe the incident with humor. The boy now very cheerfully did "K.P." duty after school, preparing vegetables for dinner while he discussed the day's happenings with his mother.

The mother herself felt that she had changed a great deal and said, "I can't tell you what a sick mind I had before. Sometimes I used to think of doing away with myself." Recently she dented a fender on the car. When her husband yelled at her, she reminded him that he had done the same himself. Only later did she realize that previously she would have been hurt and silent for days after such criticism.

After the family had been under supervision for 4 years the mother became pregnant. She maintained her increased freedom of personality function during the pregnancy. As the time for delivery approached, she said she could foresee a busy time ahead and asked to be discharged from the follow-up visit schedule. K. had not been coming to clinic with her for almost a year since it interfered with his Saturday morning baseball and other play. K. was 12 years 4 months old at the time of the last visit and was a healthy adolescent. There remained some problems, but the whole family was happier and there had been a fundamental change in the mother's personality and in her attitude toward the boy.

EARLY AND LATE SCHOOL PERIOD

In the early school period the child is less boisterous, noisy, talkative, negligent of clothing than he is in later childhood. Probably these changes are both constitutionally and environmentally determined, as are all other developmental events. Some of the changes foreshadow pubertal events; others are related to the child's increasing confidence in his ability to deal with his environment with reasonable success. School is no longer so imposing as a building or in social demands. The early consolation devices disappear, but the tendency toward repetitive acts remains, converted into a drive to collect things. This change is, of course, stimulated by the schools through the exercises assigned in making notebooks, in "show-and-tell sessions," through hobby shows, and the like. Late childhood sees the foundation of many stamp collections. This drive to make collections varies widely from child to child in tenacity of purpose and tendency to change the objects collected, but it is a rare child that shows none of it.[9]

The type of complaint in the case of K. W. is not unusual in late childhood, though most mothers are less disturbed than was this one by the activity. Many parents are able to appreciate the changes observed as evidence of maturation, and the increasing of such appreciative attitudes is the goal of anticipatory guidance at this period.

BEGINNING SCHOOL

The entrance of the child into the school is the change that marked the exit from the "yard-baby" stage of development. In the schools the child is placed in a situation demanding adaptation to a large group of contemporaries, and adaptation to a new adult in authority. Perhaps for the first time, the child must master the intricacies of a large building. He encounters the use of sex-segregated toilets, with which he may or may not have become familiar earlier. There is the expectancy that he will produce a definite result within a definite time period, a vastly different kind of succession of actions and interests than he could show in the preschool period.

The changes expected of the child are so great that educators have recognized the need for introducing them gradually. Nursery schools have already been discussed as having become functions of public education;[10] kindergartens are much more frequent and also serve the purpose of the gradual introduction of the radical changes demanded of the child. In kindergarten the social forms of schools, regular hours, obedience to rules, and conforming to the group are gradually learned under a less rigid regime than is usually possible in the first grade. "Learning" in the kindergarten is not a matter of books and pencils and exact lessons; it is a matter of learning social conformity, learning how to produce in a group rather than in an individual setting. Kindergarten helps the child create in the mediums he will later learn to discipline and use, either to learn new facts or to record impressions. It teaches him first to enjoy expressing himself before he is called upon to perform set intellectual tasks.[11]

The fostering of creativeness in the child as he learns in school does not stop at the end of kindergarten. It has become a cardinal principle of pedagogy throughout the school life of the child. There are many aspects of school life that make standardization inevitable; the maintenance of the creativeness of the pupil, of the respect for the fact that each child has an individual personality built up through the effects of its special environment on a unique constitution, is the great problem of the public school system. Educators have attempted to maintain and foster this attitude in every way possible, through teacher selection and training, through diagnostic studies of the child, and through increased communication between parent and teacher.

Teacher Selection and Training. It is probably less true for teachers than for poets, that good ones are born and not made. Still, the ability to recognize the factors that drive a child certainly varies from individual to individual. The teaching profession has made efforts to select from among people applying for teacher training those with warm, adaptable personalities who are able to recognize emotional discomfort quickly and to make adaptations to relieve strain on the individual child. The "old-maid" schoolteacher is not a personality pattern the profession itself seeks to maintain. The president of a normal school once pointed out that she was satisfied if a girl she trained taught for 2 to 4 years, then married. She considered that such girls were, because they were free enough emotionally within themselves to fall in love and marry, more likely to be warm and adaptable toward children while they were teaching. Appreciation of and adaptation to the needs of the child rather than simply covering some specified amount of classwork have become the ideals of the teacher. It has been found that the capacity to bring out the child's creative interest is more important than the ability to cover a subject before the class in an obsessive, disciplinary way.

Adaptability tends to decrease with increasing age, and probably rigidity of personality increases more rapidly in unmarried than in married people, though of course there are exceptions. There was a time when the married woman was discouraged from continuing her teaching. This was partly due to the action of the law of supply and demand—teachers were plentiful during the depression when married women were excluded generally, and they were in short supply during the war years and since, when any teacher, married or unmarried, was welcomed by most school systems with open arms. Selection of teachers is one way the schools are endeavoring to offset the routinized type of work so easy to adopt when large numbers of human beings are to be educated.

Large numbers of children have entered school in the postwar period. During the same period, there has been a decrease in the education of numbers of teachers because birth rates in many countries were low during the years 1936 to 1941, and also because of the cultural lag that has tended to keep teachers' salaries low while payment for other professions and skills was rising more rapidly. Educators have therefore been unable to exercise much selection of teachers. Educational standards have had to be lowered in order to get the numbers of teachers necessary simply to man the classrooms which must be available for the children born during the periods of high birth rate during and following World War II. It is unfortunate that precisely when the best possible teachers are necessary to cope with the large classes and inadequate buildings secondary to the population pressures, teacher selection becomes practically impossible because of the extremely short supply of candidates.

The second means of accomplishing the aim of placing the needs of the child at the core of the educational system is the training of teachers. Curricula of teachers colleges have been criticized because they contain so much material about how to teach and how to appreciate and develop the resources of the child. They seem to furnish the student in the college so little of the subject matter to be taught. Conservatives cry out for a return to the three R's, claiming that necessary basic knowledge escapes the child while too much time and attention is devoted to developing his personality. The implication is that the personality developed is an undisciplined one. One is reminded of the poor child in the progressive school who was so tired of having his own resources developed that he longed to have someone simply tell him what to do for a change. In any case, there is increasing attention given to the study of the child, his unfolding developmental patterns, and his capabilities for learning. Methods of teaching are based more on what the child can do and less on what the child is supposed, theoretically, to "cover" in schoolwork. Courses in child development and in mental hygiene are given both in teachers colleges and in in-service training courses.[12] Perhaps the most widely used technique of in-service training for teachers is the child-study method developed by Prescott.[13] In these groups, each teacher is encouraged to record and attempt to understand on the basis of available data the behavior of one or two children, submitting her data and conclusions to the group for discussion.[14,15] Through such detailed study of a child, she unavoidably confronts the specificity of that child's problems, thereby increasing her realization that each child in her classes is unique, comes from a unique family, and requires individual care if he is to be comfortable and to progress most rapidly toward a healthy maturity.

Diagnosis of the Child. Psychological testing has proved very helpful in understanding the capacities of the individual child so that educational aims may be more specifically adapted to him. The tool most used is the intelligence test. Intelligence is the capacity of the human being to learn and to apply facts. A more practical definition relates intelligence directly to the instruments used to measure it in practice: it is that capacity of the human being which determines his ability to perform tasks as set forth in certain intelligence tests.

These tasks are of several types. Rote memory is tested by repetition of numbers or of syllables. Definition of words is used to measure language development. This function correlates with general intelligence more closely than any other subtest. Another type of test measures the ability to differentiate and to generalize. Motor development and control as well as perception are tested by asking the subject to reproduce certain simple drawings. Sensory acuity also enters intelligence testing in such tasks as estimating weight. The capacity for abstract thinking is tested by the use of mathematical or other symbols and through the interpretation of fables and pictures.[16]

Intelligence tests have been developed to fit various needs. There is a constant effort to shorten them, to formulate them so that they can be given to many children at the same time, so that they are applicable to very young as well as to older children, so that they will measure the intelligence of adults as well as of children. Tests designed to differentiate various types of intelligence have been developed and proved useful. The Wechsler-Bellevue Test,[17] for example, makes possible the separate scoring of verbal and performance tests and gives some indication of what a subject can *do* in contrast to what he can *think* or, more strictly, what he can report of his thinking in words. The test method has been applied to a wide range of other problems as well. Aptitude for various types of work can be tested and, to some extent, success or failure in that line predicted. Scales have been developed that do not require the ability to read, so that basic intelligence can be determined apart from this learned ability.

All intelligence tests assume that certain stimuli are universal in the culture for which the test was devised. The test assumes that all children will have the opportunity to know numbers before they reach school age and that all children will be exposed to reading lessons. These tests assume that the stimuli to development are the same in one home as another, in one school as another. Except in terms of extremely broad averages, these assumptions are obviously not justified. A specific problem, for example, is the home in which a foreign language is spoken. It is unfair to expect a child from such a home to do as well as the average in vocabulary tests, though frequently when the child is tested in his mother tongue, the scores vary less than might be expected.

A second basic assumption that all tests tend to make is that ability is, on the average, equal in the various types of tests used. Actually there are special aptitudes that are testable, and performance ability may be on a different level from that of abstract thinking. Specific disabilities are also known that make the tests inapplicable to some children; e.g., specific reading difficulties are not necessarily correlated with general intelligence.

The intelligence test offers to all professions working with the personality functions of the human being the tremendous advantage of reducing one factor of the personality to a numerical score. By means of this score, the individual can be compared with the group or with specific individuals in the group. This ability to judge and compare in any exact, measurable sense is so rare in personality study that any technique making it possible is greeted enthusiastically. It therefore tends to receive more credit for accomplishment than is its just due. Such has been the case with the intelligence test. Educational systems have, perhaps, placed too much faith in its results and based too many administrative procedures on it, neglecting other personality factors in the use of this technique of measuring one factor with reasonable exactness. The score used is the I.Q., the intelligence quotient. This figure is calculated according to the following formula:

$$\text{I.Q.} = \frac{\text{M.A. (mental age)}}{\text{C.A. (chronological age)}} \times 100$$

According to this formula, the average I.Q., that at which the mental age equals the chronological age, is 100.

As measured by tests, mental age does not increase in adult years; tests measure capacity, and this does not increase once it has reached a plateau. The age at which this plateau is reached is not universally agreed upon. Some workers use the mental age of 16 as that of the average adult. Following World War I, this was found to be at least 2 years too high, and many clinics began to use M.A. 14 as the average of the adult population; others compromised and used M.A. 15 as the figure. The concept of mental ages has been severely criticized because it implies a stepwise growth. Percentile ratings of test scores have been substituted in some tests to avoid the introduction of the idea of mental age when making comparisons or placing a child in relation to a group. In other tests other empiric methods have been worked out to adjust to such factors as advanced age.[17]

In using the I.Q., an assumption is usually made that it has a predictive value, i.e., that the I.Q. will remain, within relatively narrow limits, constant from birth to adulthood. Thus, it should be possible to test a child when he enters school, place him in a class intended to advance at a rate fitted to his I.Q., and then be secure in the belief that that placement will remain the correct one for that child. This theoretical constancy of the I.Q. has always been questioned. Considerable experimental work has shown it to be false often enough so that the possibility of change needs to be recognized in planning for the individual case.[18] Beth Wellman has shown that the I.Q. can be raised by exposing children to a stimulating preschool curriculum in nursery school.[19] There are many cases recorded in which emotional conflicts interfere markedly with the individual's functioning in the test situation. When the conflicts are resolved these difficulties are relieved, the test score rises, and the child's I.Q. appears to have risen.[20] Various names have been applied to this condition in which the "capacity" of the child cannot reveal itself in the test situation, the most common of which is "pseudo-feeblemindedness." It is, of course, of great clinical and educational significance. Large-scale studies that tend to show consistent rises in I.Q. have been criticized on methodological and statistical grounds, so that the validity of the reported results cannot be accepted fully at the present time. Esther Richards [21] has discussed a group of children whose I.Q.'s tend to fall as they grow older, particularly as they enter the adolescent years. Studies of children brought up in foster homes show that test intelligence is influenced both by the characteristics of the true parents, who could not have had any environmental influence, and also by the foster parents, whose influence must be exclusively environmental. It is impossible to estimate the proportions of effect of these two factors, but both are operative.[22] These studies all indicate that when plans are being made for a particular child, it is most unwise to assume that the I.Q. will necessarily continue at the same level over a long period of years.

Intelligence does not correlate perfectly with social responsibility. This is best illustrated by the findings of all studies that determine the rates for feeble-mindedness for the adults and children in the same population. Invariably the rates for children are higher. In the 1925–1927 study in England, for example, the rate for children (urban) was from 17.7 to 24.2 per 1,000 of the population, depending on the part of the country surveyed. For adults in the same areas the rate varied between 3.7 and 5.2 per 1,000.[23] The reasons for this wide variation are not far to seek. Children are usually adjudged feeble-minded on the basis of intelligence tests, while in adults, the basis is social success or failure, more or less the ability to make a living. The two bases of judgment are obviously widely different. Success in living as an adult cannot be predicted with absolute reliability from intelligence scores of children. This has been clearly illustrated by Fairbank in a follow-up study made on a group of children originally tested by Campbell in 1916.[24] Fairbank's study was made 17 years later, in 1933.[25] She found that as adults the subnormal had done far better than Campbell had predicted and that almost as many of the subnormal group as of the normal population were self-supporting. Fairbank attributed a part of this result to the effectiveness of a school principal in the area, a heartening finding for those teachers—and health officers—who occasionally become weary in well-doing.

In conclusion, it may be said that intelligence tests measure with reasonable accuracy one factor in the human personality. The findings of the tests are useful, but it must always be kept in mind that their predictive value is limited so far as successful living is concerned, and the factor measured is not absolutely fixed but may vary according to environmental and developmental influence.

Intelligence varies in the population according to a typical distribution curve, the same bell-shaped curve one encounters when any human trait, from stature and weight to earned income, is measured.* In so far as this is true, mental deficiency and extremely high intelligence are equally abnormal. They become important only as they disturb the social situation in which they are found. In the schools, both must be provided for specially—the pupils of lower intelligence in classes that progress slowly according to the mental ages of the children, the highly intelligent in classes that allow them to progress more rapidly than the large middle group in the "regular" grades. Inasmuch as the slow children fail in regular grades, they attract attention and are cared for first as a rule. In practice, they are segregated in slow-moving classes that emphasize handwork and place less stress upon academic learning than the regular grades.

It appears that 4 or 5 per cent of all school children will need some sort of special educational provisions because of difficulties in learning related to mental deficiency. Most urban school systems arrange for this through special classes, varying the name according to the degree of deficiency of the children they serve and according to their age. Names frequently used include "opportunity class," "shop center," "pre-vocational class," etc. Such special classes are considerably more difficult to arrange in rural areas because of transportation problems, but there is a trend toward including them in small school systems. This trend has, in several instances in Maryland, been markedly speeded by the estab-

---

* There are exceptions to this statement in cases where the brain has been damaged. The lower end of the distribution curve is slightly loaded with these cases. Unlike those discussed here, these represent "sick" people and cannot be discussed as variations in a normal population.

lishment of mental hygiene clinical services in local health departments, clinics competent to make diagnoses and advise the special educational care necessary. In other places the same effect is gained through the establishment of psychological or psychiatric services within the school system itself. School systems are likely to exclude children with I.Q.'s below 50 from school, and special classes are usually designed to serve students in the 50 to 70 I.Q. range, though the additional criterion of difficulty in the regular classes is usually also involved. As might be expected, parents frequently object to having their children "stigmatized" by the recommendation that they attend a special class for slow children. This presents a difficulty to be solved by the teachers or principals concerned, by the school social worker or psychologist, or by the clinic personnel originating the recommendation. Ideally, of course, all have contributed to the planning and all have a function in working out the problem of the child's education with the parents.

There has been a tendency in the United States to neglect the special training of teachers for the education of the mentally defective child, and educational specialization in this field appears not to carry with it very great prestige in the profession. Observations in Italy and Yugoslavia indicate that in those countries, at least, this is not the case. Yugoslavia, for example, trains large numbers of teachers to deal with exceptional children of all types, whether they be in special institutions or in day schools, whether they be delinquent, emotionally disturbed, or intellectually defective. These teachers are called "defectologists" and have status as specialists in the educational system of the country. As specialists with pride in their specialty and devotion for their pupils, they produce special teaching materials that are particularly adapted to the children they serve.

The pupils of high intelligence are, in some progressive school systems, also segregated in classes where they are provided with a broadened curriculum suited to keep the stimulation of their intellectual growth at a maximum. The special cultivation of such children is considered by some to be of tremendous importance, since it is easily demonstrated that the future leaders of the world will come in disproportionate numbers from this group. In spite of this, special classes for bright children are usually developed only after those for duller children have been under way for some time. This is due to the fact that the quick learners are much less troublesome to educators, though frequently the unchallenged, highly intelligent child becomes a behavior problem in the classroom. On the basis of the argument that faculties not stimulated adequately tend to atrophy because of disuse, it is argued that pupils of high intelligence in regular classrooms fail to develop to their full capacity and that the world thus loses the full extent of their possible contributions. Where special classes for children of high intelligence (usually above I.Q. 120) have been established, they are much sought after by teachers; teaching this sort of "abnormal" children apparently carries special prestige. This attitude has been criticized as indicating that teachers are still too much concerned about how much a child can learn as contrasted with how nearly he can be brought to full use of all his personality assets, be they of high or low level.

The segregation of pupils of exceptionally high or low intellectual capacity into special classes or schools has been criticized because it sets up social groups on the basis of this single factor of the personality. It is pointed out that the highly intelligent will have to live with the average and the deficient as he goes through life, and that if he is to be a leader, he ought to gain the social skills of dealing with all the population, not only those who challenge him on the intellectual parameter of his personality. To achieve this end, as well as more proper classification within the broad group between the extremes, individual methods of teaching are combined with group methods and all the ranges of intelligence are taught together in the same classes. The child with low intelligence is not expected to learn more than the bare essentials, whereas the highly intelligent has a broad field of auxiliary knowledge presented to him. Suppose, for example, that a class is learning about transportation. The slow pupil may spend most of his time building a landscape with a train track and a road with automobiles and trucks and busses on it, learning to spell the names of the objects as he works. The highly intelligent pupil may be learning something about the economics of railroad versus truck-freight transportation, or even the relative efficiency of an oil versus a coal locomotive. Such teaching as this is obviously difficult and requires much more of the teacher than does the segregation method. It has the advantage of keeping the child socialized widely while he is being educated and helps him find his niche in society as he grows up.

In the United States school attendance is required by law until age 16 in an increasing number of states. This requirement places new demands on educational systems to provide worthwhile experiences for pupils who cannot successfully deal with the academic material formerly required of a rather small, self-selected group who attended secondary schools with the primary aim of preparing to go on to college. Secondary schools are being required to develop curricula for the full range of intelligences, whereas previously they were designed to fill the needs of no more than the upper 30 to 40 per cent of all children. These changes of attitude toward the functions of secondary school education have produced, and are still producing, fundamental changes in educational practices and philosophy.

Reading is fundamental to all education after the first year in school. Inability to read is probably the most common cause of the child's dissatisfaction with school attendance, and it looms high as a cause of truancy and other types of delinquent behavior. A large percentage of children show a tendency to reverse letters and words while learning to read and write. "E" is written as "Ǝ" for example, and "was" read as "saw." Such reversals are in many cases hardly to be considered as anything more than events in the process of learning. In others it appears that the difficulty indicates some sort of failure of function of the central nervous system having to do with spatial orientation. The exact nature of this dysfunction is not understood despite extensive study, although it is clearly related to the general maturational process.[26] The nonreader of this type generally improves with instruction under a specially trained teacher.

Not all nonreaders show this difficulty of spatial orientation. Another large group of children appear unable to learn to read because of lack of motivation. In nonliterate homes, for example, reading may not be valued highly and the child, reflecting the value system of his home, sees no reason to make the effort involved in learning to read. In other cases, failure to read may represent a conscious or unconscious rejection of the value system of a home or school that stresses reading too much. In some cases, it appears that attempts to teach reading were begun before the child had developed sufficiently to be able to think in terms of symbols. The child was frustrated so long by an impossible task that he became permanently resigned to failure. It is to avoid such incidents that reading-readiness tests have been developed for use with early school-aged children.[27,28] Occasionally, a child is unable to read because of actual brain damage. The numerous types of causes for reading difficulty may act singly or together. Diagnostic problems of the greatest complexity may be involved in these cases. Early diagnosis and special training often succeed in the relief of conditions that would otherwise be disturbing, and they also make possible further educational progress. Persons skilled in the techniques of remedial reading are a part of a mental hygiene program in the community.[26] Frequently the community mental hygiene clinic will be the first agency to discover reading-disability cases, though ideally they should be diagnosed far earlier, before they produce the failures of adjustment that bring such cases to clinic.

The use of the intelligence and reading factors of the personality does not solve all the problems of school maladjustment. Other personality factors have to be taken into consideration and these are, in general, less clearly defined and less measurable than intelligence. Some experimentation with special classes for emotionally disturbed children has been carried out, but on the whole, such children must be handled individually. A group which has been neglected in recent years are children reacting to gross brain damage. Special teaching methods may be successful in helping such children keep up, though the task is often peculiarly difficult because of shortened attention span, extreme repetitiveness of reaction, and difficulty with abstract thinking.[29]

The factor of brain injury as one of the causes of school and other difficulties in the lives of children is proving to be of greater importance than had been suspected. The work of Pasamanick and Lilienfeld showing the significant relationship of such injuries to the incidence of mental deficiency, epilepsy, and cerebral palsy has already been mentioned.[30] Rogers has demonstrated a similar relationship between obstetrical complications that are associated with increased risk of brain damage and school behavior problems. Her work indicates that the child psychiatric diagnostician may expect a fair percentage of children appearing before him on complaints of behavior disorders to show evidence of brain damage. If the complaints include hyperactivity and confusion, the index of suspicion should be very high indeed.[31] School systems will probably have to develop special classes to deal with the particular difficulties these children present in the educational process.

The diagnosis and the devising of treatment methods for the above types of cases are usually in the hands of specially trained personnel, although the teacher is involved in the treatment program. In the understanding of these problems and their treatment the schools have looked to the specialties of psychiatry, psychology, and sociology, the latter in terms of the social worker. The data used consist not only of the intelligence of the child, but of his past life, usually expressed in terms of his constitution as revealed in past reactions, and of the environmental factors that have played upon him. The collection and analysis of such data have reached their highest development in the mental hygiene clinic for children, sometimes called the "child guidance clinic." Some school systems maintain their own clinics, while others depend on other community agencies to furnish the service to them. Various other plans are possible as outlined in earlier chapters. The inclusion of mental hygiene in the sphere of public health, furthered in the United States by the passage of the National Mental Health Act in 1946, has made the public health department one of the agencies in the community to be called upon to furnish such service for the schools.

The psychologist in a school system usually has a considerably

broader interest than simply obtaining a figure that represents the intelligence of the child at the moment. He is concerned with understanding why this figure is what it is, whether it is alterable, whether there
are ways of increasing the child's capacity to use the ability the tests
reveal. He is interested, in short, in the child's adjustment to life as well
as his test intelligence.

The school social worker is usually trained both as teacher and
social worker. Although her main problem is maintaining the child's
adjustment in school, the adjustment in the rest of life is recognized
as a necessary prerequisite to good school adjustment. The visiting
teacher stands as a liaison person between the home and the school,
serving to bring them to jointly recognized objectives for the child. She
devises the techniques by which these two adult authorities in the child's
life can work together toward these objectives. Problems referred to the
visiting teacher comprise almost every type of difficulty a child may
get into in the school situation, from truancy and tardiness to failure
academically or in emotional adjustment. The problems referred vary
at different levels of school progress. In the early grades, scholastic
placement is a frequent concern; this becomes less important later when
the job is shifted to the more self-sufficient older child and his counselor.
The child with gaudy misbehavior is more likely to be referred than the
child who is quiet because excessive shyness prevents class participation.
This finding and the psychiatrist's concern about the shy child have
brought much criticism on the teacher, the complaint being that she is
more concerned with children that bother her than she is with children
who are maladjusted.[32]

In large school systems there are likely to be, in addition to the school
social worker, "pupil personnel workers" who have the duties formerly
assigned to the "truant officer." Unfortunately, changing the name of
the job does not change the way it is done unless the person in question
has also changed radically in outlook and training.

Parents and Teachers. When the mother sends or takes the child to
school for the first time, she has, among others, two conflicting emotions. One is a feeling of relief that for some 6 hours a day somebody else
is to be responsible for the behavior of a very active 6-year-old. This
emotion is one that many cannot admit, even to themselves; it is too
much at variance with the sentimental ideas of mother love fostered in
our society. The other emotion is likely to be one of jealousy toward
the teacher, who now has an opportunity to share the child's admiration
and, perhaps, affection. Guilt about the first and resentment involved
with the second probably account for a good deal of the frequent mutual
distrust between parents and teachers, though, of course, there are im-

mediate precipitating causes of greater or less importance, depending upon the particular case. If the mother's guilt is great because of earlier rejection of the child, and fortified by an unadmitted relief now that society has implemented her rejection, or if her own emotional life is so barren that she cannot share her child's love, only a small difference of opinion with the teacher can grow into a feud in which the child is caught. In general, in such situations the teacher is expected to show the understanding necessary to heal the breach; in spite of the efforts of the profession to improve itself, this is obviously not always possible for the teacher.

Parent-teacher associations have been developed to aid in maintaining a cooperative relationship between the home and the school. These organizations make possible reasonably regular contacts between parents and teachers. This means that the common interest in the child can be discussed when there is no acute problem to make the relationship difficult. It establishes a relationship between parent and teacher which has a better chance of remaining a cooperative one if and when a problem comes along, and it permits the exchange of information about the pupil to be put to use in working with the child in both the milieus.

In addition to this principal function of parent-teacher associations, they also afford the opportunity for parent education. School methods have advanced very far since most parents were in school, and parents need to see modern classrooms to realize how great the change has been. They have the opportunity to see what the intellectual horizon of the child actually is in terms of school life. The progressive adaptation of the home to the child's expanding knowledge sometimes forges ahead of what the child can do; at other times too little is expected and the child suffers lack of stimulation. The parent-teacher association is also something of a service club, supplying some "luxuries" that the tax sources frequently neglect to provide in public schools. Its meetings afford an excellent opportunity to educate the population on school health problems and practices, to enlist the help needed by the health officer and nurse for the summer round-up, to get cooperation for the tuberculosis survey, or to explain why it is necessary to have the parent present at the child's physical examination.

Some school systems include parent education as an objective in the total adult-education program.

SOCIAL GROUPS IN THE SCHOOL-AGE PERIOD

Informal groups, cliques, and gangs have already been discussed. Some more formal organizations have developed to satisfy the needs expressed in these spontaneous groupings. Cub Scouts for boys and Brownies * for girls are organizations that recognize the developing ability of the child to conform to social groups. These organizations offer a stimulus to this budding capacity. They capitalize on the school child's interest in "doing things" through handwork of various sorts, as well as his interest in learning things, through rewarding gains in knowledge with badges of recognition. Adult leaders for these groups are trained volunteers for the most part. Since these organizations "train" the child for group living and give him an opportunity for self-expression, they are effective as agencies for fostering the mental health of the community. These organizations, like those of the adolescent group, put before the child high ethical ideals, though these are less stressed at this age than in the older groups.

Church or Sunday schools are most heavily attended by children of school age. In our culture many parents tend to send their children to Sunday school even though they themselves avoid attending religious services. Such schools attempt to teach religious and ethical concepts to children, using as the medium the traditional stories of the sect in question. The same principles of satisfying the need of the child to gain knowledge and to do things is capitalized upon in the church school as have been discussed in connection with other organizations serving this age group. Thus, maps, geography, rote learning, appreciation of literature and music may all be parts of the work in these classes. Church schools are usually, though not always, staffed by poorly trained though devoted volunteers. In past years, most of the teaching material was poorly prepared and showed little appreciation of the needs and capacities of the child. These tended to be subordinated to the more or less rigid religious and ethical principles they aimed to teach. More recently, religious education has received a great deal of attention, however, and teaching methods and materials have been improved greatly until in many denominations they compare favorably with the teaching materials of the public schools. However, church schools still cannot compare with the public schools in having trained teachers, a deficiency probably only partly made up by a greater devotion of their teachers to their task.

SCHOOL HEALTH PROGRAMS

The modern school health program is interested not only in the child's organic intactness, but in his adjustment on a far broader basis,

---

* Cub Scouts and Brownies are used as representative of the types of organizations serving the functions mentioned. There are other organizations with similar purposes, but these are the largest and most highly organized of the type.

including the home and community. The jealousies—and lack of scientific knowledge—which dictated that the doctor and nurse cared for the child's body but left the cultivation of his mind exclusively to teachers are not tolerable when the aim of the school is to produce sound minds in sound bodies, sound personalities. Stress is on keeping the whole child in the best possible condition, not only so that he can learn better but so that he can live more happily and develop his capacities to the fullest extent.

The old type of school health program, which surveys large groups of children and records the findings, is being discarded. The stress on the diagnosing of large numbers is changing to a stress on getting the defects corrected when they are diagnosed. The attempt is being made to conserve the time available to see children whose ills are actually affecting their adjustment to life. The diagnosis of ill-health requiring medical investigation is shifted from mass surveys by physicians to the classroom teacher who observes the child's activity daily and who sees changes which, with some training and in consultation with the nurse, she can interpret as meaning ill-health.[33] The schoolteacher is concerned with the daily behavior of the child, with his ability to "fit in" socially, physically, and educationally. With the diagnosis of need for medical care being turned over to her, it is found that adjustment problems in the realm of mental hygiene reach the school health department more frequently than in the past.

Another reform in school health programs that tends to integrate the medical service more fully into the schools' concern about the life adjustment of its pupils is the emphasis upon the inclusion of the parents in the group concerned when a child is examined. With the parents present, medical histories will be more complete and behavior as well as diseased tonsils will come under consideration. The school physician will have the opportunity to become a mental hygienist, to do preventive medicine in the field of emotional adjustment, as well as in the field of ensuring organic intactness.[34] So far as curative efforts are concerned, he will be in a position to know when consultation by the psychiatrist or psychiatric clinic is needed.

Modern school health practices place new responsibilities on the teacher. She is asked, in consultation with the nurse, to determine when the child needs medical attention for any reason. To accomplish this implies an in-service training program for the teacher. In the mental hygiene aspects, this training of teachers has already reached a reasonably high state of development in some school systems. It began with the inclusion of the teacher in the therapeutic conferences of child guidance clinics,[35] the teacher becoming a contributor to the plan of therapy as well as an agent in carrying out the plan.[36] Psychiatric clinics are not nearly plentiful enough to furnish opportunity for in-service education of teachers to all those who need and want the opportunity, however. The gap has been partly filled by educators by employing the data and methods of child psychiatry, modifying them to meet the specific problems and opportunities of the schools, and teaching these principles in small groups as in-service training to teachers. Prescott's methods in this area have already been described.

Although a great deal of the effort of the educational system toward the emotional health of children is carried on independently of the medical profession, the stimulus for it has come largely from the specialty of child psychiatry. It has become independent because teachers are numerous and psychiatrists few—too few to meet the demand upon them for broadening the outlook of the teachers. The profession of education has therefore filled its need by adopting the methods and principles of child psychiatry so far as is possible by nonmedically trained personnel. The profession continues to look to child psychiatry and to psychology for leadership but has taken the task of the propagation of the principles unto itself. The medical profession is, in most cases, welcomed and invited to aid in these study programs and also in their scientific evaluation.[37]

SUMMARY

The school period marks the emergence of the child from the home into a broader social sphere. He associates with a larger group of his peers than before and includes other persons of authoritative position in his orbit. During the period he develops physically, particularly in the ability to perform coordinated and fine movements. There is an urge to gather knowledge which includes learning about sex and, to some extent, experimenting in this field both in practice and in language. In social relations, the sexes tend to be equal in most particulars, although there is a tendency for boys to play "masculine" games while girls follow a more "feminine" pattern. Social relationships in clubs are possible in the latter part of the school period, but need some trained adult leadership if the organization is to persist and be successful.

School systems are concerned with the individual child and his individual personality even though they are called upon to educate large numbers of children. In order to foster the adjustment of school children, the teaching profession has attempted to select persons for teacher training who are adaptable and have the capacity to understand and like children, as well as the ability to pass on specific knowledge. These teachers are trained in child development, specially trained workers extending this understanding to include a knowledge of the home and community and to deal with special educational disabilities.

Intelligence tests are able to measure one feature of the personality effectively, and they furnish the basis for many educational practices. The personality is, however, much broader than mere intelligence. The grasp of the other factors of personality is more difficult since they are hard to define and to measure. Methods of dealing with them are the methods introduced by child psychiatric clinics—the understanding of behavior in terms of the environmental factors playing upon the unique personality structure of the child. As school health programs improve, the mental health, the adjustment, the happiness of the child will more and more become the concern of the health officer in his school health services. With the expansion of mental hygiene services through health departments, psychiatric consultation to the schools may be included in school health programs.

REFERENCES

1. Gesell, A., and F. L. Ilg: *The Child from Five to Ten,* Harper & Brothers, New York, 1946.
2. Freud, S.: *An Autobiographical Study,* W. W. Norton & Company, Inc., New York, 1952.
3. Breckenridge, M. E., and E. L. Vincent: *Child Development: Physical and Psychological Development through the School Years,* W. B. Saunders Company, Philadelphia, 1943.
4. Campbell, E. H.: "The Social-Sexual Development of Children," *Genet. Psychol. Monogr.* 21:463–552 (1939).
5. Ramsey, G. V.: "Sex Information of Younger Boys," *Am. J. Orthopsychiat.* 13:347–352 (1943).
6. Furfey, P. H.: *The Gang Age: A Study of the Preadolescent Boy and His Recreational Needs,* The Macmillan Company, New York, 1926.
7. Thrasher, F. M.: *The Gang,* University of Chicago Press, Chicago, 1937.
8. Shaw, C. R., and H. D. McKay: *Juvenile Delinquency and Urban Areas,* University of Chicago Press, Chicago, 1942.
9. Blair, A. W., and W. H. Burton: *Growth and Development of the Preadolescent,* Appleton-Century-Crofts, Inc., New York, 1951.
10. Kellogg, R.: *Nursery School Guide: Theory and Practice for Teachers and Parents,* Houghton Mifflin Company, Boston, 1949.
11. Baruch, D. W.: *Parents and Children Go to School: Adventuring in Nursery School and Kindergarten,* Scott Foresman & Company, Chicago, 1939.
12. Bullis, H. E.: *Human Relations in the Classroom,* The Delaware Society for Mental Hygiene, Wilmington, Del., 1944.
13. *Field Program of Child Study* (multigraphed), Institute for Child Study, Daniel Prescott, Director, University of Maryland, College Park, Md., 1952.
14. Prescott, D.: *Emotions and the Educative Process,* American Council on Education, Washington, 1938.
15. Barker, R. G., J. S. Kounin, and H. F. Wright: *Child Behavior and Development,* McGraw-Hill Book Company, Inc., New York, 1943.
16. Greene, E. B.: *Measurements of Human Behavior,* The Odyssey Press, Inc., New York, 1941.
17. Wechsler, David: *The Measurement of Adult Intelligence,* The Williams & Wilkins Company, Baltimore, 1944.

18. Bayley, N.: "Consistency and Variability in the Growth of Intelligence from Birth to Eighteen Years," *J. Genetic Psychol.* **75**:165–196 (1949).

19. Wellman, B. L.: "Growth in Intelligence under Differing School Environments," *J. Exper. Educ.* **3**:59–83 (1934).

20. Kanner, L.: *Child Psychiatry,* Charles C Thomas, Publisher, Springfield, Ill., 1948.

21. Richards, E.: *Introduction to Psychobiology and Psychiatry,* The C. V. Mosby Company, St. Louis, 1929.

22. Leahy, A. M.: "A Study of Adopted Children as a Method of Investigating Nature-Nurture," *J. Am. Statistical A.* **30**:281–287 (1935).

23. *Report of the Mental Deficiency Committee,* part IV, H. M. Stationery Office, London, 1929.

24. Campbell, C. M.: "The Subnormal Child—A Study of the Children in a Baltimore School District," *Ment. Hyg.* **1**:97–147, 1917.

25. Fairbank, R.: "The Subnormal Child—Seventeen Years After," *Ment. Hyg.* **17**:177–208 (1933).

26. Betts, E. A.: *Foundations of Reading Instruction, with Emphasis on Differentiated Guidance,* American Book Company, New York, 1946.

27. Gates, A. I.: *Manual of Directions, Gates Reading Readiness Tests,* Bureau of Publications, Teachers College, Columbia University, New York, 1940.

28. Gesell, A., and Others: *The First Five Years of Life,* Harper & Brothers, New York, 1940.

29. Strauss, A. A., and L. E. Lehtinen: *Psychopathology and Education of the Brain-injured Child,* Grune & Stratton, Inc., New York, 1947.

30. Pasamanick, B., and A. M. Lilienfeld: "Association of Maternal and Fetal Factors with the Development of Epilepsy," *J.A.M.A.* **155**:719–724 (1954).

31. Rogers, M. E.: "The Association of Maternal and Fetal Factors with the Development of Behavior Problems among Elementary School Children," dissertation, The School of Hygiene and Public Health, The Johns Hopkins University, Baltimore, 1954.

32. Wickman, E. K.: *Children's Behavior and Teachers' Attitudes,* The Commonwealth Fund, New York, 1943. An excellent criticism of this work is contained in D. B. Klein, *Mental Hygiene: The Psychology of Personal Adjustment,* Henry Holt and Company, Inc., New York, 1944.

33. Maxwell, M.: "The Public Health Nurse in the Rural School," *Pub. Health Nursing* **39**:69–72 (1946).

34. Nyswander, D. B.: *Solving School Health Problems: The Astoria Demonstration Project,* The Commonwealth Fund, New York, 1942.

35. Witmer, H. L.: *Psychiatric Clinics for Children,* The Commonwealth Fund, New York, 1940.

36. Martins, E. H., and H. Ross: *Adjustment of Behavior Problems in School Children,* U.S. Department of the Interior, Bulletin 18, Washington, 1932.

37. Balser, B. H., F. Brown, D. K. Phillips, M. L. Brown, and E. D. Joseph: "Controlled Mental Health Workshop in a Public School System," paper read the 110th annual meeting of the American Psychiatric Association, May 7, 1954, St. Louis, to be published.

CHAPTER FOURTEEN

The Adolescent Period

The period of adolescence begins when the pubertal changes begin to appear and ends when the individual has developed so that he is ready physically, emotionally, and sociologically to found a family. The period includes the profound sociological change of gaining independence from the family. For a part of the period in many cultures all normal persons are still under the aegis of the schools by law; a considerable and increasing percentage spend all the period in educational pursuits. Depending on physiological factors, some enter the period early, others enter it late. Boys enter it somewhat later than girls. The sexes tend to fall apart for most of their activities in the early years of the period; at the end there has developed the pattern of association of two individuals, one of each sex, this pattern being preserved throughout the rest of life for the greater part of the population.

ATTITUDES TOWARD ADOLESCENCE

Adolescence is commonly regarded with awesome respect as a period of great emotional upheaval. This is partly because one of the most serious types of chronic mental illness, schizophrenia, first appears in this age group * as a specific cause of morbidity. In spite of this common attitude, however, the normal behavior of the period is not well studied psychobiologically. Perhaps this is because illness appearing in this stage of development is usually considered to be the result of earlier maladjustments that come to fruition under the stresses of adolescent change. In literature the period may appear as tragic. It has, almost as frequently, been caricatured and made comic, perhaps because it would be too painful to deal with its experiences more seriously.

Most people live through adolescence without carrying a load of unhappy memories about it throughout life. This is so often the case even in persons who were obviously unhappy and harassed at times during

* Childhood schizophrenia is so rare as to be statistically insignificant.

the period that one might justifiably speak of "adolescent amnesia," just as the lack of memory of infancy is called "infantile amnesia," though causes of the lack of memory must be very different in the two periods. Perhaps the fact that memories of adolescence are pleasant to most accounts for the whimsical treatment it often receives in novels and plays. The tremendous changeability of feelings in the period, from despair to complete happiness, with such small apparent cause for the changes in the eyes of adults, is rather ludicrous. Then, too, the physical and social supremacy of the female early in the period is incongruous for most cultures and probably accounts for some of the humor. Certainly radio programs and Broadway plays have used this feature as a source for humor.[1,2]

There is some scientific evidence for treating the period somewhat lightly, though it cannot be considered by any means conclusive. Lemkau, Tietze, and Cooper found that this age group presented a lower rate of problems coming to the attention of the hospitals, courts, schools, and social agencies they surveyed than did the next older and younger groups.[3] The survey depended upon someone other than the subject noticing and reporting a problem. Adolescents do not talk about their feelings easily even to skilled adults, and mental anguish does not always call attention to itself. At school age, emotions are not so much "on the sleeve" as in the preschool period; they are even less so in this period. The relatively small number of cases found by a survey of reported problems is probably not a measure of the actual existence of emotional upheaval in the persons surveyed.

Fleege attacked the question of the prevalence and severity of disturbances by submitting questionnaires to 2,000 boys in urban parochial high schools, asking them to state their problems. The study was made with the authoritarian implications of the Catholic Church inherent in the situation. While this setting may well have influenced the answers in some particulars and certainly made the group studied not a random sample of the total population of adolescent males, the results probably have some validity as to the extent to which adolescents are concerned with their adjustment to life. Fleege found that 81.5 per cent of his adolescent boys said that they were at times "pained and puzzled," misunderstood. Six out of every ten had felt embarrassed because of awkwardness. Four of every eleven had felt that they were different from others; 35 per cent complained that they felt lonely. Two-thirds of Fleege's group were concerned about the "purity" of their lives. Almost half the boys said that they felt depressed at times.[4] In a companion study to Fleege's, similar concerns were found prevalent in adolescent girls.[5]

"STAGES" IN ADOLESCENCE

From Fleege's and Knoebler's data it may be assumed that, whatever the lasting influence of these emotions may be, there are numerous concerns dealing with the practical as well as the philosophical problems of human living during the period of adolescence. Observation of individuals has tended to confirm this assumption and to relate its content and activity with "stages of adolescence." Kanner quotes "an ambitious attempt" that reports six phases of adolescence in a particular boy. The first extended from the age of 10 years to 12 years 4 months and was marked by a smooth fitting into family relationships. The second phase, from 12 years 5 months to 13 years 8 months was called a period of "feverish wishing," marked by clashes with the family, trading, a drive to earn money, and demanding various items of clothing and equipment. The third phase, 13 years 9 months to 15 years 1 month, was characterized as a phase of active spite in which the father and brother were rejected, teachers were criticized, attempts were made to escape the "oppressions" of the home, and the boy was in a mood to revolt. In the fourth phase, the spite was directed toward himself and the boy became meditative and moody. He was shy and clumsy and tried to stay by himself. Whereas before he had exaggerated ideas of his power and strength, now he sadly recognized his dependency. The next period was short but was called the "crisis." It lasted but a month, from 15 years 8 months to 15 years 9 months. In this period the boy had trouble expressing himself, complained of poor memory, had fantastic daydreams, showed a tendency to hypochondriacal trends, and was restless and absent-minded. The sixth and last phase outlined was one of relaxation and of determined ideal formation. In it he formed his first attachment for a girl. His vocational goal was settled. He looked back at the period just passed as an illness from which he had recovered.[6]

Campbell observed group activities of boys and girls and separated the adolescent period into two stages. In the first in the boys, from 9 to 14 years, pursuit games were played, girls were avoided—boys sat by boys whenever possible. Modesty was quite apparent, and the boys avoided touching women. This was followed by an interest in girls individually but a fearful attitude toward groups of girls. There was a distinct avoidance of any show of affection from anyone. Toward the end of this second period, about the age of 16 years, the boys began to show a chivalrous attitude of serving women, of waiting on them. In girls similar stages were observed. From 9 to 13 years 6 months, girls tended to separate themselves from boys, and games were classified according to the sexes playing them. There appeared to be a definite period within this stage in which girls whispered a great deal; their activities had an aura of secrecy. Toward the end of the period, more care was noted about clothing and modesty was marked. An interest in dancing appeared, but partners were girls rather than boys. The second stage was marked by an interest in the male, and the girls were acutely conscious of male attention. They selected a "favorite boy" for themselves, usually a male older and taller. Show of affection between girls was very free.[7] Furfey shows that at the age of 6 years, 92 per cent of boys played with boys and girls equally well, that at 10 years the figure had dropped to 83 per cent, at 12 to but 20 per cent, findings that tend to corroborate Campbell's results. At 14, 17 per cent of the boys had "love affairs"; the proportion had increased to 36 per cent at age 16.[8]

Studies such as these indicate the extent of the changes of attitude and activity during the period of adolescence. The discussion that follows will set them forth in greater detail and fill in the physical and physiological developmental background against which they occur.

PHYSICAL GROWTH

Sex Differences. In Fig. 4 the curve of rate of gain of weight of males shows no sudden spurt corresponding with the onset of puberty. After the curve reaches the low around 3 years, it begins a rise, reaching a zenith about the age of 12.5 years. This curve is made up of many individual curves. It is an average that conceals the vagaries of the growth spurt as it is seen in individual boys. Curves of annual increment of weight show a break in the curve of weight gain which indicates the beginning of puberty. Figure 5 shows these curves for the two sexes.[9]

The weight-increment curve begins to rise for both sexes about the age of 6. In the male, it stabilizes from 7.5 years until about 10.5, then begins the marked adolescent spurt. The peak of this curve is reached around 14.5 years, after which there is a rapid fall until adult weight stability is reached. In the female, the rise is less precipitous, but it begins earlier, around 8.5 years rather than at 10.5 as in the case of boys. The zenith for girls is reached about 12 years, and the curve is more blunt as it turns downward to reach the adult stabilization almost 2 years earlier than does the curve for males. These curves not only show the growth pattern of adolescence, but also indicate that, on the average, girls develop through this physiological reorganization about 2 years ahead of boys. This fact is of some sociological importance. It probably explains why husbands are, as a rule, about 2 years older than their wives. It also explains why, in high school, there is always the problem of allowing outside men to come to dances. The girls disdain to associate with boys of the same chronological age and tend to select partners from a group of similar developmental age. As Campbell points out, these are usually older and taller. Recognition of this developmentally determined factor by parents would relieve a great deal of the anxiety they feel when daughters begin to have dates with "older men." It is not a question, frequently, of the older man seeking a young and gullible girl, but of two people of the same developmental age forming an association. The relation of maturity of personality to the developmental age as determined by physical characteristics is another problem, to be discussed later.

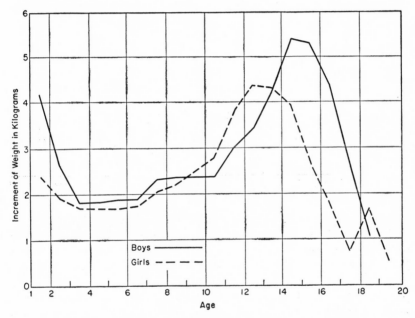

Fig. 5. Annual increments of body weight, showing that the adolescent spurt in growth occurs about 2 years earlier in the female than in the male. [Redrawn from C. B. Davenport, "Human Metamorphosis," Am. J. Phys. Anthropol. 9:205–232 (1926).]

The fact that girls in general enter puberty 2 years earlier than boys is shown by other physical characteristics than height and weight. The growth of body hair appears to have the same developmental significance in both the male and the female and is comparable for the two sexes. Growth of the genitals in the male is difficult to estimate, and in any case there is no easy observation to be made on the female to compare it with. It has been suggested that nocturnal emissions in the male are the equivalent of menarche in the female, but data on age of occurrence of the former are inadequate for comparison. No male characteristic is available for comparison with observations on female breast development. The data on the age of appearance of pubic and axillary hair in the sexes as reported by Bryan and Greenberg [10] is presented in Table 4. This study also indicated that in their group of institutionalized girls, 50 per cent were immature as to breast development at 10.7 ± .23 years, and that menarche would have occurred in 50 per cent of their sample at the age of 13.0 ± .18 years.

TABLE 4. The appearance of pubic and axillary hair in boys and girls aged 9 to 13.9 years *

Age	Girls			Boys		
	Number	Per cent immature with respect to pubic hair	Per cent immature with respect to axillary hair	Number	Per cent immature with respect to pubic hair	Per cent immature with respect to axillary hair
9	11	100	100	11	100	100
10	22	82	95	22	100	100
11	17	53	71	17	100	100
12	21	15	62	19	84	95
13	26	4	16	15	27	93
Total	97			84		

* Arranged from A. H. Bryan and B. F. Greenberg, Methodology in the Study of Physical Measurements of School Children, Part II, *Human Biol.*, 24: 117–143, 1952.

Pubertal development does not appear at the same time in all individuals of the same sex. Figures 4 and 5 present only what may be expected from a nonexistent "average individual." They indicate nothing about the distribution of the individuals making up the average. The range of individual differences is more easily obtained for the female because the onset of menstrauation, which appears about the time of the zenith of the curve of increment of weight, is an event that is easily dated. The age distribution of menarche in 680 girls is shown in Fig. 6.[11] Curves showing similar distribution can be derived for the other physical changes of puberty, including such items as the appearance of pubic and axillary hair, the beginning of breast development, the rounding of the hips, and so forth. These data have been conveniently collected in Shuttleworth.[9] As data, the material is striking, but the significance of the individual variations is even more clearly grasped from photographs showing the variation in development of individuals of nearly the same chronological age.[12] Figure 7 is such a photograph.

Males present no such climactic an event as the onset of menstruation to illustrate the age variation of sexual maturation. The secondary sex characteristics, however, are available for observation. It is interesting that the observations on males are much less complete than on females and agree less well, probably because of the lack of any obvious event such as the menarche around which to organize the data. The best studies have been on the appearance of the pubic hair in males. The pubic hair when it first appears is colorless and straight. At "pubescence," which lasts about 6 months usually, the hair becomes pigmented

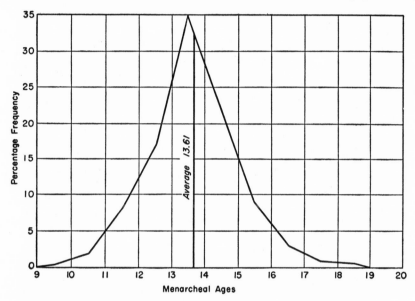

Fig. 6. The age at onset of menstruation in 680 healthy girls. The range is from 9 to 19 years. [*Redrawn from H. N. Gould and J. Gould, J.A.M.A.* 98: 1349–1352 (1932).]

but remains straight. In the "postpubescent" period, it shows for the first time the typical kink of adult pubic hair. The age range for the pubescent period has been given as from 12 to 17.5 years by Crampton [13] and from 10 to 15 years by Dimock,[14] a later worker in the field. Change of voice takes place in Crampton's pubescent stage ordinarily, Pedry having found 89 per cent of 744 boys of this stage of development showing evidence of change, though "voice breaks" occurred in all age groups he studied from 11 through 15.[15] Pedry concludes that embarrassment because of voice breaks is not severe, only 6 per cent of the 674 boys who recalled voice breaks reporting "extreme embarrassment." From what data are available, there is reason to believe that the age range of the pubertal changes reflected in these events is about 5 to 7 years. Figure 8 is a photograph that illustrates for boys the striking differences demonstrated in Fig. 7 for girls.

Awkwardness. The physical prowess of the adolescent male increases with his gain in weight and height. Strength of grip, speed of running, and general dexterity show a smooth curve, rising until the weight and

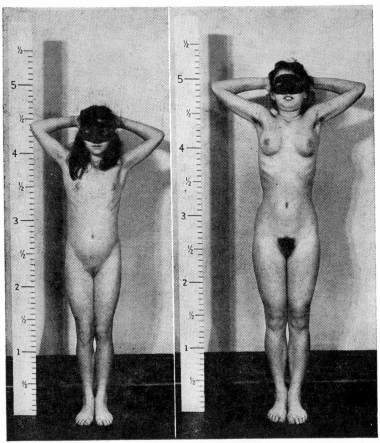

Fig. 7. Different stages of development in girls of approximately the same chronological age.

Girl A	Girl B
Age: 12 years 6 months	Age: 12 years 2 months
Height: 4 feet 8 inches	Height: 5 feet 2½ inches
Weight: 76 pounds	Weight: 102 pounds
I.Q.: 74	I.Q.: 80
Breasts: beginning subaureolar tissue	Breasts: approaching the pendulous
Body contours: undeveloped	Body contours: adult female contours
Pubic hair: sparse, straight	Pubic hair: present, kinky
Axillary hair: none	Axillary hair: present

height curves level off as the individual approaches physical maturity.[16] There is a correlation between weight and strength, i.e., the heavier postpubescent who is approaching maturity is stronger than the prepubescent boy.

The period of awkwardness is a part of the folklore of adolescence

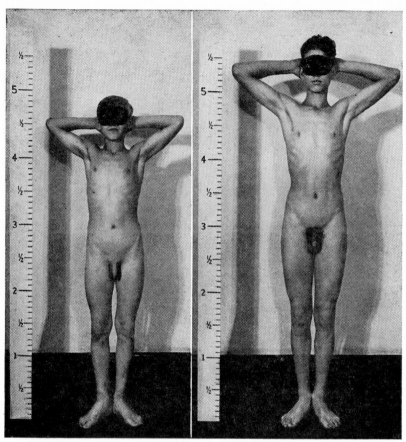

Fig. 8. Different stages of development in boys of approximately the same chronological age.

Boy A	Boy B
Age: 14 years 5 months	Age: 14 years 7 months
Height: 4 feet 11 inches	Height: 5 feet 9¼ inches
Weight: 91 pounds	Weight: 128 pounds
I.Q.: 68	I.Q.: 89
Genitals: early pubertal development	Genitals: nearing adult development
Pubic hair: light-colored, straight	Pubic hair: pigmented, curly, with persistent "shield" distribution
Axillary hair: none	Axillary hair: sparse

but has not been objectively demonstrated. It may be, however, that during the growth spurt in both sexes the body changes more rapidly than the adolescent himself realizes. The boy extends an arm he "knows" is 24 inches long to pick up a vase just 24 inches away. Meanwhile, the arm is actually 25 inches long; it meets the vase, pushes it that extra inch, it is smashed, and the boy is credited with awkwardness. Speed of movement increases during the adolescent period also; the schema of this too may lag. The result might well be stumbling and falling over the feet. Because clothing size tends to lag behind bodily growth, the folklore belief in the awkward period may be partly due to the protrusion of arms from sleeves and legs from pants. Awkwardness in adolescents is considered more marked in males. This may be due to the fact that in the male the awkward period comes at a later chronological age, when more social graces are expected. The awkwardness has been explained on the basis that adolescents are frequently unskilled socially and so are tense in social situations. This tension interferes with normal synergy in movement and gives rise to awkwardness. As social skills are acquired and excessive self-consciousness is dissipated, the awkwardness disappears.[17] It is generally agreed that the female acquires social skills more easily than the male; perhaps this accounts for the fact that awkwardness is usually less noticeable in girls.[18]

Bodily strength and dexterity do not increase through the whole adolescent period in girls. They reach a maximum shortly after the menarche, after which they tend to level off. This difference in the development of boys and girls is quite striking. It is not accounted for on the basis that girls, as has been noted already, go through the physiological changes of adolescence at an earlier age than boys. It is during adolescence that the male achieves superiority in height, weight, strength, and dexterity over the female. Earlier, boys and girls competed fairly equally in sports; after adolescence is underway, the male becomes, and then remains, the superior, in these respects, of the female.

Social Implications of Growth Factors. The enormous changes in physique taking place during adolescence are of great importance in the personality functions of the individual. The interrelations are extremely complex, since psychological and sociological maturation are taking place at the same time. To attempt to disentangle the various factors seems an almost hopeless task, yet there are some items that can be singled out. For example, the adolescent, like the infant, enjoys exercising his developing functions. The infant babbles in his crib and waves his arms. The adolescent, as though for the same reason but in much more complicated patterns, plays football or baseball or practices for track. The infant makes no comparisons so far as we can see; the adolescent makes many. His goals are social and competitive. In such a setting, it is obvious that the boy who gains weight, height, strength, and dexterity early gains also a preferred competitive position, while the late-developing lad suffers by comparison. The large, early-matured boy may gain great status on the playground where he overshadows the smaller and weaker boy. In the classroom, however, the large boy may well appear retarded in comparison with the smaller boys who are doing the same classwork at the same chronological age but quite different developmental ages. Here he suffers in the comparisons he himself and others make. There are stresses and strains in either position. In the infant and preschool child the appreciation of the child's development by the parents was stressed. In adolescence the appreciation must also be by the individual concerned. Talks on sex to adolescents should include reference to the wide age variation of the changes that take place. The understanding of such data might well allay some of the distress adolescents feel when they compare themselves with their chronological but not physiological contemporaries. Such material has a place in sex education programs, particularly when these are taught by physicians or nurses. The social implications of the secondary sex characteristics are often overlooked in favor of a too narrow interpretation of how sexual maturation affects the life of the individual. Incidentally, the facts of physical growth and development and the timing involved can and should be taught to both sexes, preferably together in groups. Depending on the local situation, it may be possible to allow such discussions to lead into co-educational consideration of the primary sex functions and drives, something that is probably desirable but frequently not to be accomplished without considerable preliminary parent and teacher education.

Standards of value for the pubertal changes are, of course, very different for girls than they are for boys. The girl may be proud of her developing feminine curves, of achieving the ability to wear a brassière like her mother, or, more likely, like the popular girl in the class who has developed more rapidly than she. Or she may be embarrassed because she remains flat-chested and slim-hipped as compared with her more matured contemporary. Conversely, the girl who has matured early may be embarrassed that she is in a class of girls who are less developed than she, just as the big boy feels inferior in the classroom situation by comparison with the smaller one able to do the same schoolwork. The earlier-matured girl may be surprised to find herself whistled at by the male "wolves" a few years older than herself. She will, perhaps, be interested in boys while her erstwhile best friend, who remains a child in spite of being the same chronological age, has not developed this interest as yet. Both she and the friend may be hurt and puzzled because they drift apart on the basis of this difference in interests. Perhaps the underdeveloped girl decides to mimic the genuine interests of her physiologically older friend. At first she may be laughed at; then she may "go too far" in her effort to be sophisticated. It is clear from the examples given that the constitutionally determined core of pattern of physical maturation may be of the greatest importance in the personality functioning of the adolescent, quite apart from the other factors that are also playing upon the individual during this period. These basically physiological problems are particularly suitable for the general physician to deal with. They also furnish a point of departure for mental health education by officials of the health department, either in collaboration with the schools or in other settings.

The variation in time of onset of puberty is likely to involve radically different standards of value according to social class. The boy of the lower socioeconomic classes is likely to be made more aware of his small size and retarded genital development than the middle-class lad who is equally retarded. Economically, the lower-class boy will have soon to go to work at a semiskilled or unskilled job, whereas the middle-class boy is usually simply facing more years of schooling. Language is more blunt and direct in the lower socioeconomic groups, and comparisons made are likely to be expressed. It can, of course, be argued that the blunt language of the lower class would not be more disturbing to the boy used to it than the subtler practices of the middle class, but this seems unlikely, particularly in the light of the greater economic imperative. Another factor applies in both sexes. Generally speaking, marriage is earlier the lower the socioeconomic class. Delay in appearance of those bodily characteristics indicating reproductive maturity may justly be assumed to be of greater importance for the adolescent who faces marriage within a few years.

The Primary Sex Functions. In the male, the testis, which has had a rate of growth similar to that of other tissues up until this time, suddenly shows a precipitous rise in rate of growth about the age of 6.5. At the peak of the rise, at age 12, it is increasing in weight about four times as fast as is the body as a whole.[19] After 12, the rate rapidly falls again, by age 20 being only a little more rapid than that of other body tissues. The penis also shows a spurt of growth early in adolescence, beginning about the time of the first appearance of pubic hair.[20] In the female, the weight of the ovaries shows a pattern of growth very like that of the testis, except that the spurt of increase in weight is less marked.[19] With the increase in rapidity of growth and the increased amount of tissue, there is increased hormonal activity, illustrated most clearly by a rise in basal metabolic rate, changes in blood pressure, and in other bodily functions.*

With these changes taking place in the body size and form, themselves important in the adjustment of the individual in his group as we have already seen, there is an upsurge and change in sex interest and activity taking place, introducing another area in which the healthy personality must achieve adjustment. In the male, sexual activity is almost always directly concerned with the primary sex organs themselves; sex and sex acts are clearly recognized as such. In girls, this may or may not be the case. It can hardly be doubted that two girls who whisper to each other as they walk down the street, with their arms about each other's shoulders, are having an experience of some sexual significance; the significance is probably neither less nor greater than would be the case if they were two boys. The boys, however, because of the localized character of their sexual feelings, might well develop the experience into a genital one of some sort. The girl, in our society, is allowed to satisfy this generalized sexual urge, while ordinarily the male is not allowed any socialized type of sexual outlet with his own sex. As Campbell has pointed out,[7] early in adolescence there is a tendency for the sexes to avoid touching one another. Girls, however, are allowed to touch each other freely; slumber parties are a typical sort of activity throughout the period of adolescence for girls. The camping out and overnight hikes of boys are the subject of more formal planning and adult supervision and do not seem to be the equivalent of girls' slumber parties. In the American culture, at least, the latter type of activity among boys would encounter parental and community suspicion in many instances, and would be discouraged. The girl is able to satisfy a less localized and more vague sexual drive by general physical and psychological contacts with her own sex, while the boy usually satisfies his more powerful sexual urge through a single channel or at least a smaller number of channels.

Kinsey notes that females have a much slower sexual pace than males in adolescence and that the peak of sexual activity in women is not reached until in the thirties. He has suggested that in the male one can speak accurately of "sex drive," while in the female a more appropriate designation would be "social drive" until the sex act with orgasm be-

* These data are conveniently collected in Shuttleworth.[9]

comes a fixed pattern.[21] This pattern is never achieved by a considerable proportion of women, as will be discussed in a later section on sexual adjustment in marriage.

Orgasm is early established as the one satisfactory means of satisfying the sex drive in males. It may be established through the appearance of the spontaneous discharge of semen during sleep. Nocturnal emissions are generally accompanied by sexual dreams that include orgasm or high sexual excitement in their content. Kinsey finds that 83 per cent of the male population ultimately has nocturnal emissions, the percentage being higher in those groups of the population in which other types of outlet are less practiced. The point is that this "physiological," unconscious outlet in the male is concerned with the sex act and that orgasm is an integral part of the function. The female also has nocturnal orgasms, usually with accompanying dreams, though the percentage of women having such dreams is almost twice as high as that of women who proceed on to orgasm in sleep.[22] The conclusion is that in the male, sex and orgasm, sex and the primary sex organs are more inevitably related than in the female, where sex urges are more general and are satisfied in less directly sexually oriented practices. It seems likely that there are physiological as well as cultural reasons for this.

Masturbation or autoeroticism is an extremely common practice in both sexes. In males, it occurs in over 90 per cent by the time they reach maturity. The practice may be well established before ejaculation is possible. It takes on much greater significance to the individual when ejaculation accompanies self-induced orgasm. The act occurs more frequently during and after puberty than before. It is usually one of simple manual stimulation of the penis but may be much more elaborate. It is practiced, usually, until intercourse replaces it. This replacement may be early or late, depending on cultural, economic, and other factors. In some cases masturbation continues until replaced by marital relations and recurs when these are interrupted. It is not unusual for it to continue as another type of sexual outlet in married men, even when marital relations are satisfying.[21]

Masturbation is frequently accompanied by fantasies, usually of sexual intercourse, but may include daydreams of other types as well, depending on previous sexual experience. If intercourse is the most satisfactory outlet, the fantasies are likely to be of the woman involved and of a particular act with her. If masturbation has been the more satisfactory outlet, some previous, highly pleasurable occasion may occupy consciousness during later acts. Animal intercourse may be the fantasy, and in homosexually experienced or oriented males homosexual fantasies may prevail. While these fantasies are present, the pleasurable sensations of orgasm are basic and are the primary reason males masturbate. The fantasies may be the stimulus for masturbation, but they are also means of increasing the pleasure. At times they are a means of justifying the act, particularly when they are of sexual intercourse.

Colloquial names for masturbation as used by adults in authority usually imply that the practice is deplorable and immoral. The word "masturbation" should be used in dealing with the subject, since it has, because of its scientific standing, less of the accusing note than "self-abuse," "playing with yourself," or "self-pollution." The time is largely past when this moral condemnation of masturbation is furthered by informed professional people, but it is still heavily propagandized by advertisements in the pulp magazines. The latter certainly express the popular view more accurately than the former. There can be little doubt that the common opinion that masturbation is physically and mentally harmful, particularly in males, is still widely prevalent and that it is an important factor in arousing anxiety in adolescents. It is an additional driving force for males toward the establishment of heterosexual patterns. Of course, it also sells the quacks' theories and medicines for the control of the practice.

The Judaeo-Christian tradition and some other religious systems as well have tended to the belief that the primary purpose of sexual acts is reproduction. This belief is very deeply ingrained in many cultures; indeed, it extends far beyond formalized religious beliefs into folklore. As has been pointed out before, folklore can hardly be regarded as other than the wisdom as well as the fantasy of the culture and as such it is worthy of respect, though it is recognized that there is often inherent in it a tremendous resistance to change even in the face of obvious new scientific facts. This "cultural lag" of moral concepts in the case of attitudes toward masturbation must be recognized. It is not lightly to be tossed aside as old-fashioned and outgrown by a more "civilized" age. Too great pressure against masturbation has been credited with forcing the idea of it into the minds of adolescents, but there is little doubt that a permissive and tolerant attitude would have the same effect, though perhaps on different individuals. It is possible that neither attitude is quantitatively very important in relation to the constitutionally determined forces to be dealt with. The man who has to face the question before an audience, of whatever age, will have to respect as a fact the prejudices of the general public against masturbation. He will have to direct people from obviously cruel and patently ineffective prohibitions to some more generous and experience-determined viewpoint. An attitude of sympathetic guidance is the aim; this will usually have to be in terms of "control," or the major part of the audience will reject the concept entirely. It can be said definitely that there are no scientific data to support the assumptions that insanity, sallow skin, pimples, or any of the other ills popularly ascribed to masturbation are in any direct way related to it.

The anxiety and self-depreciation that males go through because of masturbation which they want to but cannot completely control is considerable. As noted above, Fleege found two-thirds of high school boys concerned about the "purity" of their lives; this probably was a concern about masturbation in many cases. The pattern is extremely common. The assumption is easily made that it is good mental hygiene to relieve this anxiety and self-depreciation and that this should be done by a revision of popular concepts about masturbation. It is well to recognize and, perhaps, to publicize that masturbation in males is a part of normal sexual development, that the management of it is a matter of concern to most adolescents, and that the individual need not feel that he is different from others and a sinner because he occasionally indulges. Condemnation of masturbation should not force adolescent males to injudicious intercourse and the social and health problems that may follow in its wake.

Whereas most males have opportunity to learn about masturbation from other males, this is much less likely to be the case in females, who talk much less among themselves of sexual activities.[22] About 60 per cent of all females masturbate at some time during their lives, the percentage reaching orgasm being a little less. Prepubertal masturbation may be more common in the female than the male, though Kinsey's published data on the male is less complete than on the female. As in all other sexual activity the rise in percentages of females masturbating is far less precipitous than in the male. There is considerably less guilt feeling and worry about masturbation in the female than in the male, only 47 percent of Kinsey's sample of females showing worry. Perhaps this is because the female has no ejaculation; most religious systems place a high value on the ejaculate, and it is frequently referred to in terms of its equivalent in blood (with tremendous exaggerations) or a "life fluid." The similarities and contrasts between masturbation in males and females are conveniently tabulated in Kinsey.[22]

Moral codes that approve sexual relations only for the procreation of children, or the satisfaction of the need of the marital partners for emotional and physical response to each other, are dominant in many areas in our culture. There are, also, areas where they do not hold, but these subcultures are small and not influential and are usually of lower educational status than the country as a whole.[23,24] The idea of rigid control of sex impulses before marriage is supported by law, but the laws are poorly enforced. There were many who argued that the prohibition law in the United States should be repealed because it was unenforceable, but the laws against sex activity outside marriage, though subject to the same deficiencies, are not questioned in this fashion. Mankind appears to be satisfied to encode what it considers ideal, but to live by quite another pattern. It calls the pattern wrong, yet by not attempting strongly to change it, tacitly states that it is right. This situation, like the prevailing attitude toward masturbation, is so contradictory that it makes clear-cut action extremely difficult. The psychology of man is not well enough understood in these areas to justify any single line of attack. A propaganda approach is certainly not to be considered. The conflicting modes of action and thinking in our culture represent values too nebulous yet too important to be impudently dealt with. In so controversial a field as the control of premarital sexual relations, and with no scientific information available to indicate the goal, it is certainly inadvisable to initiate a public health program that would have to be based entirely on opinion unsupported by demonstrable fact.

Granted that in some cultures the ideal of the rigid control of nonmarital sex outlets remains established, how great is the deviation from this ideal in actual living? Masturbation has been discussed as extremely common among males. Premarital and extramarital intercourse are also common. Leiby and Larimore, studying an army population, found by relatively simple questionnaire methods that 65 per cent of white and 76 per cent of Negro soldiers admitted extramarital sexual experiences. Analysis of these data by religious group membership indicated that the practice among Jews was somewhat less than among Catholics and Protestants, but that the latter two groups were equally involved. Single men admitted premarital intercourse in 81 per cent, married men extramarital intercourse in 51 per cent of those questioned. The practice was found to be consistently lower the higher the education of the group in question. For white soldiers, the figure for those with less than eighth-grade education was 70 per cent; for the college-educated men, 57 per cent. According to this study, the rate for white males was 121.1 extramarital sexual experiences per 1,000 men per week; for Negroes, 214.0.[25] Incidentally, men in the armed services are usually less active sexually than they are when civilians.[21]

Kinsey reports that 89.9 per cent of the unmarried male population of eighth-grade education or less have had sex relations by age 25; for college males the percentage is less, 64.4 per cent. For females the proportion in both these educational groups is smaller but the direction is reversed—26 per cent of the less well educated group having had premarital coitus and 39 per cent of college women. Homosexuality occurs to some extent in 50 per cent of all males, 4 per cent being exclusively homosexual in form of sex outlet; the corresponding figures for the female are about half as large.

Frequency of sexual outlet in the male from adolescence to age 30 was 3.3 per week; for the female, markedly less. The rate of outlet tends to begin to fall in the male after the late teens; in the female it rises to age 35, then falls only very gradually. One of the most remarkable of Kinsey's findings is the extreme variability of sexual functioning in human beings. He shows that some are many thousands of times as active sexually as others.[21] With such enormous individual variation it again seems pertinent to state the dangers of any effort under public health or other auspices to influence this activity one way or another. There is no scientific basis on which to set an aim; there are too many patterns that appear biologically and socially successful. On the other hand, recognition of the tremendous range of what must be considered "normal" may well have some preventive value. Many persons suffer from the fear that they are "sexual perverts" because of an occasional homosexual or other type of sexual outlet not within the "accepted" code. Many married couples, Kinsey estimates as high as 60 per cent in those who have attended college, make use of mouth genital stimulation in their sexual life together. Many of these couples feel guilt about the practice which might well be relieved if the range of normal sex activities were better known. Some of the cruel legal punishments dealt out to sex "perverts" might well be modified if our laws could be reconciled somewhat with what is apparently biologically tolerable.

The meaning of such findings as these points again to the fact that in the sex aspect of mental hygiene attention must be paid not only to what people do but also to the more or less fixed attitudes toward what is done. The fact that half of all men have some homosexual outlet during their lives does not necessarily justify cessation of all efforts directed toward the suppression of homosexuality. Such a conclusion would challenge, with very little evidence, concepts that may be the result of accumulated wisdom, the evidence for which we do not know and the effect of the abolition of which we cannot prognosticate. Caution and individualization in the field of the mental hygiene of the sex life seem the attitude of choice so far as public health is concerned. On the other hand, recognition of human variability may well increase tolerance to the point where individual sex offenders are studied and dealt with more rationally and with less of the cruelty born of unrecognized prejudice and incomplete knowledge.

The data already given indicate that patterns of behavior in the male and female are significantly different at many points. Kinsey's studies support Davis's earlier findings that orgasm has occurred in only a little more than half of all women by the age of 20, whereas the corresponding figure in men approaches 100 per cent.[25] One of the most interesting facts that Kinsey finds is that the variation of sexual behavior between different social classes is less in the female than the male. The female has often been called the carrier of the culture and the stabilizer of cultural patterns. It is interesting to speculate about the relationship the apparent greater uniformity of female sexual activity has to these observations. "The Colonel's lady and Judy O'Grady are sisters under the skin" may show poetic insight into the biologic facts.

The expression of affection between girls is accepted as "normal," whereas a similar expression between males is considered unsuitable in our culture. Davis finds that these expressions go on to actual sex play in 25 to 30 per cent of the unmarried women in her group.[26] This finding, as well as the greatly reduced incidence of homosexuality in all married groups studied by others, is confirmed by Kinsey. Female homosexuality appears to be less often associated with disturbing social activity than the same trend in males. Women homosexuals appear to be more rarely promiscuous, and their relations are more often of a man-and-wife character than male homosexual partnerships. It also seems likely that distinctly homosexual activity in adolescence less often presages a settling of sexual drive in that direction than is the case in men.

Premarital intercourse in females is much less prevalent than in males, possibly because the sex drive can so frequently be satisfied without orgasm and because sex feelings are not exclusively genitally centered. In working with adolescent girls arraigned in juvenile court because of promiscuous intercourse, one is impressed by the fact that the experience is rarely entered into for personal pleasure; it is, rather, simply an accommodation to some male. Frequently the act appears to mean very little to the girl. The problem of stopping the activity of such a girl is largely one of interfering with opportunity. It is remarkable how rarely the girl rebels because the sex outlet with men is cut off. In the court setting, of course, the law dictates that the activity shall be stopped. When one considers the social results in terms of illegitimate children to be born to an immature mother and cared for by an adolescent girl and with no male parent, the modification of the activity in these girls seems justified. It is difficult, however, to escape the conclusion that it is a matter of accident that one girl is "caught." It is clear that the promiscuous intercourse for which she was apprehended is actually so common in her social setting that her apprehension and detention cannot possibly have any effect in the large picture. Perhaps the suppression demonstrated in the few cases is somewhat effective in preventing an activity that is not very highly valued in the female of this age in any case. The social, psychological, and psychiatric reasons for delinquency in the male appear to result in violation of laws protecting person or property, while in the female they lead to flaunting laws and customs relating to sexual activity.

The onset of menstruation is evidence to the girl of the changes within her. It is an event marked by the external discharge that all may see unless proper means of caring for it are practiced. Its appearance, whether frightening or not, may certainly prove embarrassing to the unprepared adolescent girl. In spite of the obvious reasons for preparing girls for the onset of menstrual bleeding, most studies indicate that a large number of females in our culture are allowed to go through the menarche without any anticipatory guidance. Landis reports that a third of his 153 highly selected "normal" women had "little or no preparation for menstruation." [27] Deutsch, agreeing that lack of preparation for menstruation is common in girls, doubts that this is always the fault of the environment. She ascribes it, in some cases at least, to the girl's repression of her knowledge, leading to denial that she ever received it.[28]

Wootten found that 45 per cent of her 56 carefully studied pregnant women had no memory of knowledge of menstruation before it occurred to them.[29] Many of them believed they had been injured in some way or entertained other anxious fantasies. These are well illustrated in Rogers's analysis of the questions asked about this function by women enrolled in classes for instruction.[30] Although pointing out that there are many opportunities for most girls to learn of menstruation in our culture—it is a common topic of the whispering period—Deutsch elaborates at some length on the fact that it is peculiarly difficult for mothers to talk to their daughters about it. They may prefer that the younger sister get the knowledge from an older sister. A mother rarely allows a daughter to observe that she herself menstruates, though the daughter frequently seems to know, however vaguely, and recognize the fact.

Menstruation is subject to many disorders, the most common being absence of periods and pain during periods. The fact that the periodicity is rarely regular in the first few years after menarche [31] gives opportunity for fears and fantasies of pregnancy and of diseases or abnormality. The former fears are sometimes enhanced by the parent who warns the daughter of the possibility of pregnancy after the first menstrual period. Lacking specific knowledge of the act of intercourse, the girl may imagine pregnancy as originating from a kiss, the use of a bathroom, etc. Naïve as these fears are, they are nevertheless prevalent and genuine, though they may be based on the repression of capacity to gain knowledge easily available. Under these circumstances the girl may suffer unnecessary tensions which, at least to some extent, knowledge can relieve.

Pain with the menses may be related to anatomical or physiological malfunction not related to psychic processes, but the opposite and mixed situations are probably more common. It would appear that this is distinctly a problem for individual management. Yet there are some factors that might, if taught properly to groups, modify the prevalence and severity of menstrual disorders. Unsupported clinical impressions are notoriously unreliable in such questions, but it appears that there is now less dysmenorrhea than was the case a generation ago. This may be the result of the greater freedom women have now. It may be due to the fact that the efficient sanitary pad has replaced the difficult and tedious methods of handling the flow that then were prevalent. It may be that more women expected to be "sick" then, whereas now they expect to function with reasonable regularity, menstruating or not. No study has appeared on the subject, but it would be interesting to know whether folk terms for menstruation have changed over the years. The terms now used—"the curse," "falling off the roof," etc.,—indicate a sort of good-natured tolerance for an inconvenience. Benedeck and Rubenstein have shown that there is a relationship between the menstrual function and the character of dreams. This probably indicates an effect on psychosexual attitudes during the waking state as well.[32]

It was stressed earlier that the tremendous variation in age of onset of all the pubertal changes and the social consequences thereof might well be included in programs of sex education. It would appear that a clear statement of the function of menstruation might be included also. The teaching of the "danger" of pregnancy can probably be delayed until menstruation is established, allowing the two to come as separate pieces of information, since there appears to be a period of adolescent sterility of approximately 2 years between menarche and the possibility of pregnancy occurring.[33] It is clear that any program to be devised now would have to be experimental and that caution rather than an uncritical, all-out type of attack would be advisable. Such programs should be worked out in collaboration with a health council including clergymen, educators, scoutmasters, school counselors, and, of course, representative parents. The present tendency is to include such information as incidental to larger courses in social hygiene which include broader information on homemaking and community responsibility.[34] While this is, in general, to be encouraged, care should be taken that a broadened aim is not used as an excuse for neglecting relatively specific information concerning menstruation. It should also be recognized that education concerning menstruation must be given no later than the fourth grade if it is to precede the onset of the function, while the type of information with which it is usually combined comes more appropriately in the secondary school years. There are numerous well-written pamphlets and other aids available for education concerning the menstrual function, many of them prepared by commercial firms producing materials needed in the social management of the function.

ADOLESCENT PERSONALITY

The personality of the adolescent has been the subject of much writing and comment, but too little of what can be considered critical research has been done. Tryon investigated the problem by trying to discover how adolescents evaluated certain traits in each other. The method dictated what traits were evaluated; the children were not free to record traits of their own invention. On the other hand, the range of items used in the test was broad and inclusive, and the results are interesting. Boys of 12 were found to have a tendency "to emphasize the desirability of activity of any sort; to prefer aggressiveness, boisterousness, and unkemptness to submissiveness, reserve, and tidiness; to appreciate certain 'feminine' components if associated in the individual with the 'masculine' qualities; to respect above all competence in group games." By the age of 15, however, the pattern of desirable traits in the eyes of the boys is slightly different.

> Attributes which are frequently considered "masculine," such as skill in games, fearlessness, and self-assertion, continue to be important determiners of prestige for the 15-year-old boy. However, equal emphasis is placed on personableness and social ease and poise in heterosexual situations. Cheerfulness and a sense of humor are important, but boisterousness and hyperactivity are regarded as rather childish and unimportant.[35]

The factor of boisterousness has, perhaps, been evaluated more in terms of skill than in terms of mere movement; controlled management of social situations has become more important than obstreperous neglect of clothing and personal neatness.

The patterns for girls obtained by the same techniques are also of interest. Tryon's summary for 12-year-old girls is as follows: "The qualities most indicative of prestige for the girl at this age are neat, attractive appearance; friendly but rather demure and docile social manner; quiet good humor; and controlled behavior conforming to adult standards. A certain amount of tomboyishness is acceptable, but raucous, noisy activity is not." With such a contrast between their ideals for personality, is it any wonder that at 12 boys and girls tend to separate rather than play together? By 15, two patterns of prestige-gaining traits are apparent. "Prestige for these older girls is achieved through two major channels, either through buoyant, rather aggressive good fellowship with both boys and girls or through sophisticated, glamorous qualities which attract the boys.[35] It would be interesting to correlate these two channels with extent of sexual development in the individual girls questioned. There is a curious contrast in many cultures between the fact that secondary sex characteristics and social skills appear to develop more rapidly in girls than in boys and the fact that, so far as actual primary sex function is concerned, boys are much more developed than girls of the same chronological age.

The change of values for personality traits during adolescence appears to be in the direction of more tolerance for variability between individuals toward the close of the period. Early adolescents are likely to be very insistent on being like the gang in speech, dress, manner, hours, and even political enthusiasms. In early adolescence athletic skills are likely to be all-important, but later intellectual brilliance, musical and graphic-art talent, and skill in debate are also valued traits. It has been pointed out that schools have not been able to build a social system within their subculture that fosters high valuation of mechanical skills, though some progress is being made in this direction. Jones's excellent longitudinal study shows the value changes that occurred in a boy's own evaluation of himself and of his classmates as he progressed through the adolescent years.[36]

RELATIONSHIP TO PARENTS

The adolescent is attempting to abolish the dependent relationship he has had with his parents for many years and in doing so he swings widely—and wildly—between "proper" respect for parental opinion and complete disregard for it. With the broader knowledge of people he has gained since he came under the influence of teachers and has made investigations in the homes of his friends, he sees his parent more objectively and has trouble with the Biblical dictum "honor thy father and thy mother." The pain that an adolescent feels when he finds that he cannot completely carry out this dictum may be exquisite. The delinquent adolescent, for example, will frequently deny his mother's obvious prostitution or mitigate his father's alcoholism. Rather than face the fact that his parents are hardly worthy of his love and respect, he becomes unable to interpret logically the facts that are only too apparent to the more objective person. With perhaps less intensity this same sort of conflict exists when the child sees more objectively than before inconsistency, irritability, or inefficiency on the part of his parents. This conflict may be severe enough, as it frequently is in juvenile delinquents, to result in antisocial behavior of real significance. On the other hand, the difficulty may be confined to the home, where it appears as flippant, supercilious disobedience, sullen uncooperativeness, or temper outbursts of more or less severity.* This conflict of dependence versus independence has many different facets touching almost every area of life in the home. When he is considered by society adult enough to drive a car, he still has to "demean" himself by asking his father to use it. He is encouraged to express his maturity by selecting and buying his own clothing, but he asks for the money to buy it. It is perhaps this conflict that makes adolescent males, in particular, so anxious to earn money. This is a common trait and one that has been, perhaps too often, thwarted by child labor laws that confine to very narrow limits what young men—even those who are very husky so far as physical development is concerned—may do. The allowance idea of defining a range of spending and freedom for the adolescent, in money as well as in nights out, time of coming in, etc., was invented to relieve the child of too frequent confrontations with the dependence that he is outgrowing and against which he struggles. Because the method defines consistent limits within which the adolescent can exercise decision and have freedom, it is generally a good one. The parent who can restrain himself from pressing into these areas of freedom after they have been granted is greatly appreciated by the adolescent. In general, he stands a better chance of remaining a counselor of his child, though probably not a confidant, since no older person is likely to be given that status.

The problem of emancipation for the adolescent is a family problem. The parent is the emancipator; it is he or she who must allow the child to grow into adulthood. The changing relation presents its conflicts and stresses to the parents as well as to the child. The parents

* Some of these patterns are seen in the case recorded on pages 360–365.

may fall into exaggerated responses almost as uncontrolled as those of the child and frequently no more clearly understood by the parent than the adolescents' are by themselves. There are several people living through the emancipation of the child, all of whom may be showing strain by inappropriate or extreme emotional reactions, each playing upon the other.

RELATION WITH OTHER ADULTS

The relation of the adolescent to his teachers is quite different from that with his parents. It is an interesting fact that, while there are relatively few books on how parents can furnish guidance to their adolescent children (as contrasted with the number on the management of the preschool child, for example), there is a large literature on the guidance of adolescents for teachers and other specialists in this field. This appears to indicate cultural acceptance of the different positions of the parent and an unrelated counselor. The educator has no conflict about the child's acquiring independence and self-reliance; this is the aim of education. The parent, however, may have deep regrets at losing his child's earlier dependence upon him. The teacher does not demand personal affection of the adolescent, whereas the parent is likely to have this in mind as a goal in dealing with his child. The teacher asks—so far as surface appearances are concerned, at least—only that the child give intelligent attention to problems, though the actual effectiveness of the counseling is recognized to depend upon a manipulation of both ideas and feelings. The educator's entree is usually on the level of plans and goals; the parent's relation is on the basis of daily behavior and conduct.

These considerations have perhaps been effective in making the growth of school counseling so rapid and the program so complete. There are other broader cultural reasons, to be sure, not the least of which is the complicated pattern of our industrial civilization which has made job placement so highly technical a procedure.

This partial transfer of guidance of the adolescent from the home to the educator has been criticized as being damaging to the child-parent relationship; it is often said that the place for children of any age to get advice and guidance is in the home. This is an attractive argument that is used whenever there is an educational effort that threatens to invade the emotional life of the child, whether it be the establishment of nursery schools or of high school guidance programs. It invariably arises in connection with sex education. The answer is that the home too often does not do the necessary job and that the aim of the program is not the supplanting of the home and its functions, but a cooperative effort directed toward a desirable goal. The home is being aided in the adjustment of the child by many types of technical personnel. Because of the emotional conflicts for parent and child concerned with emancipation from the home, outside technical help in maintaining healthy adjustment of the adolescent during this period seems desirable and has proved in practice to be effective.

The aim of educators in counseling is not merely the presenting of facts to the child. The ideal is "to obtain a full understanding of each student in order to adjust educational offerings to his needs so that he may be prepared for a role wherein highest achievement and satisfaction may be realized." [37] Quoting further:

> From this point of view, guidance and education are intimately related. As a matter of fact, educational guidance, vocational guidance, and all other desirable types of guidance are merely different phases of a single program whose purpose is to build the happiest and most fully integrated personality possible upon the foundation with which nature and previous experience have provided the individual.[38]

This ideal is certainly one that the mental hygienist can hardly take exception to. Educational and vocational guidance, counseling with the pupil as to what sort of courses he should take in school and what sort of work he should prepare for, are perhaps the most highly developed nonmedical types of counseling in school systems. Integral in these types of guidance is the use of tests—intelligence and aptitude tests primarily, but some "personality" tests also. Intelligence tests have already been discussed; their application at this level is clear. It is known, for example, that various types of work require various levels of intelligence. It is futile for a child with a known I.Q. of 80 to hope to be a physician, since it is impossible for him to gain the necessary knowledge to achieve his end. Frustration and unhappiness may well result from his inevitable failure. Similarly, it is seldom wise to leave undisturbed the conclusion of the highly intelligent girl that she wants to be a cashier. She will probably be unhappy at the job which does not use her capacities fully. She needs a higher goal.[39] Aptitude testing has the aim of avoiding maladaptations in a similar fashion, though the techniques are less well established and reliable than those of intelligence testing. Nevertheless, the tests can discover special aptitudes and lack of them and thus avoid placing the subject in frustrating circumstances. Most personality tests, in their present state of development, are not dependable for guidance, except in the hands of a few highly trained and experienced workers. They are hardly useful in programs involving large numbers of people.

Testing of whatever sort is not the end of guidance but only the beginning. The problem is to influence the adolescent and, frequently, his parents to take into consideration the findings of the counselor. Nor are test results the only findings to be considered. A plodding, persistent person with secure background and an even tenor emotionally may be able to accomplish a good deal more educationally and vocationally than a more intelligent but less stable person. The boy who comes from a home of high educational standards will have to have a different sort of a job than one who will equal his family regardless of what level of work he takes up. Guidance is based on a multiplicity of factors, of which tests are but one. Its aim is the mobilization of the facts with the subject and a collaborative consideration of them leading to a conclusion that is the subject's, though influenced by the facts marshaled and by the emotional relationship with the counselor.

The adolescent's relationship to the teacher or counselor may become a "crush," a falling in love with him or her. Such crushes are not uncommon in either sex. The emotional force they possess may be very great. It would appear to arise from three main sources. First, there is the affection for the parent, unsatisfied at home because of the problems concerned with freedom there; second, the force of emotion that is likely to well up when two people work together over the personal problems of one of them; and finally the idealized sort of love relationship of which adolescents are capable. Such crushes can be embarrassing to the adult so idolized; fortunately they are not likely to last long.[16]

The social groupings of boys and girls at this period are most interesting. Boys tend to have larger numbers of friends than girls, and their friendships are likely to be less intense.[40] Whether this is culturally determined as a response to the fear of male homosexual tendencies to which our culture reacts so violently, or whether it represents a constitutional difference between the sexes is not determined. Group loyalties appear to be stronger in males than in females of this age.

Boys' societies are usually more successful than girls', probably for this reason. Girl Scouts are not so numerous as Boy Scouts, and troops of the former have, as a rule, shorter lives. Toward the end of the period of adolescence, DeMolay, Hi-Y, and other types of groups become established. From these the male tends to graduate to the permanent fraternal organizations of the adult years. Girls seem less able to form lasting groups in such organizations; they are likely to break up into small cliques, rather than remain in solid, large-group efforts. This may, of course, be secondary to the fact that the male is, in most cultures, granted the position of leadership in the social activities of the family.

The success of the Boy Scouts of America * in many cultures makes it reasonable to assume that the programs include principles and practices that satisfy the needs of the adolescent in large degree. The organization makes use of the opportunity offered adult leaders not involved in the home relationships of the boys. Offering a stable organization, it satisfies the boy's need for a larger group of friends. The fact that it has high ethical and religious aims is no less important. The tendency of the adolescent male—the trait is present in the female also but probably not so strongly—to adhere to an idealistic vision of the world and strive for conduct that will bring the vision into being appears fundamental in the psychology of adolescence. The glorification of motherhood and all womanhood is a part of the general ethical ideal; it serves a purpose in helping control the primary sexual pattern of the male. This technique of controlling sexual activity of the male is typical of adult fraternal organizations also. Boy scouting also appeals to the adolescent male's devotion to health and bodily strength. It offers active games, hikes, and opportunity to acquire skills. It awards advancement in status and prestige for the completion of certain tasks that require learning as well as physical activity. In capitalizing on the boy's desire for physical skill the organization meets a basic need directly. It also takes the position that physical activity is a means of making the sexual urge somewhat easier to control. This concept, usually expressed as "sublimation," is that the expenditure of physical and psychological energies will rob sex desires of some of their force. Sublimation is particularly effective, according to ancient religious tenets, when the expenditure is in service to others on a rather idealistic plane. Kinsey finds no evidence that sublimation is effective in his cases and doubts that the concept is defensible scientifically.[21]

From the success of organizations of male adolescents that typically feature religion, high ethical standards of helpfulness to others, the glorification of womanhood, loyalty, physical skills, and knowledge, these may be considered important features of the thinking of the male adolescent. The fact that such groups usually have more or less complicated, rather mystical rituals indicates another trait of the adolescent. Ethical and religious beliefs learned as rote prayers or recitations

* The Boy Scout movement is the largest of several similar organizations and is used as typical of the group.

at preschool or school age now take on meanings and are subjects for reverie.

Reverie is itself a prominent feature of the period in both boys and girls. Both may daydream of careers and high success. In boys this is more likely to be success in work; in girls, a satisfactory love relationship and a home.

The loyalty factor in group relationships of adolescents is important. In the "normal" situation this loyalty will be to the group goals as indicated above; this tendency may be "perverted" so that the loyalty is to a gang with antisocial aims such as robbery. This pattern which becomes established, described by Jenkins and Hewitt under the name "socialized delinquent," appears to be dependent upon certain traumatic environmental factors.[41] The perverted loyalty makes the delinquent showing it particularly difficult to readjust, since it has some ethical features that are attractive and valuable in society. In fact, the boy himself is frequently attractive; witness the popularity of the Dead End Kids of the movies a few years ago. The dilemma these boys pose for the person charged with their treatment is not an easy one.

JUVENILE DELINQUENCY

The prevention and treatment of juvenile delinquency was the goal of the first organized efforts in child psychiatry and has always been a prominent goal in the work of guidance clinics. In spite of the general impression that individual treatment of juvenile offenders leads to success, there is little evidence to support this view. The only large and controlled experiment in attempting to change by individual counseling methods the pattern of children considered to be predelinquent led to the conclusion that such treatment is, on the whole, ineffective.[42] It would appear that the nontreated controls improved as much as did the counseled cases. Other work has indicated that maturational factors may be more important than treatment factors in the prevention of delinquency.[43] On the other hand, Shaw has shown that organized efforts to change attitudes and to increase activities of a nondelinquent, recreational type are successful in prevention to a significant extent.[44] The environmental factors in the production of delinquency are so powerful that the Gluecks have been able to construct a prediction scale for the appearance of delinquency.[45] The elements of the scale have to do with the health of the child involved, the marital status and happiness of the parents, socioeconomic level, community standards, and the like.

In general, there may be said to be three types of delinquency, though none ever appears in pure culture and usually factors of all three may be found in every case. The first type is "normal delinquency" in which behavior is within the range of usual activity for the subculture but is intolerable to the classes that make and enforce the laws. In the subcultures that produce the largest proportion of delinquency, delinquent patterns are a part of a way of life for the majority of the children. Under these conditions, delinquency does not indicate individual pathology. Treatment will consist mainly of inculcating respect for the mores of another subculture, that which controls law enforcement. In most institutions for the treatment of juvenile delinquents the setting is one of coercion, which is not conducive to attitude changing—particularly in adolescence, when all authority is likely to be summarily rejected. The irreconcilability between the need for an ideal learning situation and the restrictions necessary for the protection of the public is the dilemma of the institution for the care and treatment of juvenile delinquents. The problem presents challenging research opportunities.

The second type of delinquent is the neurotic child who attempts to act out his conflict in aggressive attempts to injure the social system, which he realizes—however vaguely—has somehow put him in a personally intolerable situation. This is probably the type of delinquent who profits most by intensive psychiatric treatment. The proportion of delinquents predominantly of this type is unknown, but it is probably not as large as the first group.

The final type of delinquency is that which appears in children who are emotionally deprived by neglect in early childhood and have lost the capacity to relate emotionally to others or to any social system (see Chap. 11, page 191). According to present theory, these cases are untreatable. Although many workers believe there are no untreatable cases of delinquency, it is wise to keep this group of fundamentally damaged children in mind. It can serve as a corrective to the over-optimistic and unrealistic estimates of possible success under ideal conditions that are frequently and irresponsibly made by enthusiasts for one or another treatment method. In many cases, the increasing tendency to social conformity that accompanies the aging process appears to be the fundamental reason for success, and it is probable that treatment efforts are most successful in so far as they speed up this maturational process, which has been delayed by earlier mistreatment or other type of damage.

SUMMARY

Adolescence is the period between the beginning of the pubertal growth spurt and the arrival of the individual at a level of maturity at which he is ready to enter upon courtship with the aim of establishing his own home. It includes massive endocrinological changes reflected in physiological changes that take place about 2 years earlier in the female than in the male. Sexually, the male is largely confined to the primary sex organs and orgasm for satisfaction of this urge; the female is less genitally centered, and more general sensual experiences appear to satisfy the less clearly recognized sexual urges. There is tremendous variation in the age of onset of the changes incident to puberty in different individuals; this variation is highly important in the social adjustment of the individual. Group loyalties are more typical of the male; intensive friendships, of the female. The struggle for emancipation from the home makes the child-parent relationship tend to be strained and distant; neutral, more objective teachers and group leaders are frequently more readily acceptable as counselors than parents. Religious and ethical considerations are important in the preoccupations of adolescents and are useful in the management of their behavior. Juvenile delinquency is a complicated and difficult social issue involving deep-seated social and individual problems not to be easily solved by any single method but requiring consistent, thoughtful work and research.

The public health officer may capitalize on the adolescent's interest in physical condition in the teaching of health rules and in establishing health habits. Sex education should include the interpersonal implications of the timing of pubertal changes. It is necessary to respect the dicta of the culture as regards sex practices of adolescents. The dilemma presented by the wide gap between the encoded ideal of the culture and actual practices encountered would appear to indicate great caution in devising programs of sex education. Knowledge of what the actual practices are may well serve to make the health officer more objective and tolerant in his estimation of sex delinquents. The tendency to form loyal groups with high ethical ideals offers an opportunity to the health officer to use groups in campaigns designed to "help" the community.

REFERENCES

1. Herbert, F. H.: "Kiss and Tell," Dramatists' Play Service, New York, 1943.
2. A Date with Judy, Henry Aldrich, etc. (radio and television programs).
3. Unpublished analyses of data of the 1936 survey of the Eastern Health District of Baltimore, Md.
4. Fleege, U. H.: *Self-revelation of the Adolescent Boy,* The Bruce Publishing Company, Milwaukee, 1945.
5. Knoebler, M.: *Self-revelation of the Adolescent Girl,* The Bruce Publishing Company, Milwaukee, 1936.
6. Kanner, L.: *Child Psychiatry,* 1st ed., Charles C Thomas, Publisher, Spring-

field, Ill., 1935; quoting H. Ruppert, *Aufbau der Welt des Jugendlichen,* Leipzig, 1931.

7. Campbell, E. H.: "The Social-Sexual Development of Children," *Genet. Psychol. Monogr.* 21:(4) (1939).

8. Furfey, P. H.: "Case Studies in Developmental Age," *Am. J. Orthopsychiat.* 1:292–297 (1931).

9. Shuttleworth, F.: "*The Adolescent Period,*" Monograph of the Society for Research in Child Development 3 (3), ser. 16, Society for Research in Child Development, Washington, 1938.

10. Bryan, A. H., and B. G. Greenberg: "Methodology in the Study of Physical Measurements of School Children," part II, *Human Biol.* 24:117–143 (1952).

11. Gould, H. N., and M. R. Gould: "Age of First Menstruation in Mothers and Daughters," *J.A.M.A.* 98:1349–1352 (1932).

12. Priesel, R., and R. Wagner: "Gesetz Mässigkeiten in Auftreten der extragenitalen secundären Geschlechtsmerkmule bei Mädchen," *Ztschr. f. Konstitutionslehre* 15:333–352 (1930).

13. Crampton, C. W.: "Anatomical or Physiological Age versus Chronological Age," *Pediatrics* 20:341–355 (1908).

14. Dimock, H. S.: "Research in Adolescence," *Child Development* 6:177–195 (1935).

15. Pedry, C. P.: *A Study of Voice Changes in Boys between the Ages of Eleven and Sixteen,* Research Annual, vol. 12, Speech Monographs, 1945.

16. Breckenridge, M. E., and E. L. Vincent: *Child Development: Physical and Psychological Growth through the School Years,* W. B. Saunders Company, Philadelphia, 1949.

17. Kuhlen, R. G.: *The Psychology of Adolescent Development,* Harper & Brothers, New York, 1952.

18. Jones, H. E.: "Adolescence in Our Society," in J. Seidman (ed.), *The Adolescent: A Book of Readings,* The Dryden Press, Inc., New York, 1953.

19. Harris, J. A., C. M. Jackson, D. G. Patterson, and R. E. Scammon: *The Measurement of Man,* University of Minnesota Press, Mineapolis, 1930.

20. Schonfield, W. A.: "Primary and Secondary Sexual Characteristics: Study of Development in Males," *Am. J. Dis. Child.* 63:535–549 (1943).

21. Kinsey, A. C., W. B. Pomeroy, and C. E. Martin: *Sexual Behavior in the Human Male,* W. B. Saunders Company, Philadelphia, 1948.

22. Kinsey, A. C., W. B. Pomeroy, C. E. Martin and P. H. Gebhard: *Sexual Behavior in the Human Female,* W. B. Saunders Company, Philadelphia, 1953.

23. Johnson, C. S.: *Shadow of the Plantation,* University of Chicago Press, Chicago, 1943.

24. Whyte, W. F.: "A Slum Sex Code," *Am. J. Sociol.* 49:24–31 (1943).

25. Leiby, G. M., and G. Larimore: *A Study of Factors Allied with Venereal Disease,* Headquarters, Third Service Command, Baltimore, 1945.

26. Davis, K. B.: *Factors in the Sex Life of 2200 Women,* Harper & Brothers, New York, 1930.

27. Landis, C., A. T. Landis, and M. M. Bolles: *Sex in Development*, Paul B. Hoeber, Inc., New York, 1940.

28. Deutsch, H., *Psychology of Women*, vol. II, Grune & Stratton, Inc., New York, 1944.

29. Wootten, B. G.: "The Emotional Status of 56 Prenatal Patients: Correlation with Obstetrical Experiences," thesis, The School of Hygiene and Public Health, The Johns Hopkins University, Baltimore, 1951.

30. Rogers, M. E.: "Responses to Talks on Menstrual Health," *Nursing Outlook*, 1:272–274 1953).

31. Engle, E. T., and M. D. Shelesnyak: "First Menstruations and Subsequent Menstrual Cycles of Pubertal Girls," *Human Biol.* 6:431–453 (1934).

32. Benedeck, T.: *Psychosexual Functions in Women*, The Ronald Press Company, New York, 1952.

33. Mills, C. A., and C. Ogle: "Physiological Sterility in Adolescents," *Human Biol.* 8:607–615 (1938).

34. *A Tentative Course of Study in Problems in Democratic Living for Grade Twelve*, Baltimore County Public Schools, Towson, Md., 1950.

35. Tryon, C. M.: "Evauation of Adolescent Personality by Adolescents," in R. G. Barker, J. S. Kounin, and H. F. Wright, (eds.), *Child Behavior and Development*, McGraw-Hill Book Company, Inc., New York, 1933.

36. Jones, H. E.: *Development in Adolescence: Approaches to the Study of the Individual*, Appleton-Century-Crofts, Inc., New York, 1943.

37. Patterson, D. G., G. G. Schneidler, E. G. Williamson: *Student Guidance Techniques*, McGraw-Hill Book Company, Inc., New York, 1933.

38. Trabue, M. R.: "Recent Development in Testing for Guidance," *Rev. Educ. Research* 3:41–48 (1933).

39. Ruch, F. L.: *Psychology and Life*, Scott, Foresman, & Company, Chicago, 1941.

40. Wellman, B. L.: "Sex Differences," in C. Murchison (ed.), *A Handbook of Child Psychology*, Clark University Press, Worcester, Mass., 1933.

41. Hewitt, L. E., and R. L. Jenkins: *Fundamental Patterns of Maladjustment: The Dynamics of Their Adjustment*, State of Illinois, Springfield, 1946.

42. Witmer, H. L., and E. Powers: *An Experiment in the Prevention of Delinquency: The Cambridge-Somerville Youth Study*, Columbia University Press, New York, 1951.

43. Glueck, S., and E. Glueck: *Later Criminal Careers*, The Commonwealth Fund, New York, 1937.

44. Shaw, C. R.: *Change the Street: The Chicago Area Project*, Annual Report, 1949–1950, Chicago Area Project.

45. Glueck, S., and E. Glueck: *Unraveling Juvenile Delinquency*, The Commonwealth Fund, New York, 1950.

CHAPTER FIFTEEN

The Young-adult Period

The end of adolescence finds the average individual adjusted in some fashion and to some degree to the stresses and strains imposed upon him, from both within and without. His full physical growth has been achieved, the flattening of the height and weight curve appearing about 18 in the male and 16 in the female. He has achieved some degree of independence from his parents and has reached a way of looking at them that relieves him from acute conflict about his relationship to them. He has grown out of the period in which he hesitated and feared even to touch the other sex and has arrived at one where association with a member of the other sex is attractive. The intensely individual and egocentric outlook of the adolescent has given way to a sense of personal security, making it possible for him to appreciate another's situation sufficiently to enjoy personal relationships. With the settling of his own individual status, there is enough internal security to act as a point of departure for knowing and loving other personalities.

The young-adult period begins when the individual starts out on his own adult pattern of living. Typically, he will marry and have children. The end of the young-adult period is defined as the time when these children are emancipated from the parents. On the average, marriage will occur at the age of 21.6 for the female, 24.3 for the male.[1] The children born of the marriage will reach the end of adolescence about 20 years later. Obviously there will be wide variations in the chronological ages of different individuals reaching the end of the period. For our purposes, the menopause is considered to take place shortly after the end of the young-adult period.

This period includes courtship and marriage, the establishment of the home, and the populating of the home with children. It includes the formation of a work pattern and with it financial independence from the parental home and financial responsibility for a new home. A ripening and adjustment of physiological sex drives take place in the building of an emotional response pattern with an individual of the other sex. This emotional tie, at first rather exclusive, broadens so that children and, to a certain extent, the community are included in its scope without excessive strain. This is the period of maximal physical and intellectual development and stamina. In the female, it includes the massive endocrincological and physiological changes consequent to pregnancy, and in both sexes, the adaptations to be made in the rearing of children. These momentous events are nearly all of interest to public health, and many offer opportunities for mental hygiene efforts within public health.

MAXIMAL PHYSICAL ATTAINMENT

Figure 8 indicates that maximal motor efficiency is reached about age 25. The curve then begins a slow and gradual decline, becoming more steep as middle and old age are reached. Visual acuity and other sensory phenomena show a similar curve; all bodily functions appear to be at their best during this period just after the cessation of bodily growth. Intelligence, defined as ability to do tests, is also at its peak. Endurance, reduced during adolescence by the expenditure of energy in physical and emotional growth, is at its maximum. This maximum capacity—sensory, motor, emotional, and intellectual—is immensely variable. For one individual, this maximum may be the highest known human capacity; for another, it may be at a relatively low level. Each individual is at his own best during this period so far as the factors thus far discussed are concerned. Most capacities are still rising at the beginning of the period and gradually decline in the later years of it, though judgment may not follow this rule. Judgment, the capacity to weigh and decide wisely, is exceedingly difficult to define and measure. It appears to increase during the young-adult years and reaches its maximum toward the end of the period or even later. This theory that judgment and wisdom increase during the young-adult years is supported by the fact that the lower the income, the younger the age at peak income. Skilled and unskilled laborers, where wages depend to a large extent on physical efficiency, reach maximum levels in the 35 to 40 age bracket. Professional men and executives, in whom a high order of judgment is required, reach peak incomes later, around 45 to 50.[2]

The great importance of the earlier years for the formation of the personality is apparent in the earlier chapters of Part 2. During these years the personality traits are built; the individual's capacities are continually increasing and are coming under the disciplined control necessary for their full use in solving problems. From the totally dependent infant, the individual matures to become sufficiently independent to leave his parental home and set forth to direct his own fate. But the maturational process does not end just because maximal capacities for motor and sensory function are reached. Skills in the use of personality traits continue to be learned. The personality structure encounters stresses and adapts to them, the result being a modification of the structure previously present. Personality is present before birth, and it is in process of modification to the very end of life.

REACTION TO ILLNESS

Physical disability due to acute and chronic disease is less likely at this period than it will ever again be in the life of the individual. The rate of disability increases sharply as middle age approaches.[2] Health hazards exist, to be sure, but poor health is less likely to strike at this period than at any later one. On the other hand, because good health is the expected state, and because responsibilities are great and are clearly recognized, illness is a heavy blow when it falls. It is likely to be a severe emotional stress for the individual. He is likely to act irrationally, and the extent of the irrationality of his reaction usually bears some relation to the severity of the blow. For example, the workman who breaks his finger is likely to seek medical care at once and to carry out the recommended procedures, since he realizes that the illness is acute and full recovery can be expected within a short time. He may even be able to work while undergoing treatment. The blow is not very severe. If the illness is tuberculosis, however, the blow is very great. In the first place, the onset is insidious. There is frequently a long period of aggravation at himself because of early symptoms that appear before the diagnosis is made. There may have been friction with the employer because of absenteeism during this period, introducing a large element of anxiety even before the final blow falls. Easy fatigue, characteristic of early tuberculosis, may have given the family the idea that the victim is lazy; this may be another source of anxiety for him. At the end of some such series of events, a diagnosis of tuberculosis is made. In spite of all the educational efforts and publicized cures, an aura of fear and disgust still hangs about the disease. Even if this common fear has been overcome by previous public health educational efforts, there remains the long period of hospitalization and the probability of limited activity for years. These constitute a threat to the individual and to his family.

The disease is a blow to his vanity. He is only a little time removed from the adolescent overevaluation of physical prowess. He must now look upon himself as an invalid, not as a strong, dependable, virile young man. He is unable to earn his way, unable to care for his wife and family. He is a failure, subjected to the indignity of accepting charity for himself and his family. Emotional threats of equal severity confront the young adult woman. She fails in her job as a mother, she deserts her husband and family, she exposes her husband to temptations to profligacy while she is in hospital. Under such circumstances, the tuberculous individual may well defend himself by denying the severity of his disease. The illness cannot strike him so severely as the physician says it has. He, with all his good intentions toward his family, could not possibly be the danger to them that the doctor says he is. He has always had good health, he cannot be seriously ill now. Just wait; he'll stay home and take it easy and the doctor will be proved to be wrong. So he refuses hospitalization. Usually in a few months he has to accept it anyway, but enough time has now passed so that the emotional factors are less acute and he is better able to accept the radical change in his life pattern that is necessary for the arrest of his disease.

The problem of the public health nurse and medical officer in such a situation is to speed up the process of adjustment to the recommendation for treatment so that it can be accepted, the family and public thus receiving maximal protection and the individual receiving early treatment. There are several ways in which rapid hospitalization can be achieved. In many places, the health officer has the legal power to incarcerate the patient in hospital.[3] This type of management has been used most frequently not in tuberculosis cases, but in venereal-disease control. There, because of the more irresponsible types of people to be dealt with, it is perhaps a reasonably suitable method when others have failed. In other situations it is, however, less applicable.

In tuberculosis the mental state of the patient is agreed to be very important in relation to his cure. Anger and rebellion are destructive emotions which, while making the patient difficult to handle medically, also make him easier prey to the ravages of the bacillus. Impatience and anxiety take up energy that the patient needs to combat his disease. While legal force may be necessary to protect the public from an infective tuberculosis patient, it should be recognized that hospitalizing him against his will may retard his recovery, particularly if he is allowed to lapse into a chronic resentful state after hospitalization. The acceptance of hospitalization may be made easier for the patient as a voluntary decision on his part if he is given the time to mature his decision in a series of interviews that take up the important factors in his own case. These factors may be clear to the health official at once; they are not effective in leading to the desired action on the part of the patient until he too recognizes them and adjusts to them. The patient, provided that he is not caught up in long-standing irrationalizations secondary to past emotional strains—that he is not mentally ill—will usually come to the point of bringing up the pertinent factors and adjusting them for himself if allowed to do so. The means for doing this is a permissive, nonforcing type of interview which takes into consideration the fact that he is a part of a larger social situation to which he has real responsibilities and that he is a citizen who cherishes and has pride in his free will. Such interviews cannot be successfully carried out by the health officer who begins with the concept "My God, another uncooperative patient." They can succeed quite regularly, however, for the official who is willing to take the time to understand the host factors in the etiology of tuberculosis as well as the bacterial ones.[4,5] The former are as much the province of public health as the latter. The issue is to cure the man as well as to kill the bacteria and stop their spread.

Getting the patient into hospital is not the only point where mental hygiene and the care of chronic disease are associated. The peace of mind of the patient in hospital is also important to his cure. This is achieved through the attention given to such problems as social service to the family. This cannot be successfully carried out without attention to personality and attitude factors as well as to financial ones; visiting arrangements, including transportation of families to the hospital; and gentle honesty in explaining the progress of the disease to the patient. The patient's feeling of responsibility to those on the outside who love and depend upon him should be preserved. Problems successfully faced and solved are better for the patient from the mental hygiene standpoint, and probably from the point of view of the healing of the lesion, than a realization by the patient that problems are being kept from him. Unless his responsibilities are continuously discharged by the patient, they may well appear to be a burden he cannot face when he leaves hospital. In such cases relapses just before time to leave hospital are likely to occur.[6] Or the patient may become so thoroughly hospitalized that he fails to leave the protective environment even when well enough, simply because he fears to face the outside world again. Instead of taking up where he left off with his family, he may completely desert them, feeling that they survived so long without him that they no longer need him and would not have room in their emotional lives for him again.

In some tuberculosis hospitals as many as 75 per cent of patients leave hospital against medical advice, and percentages above 50 are not uncommon. Weber has shown that the proportion of discharges of this type can be significantly reduced by even small amounts of psychiatric consultation within the hospital,[7] and probably a similarly controlled experiment would indicate the value of social-service work as well. No one who has observed families one of whose members is hospitalized can doubt the importance of marriage counseling for the patient and the spouse. It is to be hoped that the modern surgical and drug treatments will sufficiently reduce the length of hospitalization that there will be less time for the family to close ranks to the exclusion of the sick person. Counseling will nevertheless be important for some time to come in the design of a complete treatment for tuberculosis.[8]

The progressive development of antibiotic and other types of drug treatment for tuberculosis is already leading to the home care of tuberculosis patients and may, in the future, reduce the extent of hospitalization considerably. Home care will require major shifting of roles within the family for the period of illness. In many instances success or failure will depend as much on the capacity of the individuals to change their roles, yet maintain confident and appreciative relationships, as it will on the drugs and regimen used.

Tuberculosis has been used to illustrate the place of psychosomatic thinking in dealing with diseases that break up the family group for a time. Similar considerations apply to any other disease involving hospitalization. If the hospitalization is for mental disease, the problem is even more complicated. In such cases the patient's ability to collaborate is interfered with by the nature of his disease. It is well to keep in mind that his ability is only interfered with, not abolished; even more effort, more acumen, and more patience are required on the part of the physician or nurse than with patients whose communicative and collaborative capacities are not directly affected by their disease. Crass legal incarceration in hospital is even more to be avoided in mental disease than in the more somatic types of illness. When authority must be used, it is best preceded by honest explanation and carried out with gentle determination. The physician who takes, or advises someone else to take, a mental patient for a "ride in the country" and dumps him at the doorstep of the psychiatric hospital deserves to have the same thing happen to him. Even more, he deserves to be the psychiatrist whose job it becomes to treat a patient who has had such an education in the integrity of the medical profession. Inasmuch as the public health officer is the physician charged with responsibility for the administration of commitment procedures in some states and in many countries, this material is pertinent to public health practice.

The understanding of personality factors, of attitudes, and of the environmental situation in which the patient experiences his illness is important in getting the patient into hospital, in getting him well there, and in the reestablishment of his life outside hospital. These factors are as much the responsibility of the health department as are the laboratory and physical findings in the case.

COURTSHIP

As the end of the period of adolescence draws near, the individual finds himself seeking the company of members of the other sex. The female generally completes adolescence in the physiological sense and in general maturity about 2 years before the male, and eventually she marries about 2 years earlier than her male contemporary. Between the time she begins to "go with" boys and the time she marries, she is likely to have fallen in and out of love several times.[9] These affairs usually begin as dates, frequently sought for the first time because of some social event demanding a partner. At first there may be considerable resistance to this on the part of the boy; there is a remainder of the tendency for the sexes to separate which must be overcome before he can be comfortable in a dating relationship. More or less quickly, depending on the couple, the relationship tends to become stabilized and is accepted by both parties and by their friends as an expected association. The relationship may go on to culminate in marriage. Frequently such courtships disintegrate, often by tacit mutual agreement, but the breakdown may also come through the building up of a new association by one or the other party. In that case there may be strain on each of them at the transition. The reasons for the breakdown of these early dating relationships have not been widely studied, but they probably have to do with the immaturity of the two individuals involved and with the discovery of unliked patterns of thinking or culture of the one member by the other as the acquaintance ripens. In some cases it may be the realization that the other does not fit the dream that has grown up of the type of husband or wife wanted. It may be that the one demands petting intimacies the other refuses. It may be that although the individual concerned is acceptable, his or her family standards are too different to be fitted into comfortably. It may be that one, usually the boy, refuses to be pushed by anyone or any group into a position where he is "expected" to act in a certain way—he is still fighting to be independent and free. Whatever the cause, such early courtship adventures may not continue into marriage. Usually they include an expectancy of marriage by both partners, though no public statement is made to this effect. There is little information on the number and duration of these "puppy-love" affairs, but they are known to be frequent enough to be called a part of average experience and may be looked upon as developmental activity eventuating in an attachment that leads to marriage. There is some evidence that persons who have had several close friends of both sexes before marriage are likely to have more success in marriage than more solitary individuals.[10]

Later love affairs that culminate in public engagements are better studied, particularly for the highly selected group that attends college and, of these, those individuals who take courses in preparation for marriage. These data have to be used with extreme care because the college population is certainly not representative of the whole population. It is particularly different from the one-third of the population that is the principal concern of the health officer at the present time. Burgess and Locke report that of 1,000 engaged couples they studied, 238 of the men and 358 of the women had been engaged one or more times previously.[9] The college campus is highly competitive in the sense that some men and women "rate" and are avidly sought after by groups of suitors, and also that it may be a mark of prestige to gather fraternity and sorority pins. This situation probably accounts for these high figures, which may not be at all the pattern where engagement means an announcement to the community that a marriage will take place. Probably in the general population the announcement of engagement still approaches more nearly the traditional posting of marriage banns, though there are no data available to support this surmise. The abolition of the breach-of-promise laws in many states indicates that, in American culture, engagement no longer implies a contract but is rather simply a statement of intention.

As the courtship matures, or as a part of dating before the relationship is mature enough to be called a courtship, petting and necking are likely to appear. Of Terman's 752 married couples of "the middle and upper middle classes of urban and semi-urban Californians," 153 of the men and 255 of the women denied "petting" at all, 21 and 34 per cent, respectively.[10] The couples of this study were adolescent in the years 1900 to 1930; Terman states, "Although the custom in question has grown more popular in recent decades, it was a fairly well-known institution when our oldest subjects were boys and girls." Although Terman found a slightly higher ratio of marital happiness among couples of which the wives had never petted, in general, his findings tend to indicate that both those who decry it and those who encourage it as a preparation for marital life are probably merely expressing opinions not justified by demonstrated biological success or failure. Kinsey's more recent data indicates that approximately 90 per cent of women have had some experience with petting by the age of 25, and that about

80 per cent recognized definite sexual arousal in petting. By this age orgasm has occurred in connection with petting in around 30 per cent of his sample.[11] Whatever its teleological significance, it is recognized as a part of most courtship experiences. Petting and necking may lead to the complete sex act.

It has already been noted that perhaps 80 per cent of men and 25 per cent of women have had intercourse before marriage. What are considered to be certain important reasons for the difference in men and women in this practice have been detailed in the preceding chapter. Rockwood and Ford, in a study of college students, indicate that the "double standard" in this regard is generally accepted by both males and females. Although 72.5 per cent of the 364 college students felt that the control of petting rested equally on both partners, 25.8 per cent believed it to be the responsibility of the girl alone and only 1.6 per cent felt that control rested only with the male. When 173 students (73 males, 100 females) were asked their attitude toward premarital sex experience, 49 per cent of the males and 76 per cent of the females felt no sex experience before marriage to be the desirable standard. Eleven per cent of the women and 23.3 per cent of the men said they believed that men but not women might have sex experience before marriage, while 15 per cent of the men and 6 per cent of the women approved relations for both sexes, particularly if engaged and if marriage was blocked for a period of time.[12] Again it is apparent that the standards for sex activity and the actual activity are quite different, although attitudes tend to show recognition of the existing patterns of activity in that men are less "conservative" in their standards than are women, at least in the college group. The data appear to indicate that women expect men to be less chaste than themselves.

If 80 per cent of men and but 25 per cent of women have premarital intercourse, it is clear that some women will have to be definitely promiscuous, particularly since it is probable that a great many women who do have premarital intercourse practice it only with a fiancé or with a very few men. In some cases, promiscuity will have deep psychological roots based on dissatisfactions in the family relationships or on factors that seem constitutional. In other instances, the pattern will be culturally determined, i.e., the usual pattern of activity of the adolescent and young-adult woman will be to have intercourse with a number of males before marriage. In still other instances, the activity will be an expression of a hate for the female sex, possibly based on the envy of male prerogatives, and the promiscuity a means of bringing the vaunted male under control through the use of the sex impulse. Again, it may be the response of the girl to a desire to "mother" males, using her sexual resources to accomplish her end. In some, there may be the effort to "hold" the man, the woman having a sense of inferiority that keeps her from believing that her other resources are sufficient. The economic factor has been stressed both from the point of view of the girl who has no other means of support and from the angle of the racketeer who preys on her for financial gain. Helena Deutsch's study of the intricate psychology underlying prostitution and promiscuity clarifies and illustrates with case studies some of the concepts noted above.[13]

VENEREAL DISEASE AND ITS CONTROL

The control of promiscuity in a population is, of course, a public health problem of first magnitude because of its relation to venereal-disease control. The problem of controlling male promiscuity usually has a limited aim; it is recognized that no known control measures will work for a large part of the male population. However, the factor of moral responsibility is kept before the male; the chaplain in the Army or the clergyman in the community is a member of the control team. The ideal of the virginal male and female at marriage is upheld, even though it is recognized as unattainable for many. For an unknown percentage the ideal may be a deterrent to exposure, although it may add to the difficulties of treatment by producing great anxiety in the patient if and when infection does occur. For patients who present psychologically fertile ground, this arousing of anxiety seems to precipitate certain types of mental illness. From the purely mental hygiene point of view the scare technique seems ill-advised, however valuable it may appear to be in practice—a value that is not demonstrated at all clearly as yet. Regardless of the type of education, those who know more about venereal disease tend to have less of it. The impact of this fact is much less because men with higher general educational level show less total sexual activity and the exposure rate is therefore lower.[14,15] Another way of reducing male promiscuity is to make the opportunity for sex contact difficult. As in the effort toward moral and religious persuasion and in education, it is not hoped that this effort will totally prevent sex contacts. It is expected that if contact is made difficult, a part of the group seeking intercourse will fail to find a partner, or become discouraged enough so that educational or moral considerations will prevail over the sex drive and the other factors leading to promiscuous sexual activity.

No definite experiments have been done to show whether any mental hygiene program can affect promiscuity and therefore be helpful in the prevention of venereal disease. Nevertheless, much is frequently expected of this field. Adequate sex education of children, attention to the stresses placed on the individual by the appearance of the secondary sex characteristics, frank recognition of the sex urge and of the sociological reasons for its control appear to many to be effective in influencing the frequency of the sex act and therefore the frequency of risk of exposure. Strongly religious people have somewhat less sex exposure than others; particularly is this true of males.[15] Like the alleged effect of education, however, this fact is less helpful for planning than it might be, because regularity of religious observances is usually combined with other traits of self-discipline. Both the religiousness and the sexual control may stem from a common personality pattern. Education in the use of prophylactic devices has not proved highly successful and usually offends many in the community because it implies acknowledgment of defeat in the control of the sex impulses. While such attitudes may be ridiculed as impractical and disregarding the biological realities, they will characterize the thinking of many who are the health officer's allies on other fronts and must therefore receive careful consideration by him. There is a great deal of careful research to be done in this field.

The treatment of the venereally diseased person offers an area where mental hygiene concepts and methods might be helpful. The problem of treatment is threefold—to cure the disease, to prevent infection of a population and to prevent recurrence. Within the limitations of modern treatment, cure of most venereal diseases is dependent upon the patient's presenting himself for treatment after the diagnosis is made. The problem of the completion of treatment is no longer a serious one, though long-term follow-up continues to present the same research opportunities. Cowper and Clark were able to demonstrate that better educational methods used in clinics tended to result in more regular attendance.[16] This work is subject to several interpretations; it is suspected that the better results were due as much to the increased intensity of relationship between patient and clinic personnel as to the material taught.

The essential problem in venereal-disease control at the present time is that of reinfection. Multiple reinfections are characteristic of only a small number of cases, probably less than 10 per cent of all cases of venereal disease. Thus far such cases have not been studied psychiatrically to any satisfactory extent, nor has their sociological background been described thoroughly.[17] It is probable that the multiple-infection cases are distributed in the population as are other people who tend to show the multiple problems of mental and physical ill-health and dependency.[18]

The interview with the patient who has infectious lesions, to discover the names and addresses of those people with whom he has had intercourse since he became infectious, is an area for investigation that is already under consideration. Expert interviewers can obtain more accurate and complete lists of contacts than can untrained personnel.[19] The technique of interviewing is the tool that the psychiatrist and mental hygienist use in all their work. The contact interview would appear to be a place where their skills could be put to work to good advantage. Various interviewing techniques could be tested, results being gauged by the number of verified contacts obtained by various interviewers, checked also by the condition of the person interviewed as indicated by his completion of treatment and reinfection experience.

A special case in the control of venereal disease is the rehabilitation of the prostitute. This has been recognized as a psychiatric concept, though in many instances the people actually working in the field are social workers. There are still too few experiments reported to draw any definite conclusions as to their long-range effectiveness. What reports there are indicate that some success may be expected, both when the service is offered for voluntary acceptance or rejection by the person concerned and when it is a condition of probation by direction of a court. The problem is being clarified, and the methods are being reduced to techniques that can be applied generally. The promiscuous woman has been discovered as a person, not a specter to be emotionally discarded by all in society. Some will respond to sincere efforts to rehabilitate them in a way of life that is not a threat to the public health.[20,21] When successful, such rehabilitation prevents venereal disease through methods of mental hygiene.

MATE SELECTION

In a maturing courtship, the relationship between the two partners becomes something to be taken for granted by each of them and by the people with whom they live. Theoretically, in Western European cultures, people choose their own mates without duress from others, in contrast to many other cultures where mates are selected without or with very little reference to the persons mated. In actuality this is far from true; if it were more true we should have fewer of the difficulties attributable to the social isolates discussed earlier and perhaps fewer classes and special groups in our society. The specific persons may not be selected for a particular marriage, but the range of selection for any one person is definitely restricted by his circumstances. In a study of 5,000 consecutive marriages in Philadelphia, for example,

Bossard found that 51.9 per cent of the partners lived within 20 blocks of each other and that 12.9 per cent lived at the same address before marriage.[22] More than half the marriages occurred, apparently, because the partners had a better opportunity to become acquainted with a neighbor than with a person far distant. Similar findings are recorded for the various occupations, it being shown that people from the same occupations marry much more frequently than chance would dictate.[23] Educational opportunity, which is not usually entirely dependent upon the individual's decision, is another limiting factor in mate selection. Religion reduces the range of selection of mate for the members of many sects, as does color for most people. Such constitutional factors as height and weight and general intelligence still further constrict free marital selection. More definitely personal factors are the variation of need for dominance and for passivity and the tendency to marry personalities that are like the parent of the opposite sex, or similar to some greatly loved and admired person. The conclusion is inescapable that the selection of the mate is far less free even in our culture than is implied when the statement of free choice is first encountered. Nevertheless, though the range of selection is restricted by many factors, there is still a considerable freedom for the individual.

The factor that makes the final selection may be called "falling in love." While many features of this reaction are understandable with sufficient study, there is still considerable mystery about it that cannot be explained; in fact, it is an evidence of that spontaneity of the human being that many feel is the most to be treasured of all human traits. Even though the circumstances are clear as to why two people were in a particularly propitious setting for falling in love, there remains the fact that these two actually did; there were others whose situation seemed identical, yet with them, the falling in love did not take place. There is a tendency in our culture to overestimate the romantic factor with regard to marital happiness, yet most agree that for a truly companionable and happy marriage there must be some degree of "falling in love," and this romance must be present recurrently for most marriages to be successful.

As the popular songs tell so vividly, romantic love is not always a comfortable emotion. The "puppy love" of late adolescence makes its victim, according to the jokes, absent-minded, unable to deal with any practical matters, neglectful of all responsibilities. Such a state of mind is hardly compatible with the hard facts that have to be faced in marriage. Just as the adolescent's excessive rebellion toward the parent matures into a less intense but more practical type of relationship, so romantic love matures. It becomes perhaps less exciting but much more practical. It is capable of existing without consuming all the energies of the individual. It is capable of reaching high intensity at times but it is also a general comfortable attitude toward the partner that does not demand constant high intensity of feeling.

Courtship is the process whereby two people achieve the maturation of their relationship so that their love for each other is secure. It has reached a state in which they can begin to consider the practical aspects of the affair; there is enough security in the relationship to make possible planning for a home. Such a maturation requires the passage of a certain amount of time. It also involves sharing a number of experiences in which each partner can learn the reactions of the other so thoroughly that there is no longer anxiety that shocking, unexpected, vast differences of attitude and practice will appear. It is this secure type of relationship that appears most favorable to the foundation of a successful marriage. The length of time this maturation of the love relationship takes varies widely, as does any other time factor in maturation. Burgess and Locke review the literature on the subject and conclude:

> Courtship involves exploration, the purpose being to discover the actual kind of person the other is. If the exploratory gestures are carried on only over a few weeks time, chances of happiness in marriage are reduced. On the other hand, "keeping company" for not less than one year, and preferably longer, affords the opportunity of discovering the differences between what the love object is imagined to be, and what the person actually is, and if the difference is too incompatible, of separating oneself from that person. Also, a long period of premarital association enables the persons to become accommodated to each other on the basis of companionship rather than romance.[24]

The human being appears to have a basic need to live with someone of the other sex to the fullest possible meaning of the words "live with." This need has been termed the need for "response." Mowrer says: "The desire for response is universal among human beings. In the marriage relation it involves the demonstration of affection, the sharing of interests, aspirations, and ideals by husband and wife."[25] Courtship is the time during which secure response patterns are matured. The dependability of the satisfaction that the partners can get from the relationship with each other appears to be what determines the happiness or the failure of a marriage.

Most of the factors that make for happy marriages as opposed to unhappy or unsuccessful ones can be interpreted as circumstances that relieve rather than place strain on this response pattern. For example, the happy marriage of the parents of both marital partners shows a high correlation with marital happiness.[10] This finding is, of course, subject to many interpretations, including a constitutional factor; the children of adaptable people are more likely to be capable of setting up a lasting response relationship. On the other hand, if each member of a couple comes from a happy home, they have a fund of experience that is similar. Both have seen people make compromises and act responsibly, and thus each can depend upon the knowledge of the other that such processes are necessary and useful within marriage. The response pattern of each is more dependable in the eyes of the other because of a common fund of experience. Similarly, approval of the marriage by both sets of parents of the couple is correlated with a high rate of marital success. In such a situation the response pattern seems more likely to be stable and dependable than when one partner struggles to justify the attitudes and actions of the other in the light of family criticism. There is less opportunity for the ambivalent attitude "maybe they were right and I was wrong" to interfere in the relationship of the partners. When family backgrounds are similar financially, in religious patterns, and racially, the chances are better for a happy marriage resulting. All this would appear to indicate that the more the lives of the two partners are different before marriage, the greater the strain on the response pattern. The one partner acts in a certain way because of past experience the other has not been exposed to and cannot easily understand. A great many factors have been subjected to analysis as to their relationship to marital happiness. Almost all indicate that the more the one party has to learn about the environmental and emotional background of the other, the less of a common heritage of experience they have, the poorer is the chance that marriage will be successful. Bossard's study of the blending of the family rituals of the two parental households in the newly formed home indicates the multiplicity of adjustments to be made as well as the intensity of feeling surrounding such matters as birthday and holiday celebrations.[26] Most studies indicate that these background factors are more important to marriage success than the sexual adjustment of the partners. The studies on which the statements of this paragraph are based are those of Terman, of Burgess and Locke, and of Davis.

Many methods have been developed for attempting to place such data before persons who contemplate marriage. Colleges, and more recently high schools as well, have developed marriage preparation courses for this purpose, but in spite of their excellent progress, by far the largest part of the population remains untouched.[27,28] A few cities have marriage counseling agencies * which attempt both to guide in-

* The National Council on Family Relations, 1126 East 59 Street, Chicago 37, Ill., is a nation-wide group of lawyers, ministers, sociologists, psychologists, and physicians which is concerned with the field of marriage and family living and can advise on

dividuals and to teach community groups the known facts to be considered when marriages are contemplated.[29,30] Religious leaders of all faiths have recognized the opportunity of premarital education, and many insist on several hours of consultation with couples they are asked to marry. Some clergymen work with physicians in such ventures, so that the health status of the partners may be known and the problems of sexual adjustment may be discussed in the medical as well as the religious setting.[31]

The question as to whether premarital consultation and education help ensure happy marriages cannot be answered statistically at present. The heiress who is about to marry the chauffeur does not intend to change her plan because the clergyman insists on several hours of conferences with the parties before he will perform the ceremony. Nor will such a couple extend their engagement for a longer period in the light of the vast differences of background that might be adjusted or discovered to be unadjustable. The soldier, sexually starved in his own belief and glamorously in love with a 2 weeks' acquaintance selected from the community nearest his camp or from the population of a foreign country, is not likely to stop his marriage plans to build up a dependable response pattern before marriage. Couples in these situations are always sure that adjustments will be easy, that the energy of romantic love will carry them through any stress of adjustment. The situation is rather similar to that of controlling male promiscuity. The aim cannot be to stop all ill-advised marriages. It is rather to prevent some of them, to reach those for whom retreat or delay is still possible.

Delay of itself has been made a legal requirement in many states and is probably effective in preventing some of the most ill-advised marriages. In some couples the usual 2 or 3 days' delay legally imposed is sufficient for the expiration of a very superficial response pattern. The requirement of a serological test for syphilis before marriage delays some marriages long enough for the plan to be dropped. Variation of state laws, of course, tends to defeat the purpose of preventing these hurry-up marriages and is one of the arguments for the establishment of Federal marriage laws. How many marriages are stopped by laws imposing delay is unknown; it is probable that some are. It is very unlikely that any that ought to be consummated are interfered with.*

---

programs in the field. The organization publishes a quarterly journal, *Marriage and Family Living*. There are other similar groups also organized with the aim of making marriage and family life more stable.

* The statistical problems involved in determining the effect of waiting period and serological test requirements on the rate of marriage are complex, and satisfactory data are not available. For a discussion of the subject see 59th Annual Report of the State Department of Health, New York, pp. 83–87, 1938.

Many attractive arguments can be presented for the idea that it is a proper function of the health department to foster and preserve sound marriages. The importance of the family in the healthy maturation of the personality has been demonstrated. If there is to be preparation for the unpredictable stresses of living, stable family life is almost essential. Thus the health department, working toward the promotion of mental, physical, and social well-being of the population, should engage directly in those procedures that are assumed to make for family stability. Premarital counseling appears to be one of these procedures. Since the health department is frequently involved in the performance of serological tests for syphilis before marriage licenses may be granted, perhaps it should also take on the job of premarital counseling. So far as can be discovered no health department has accepted this responsibility, and probably none is prepared to take it. It would appear that the techniques of this work are still too ill defined for general application by a public agency, and there is no qualified personnel available in the health department to tackle the job as a community-wide venture. That it is a field where the health department might be a cooperating or referring agency is, however, quite clear. These remarks apply, of course, only to marriage counseling as a specialized service. The involvement of this type of work in the ordinary activities of the department is discussed below.

THE FAMILY

Historically, the family has been the economic unit on which the individual has depended for his livelihood, his food and shelter. The family required the services of the father to bring in the large items of food and to provide shelter; of the mother or wife to produce the smaller items, to prepare the food, and to care for the house. The children helped in both the production of food and the duties necessary to the comfort of the home. They also provided for the protection of their parents when the latter reached nonproductive ages. There was a pattern of interdependence in the household which it was practically suicidal to disregard. The industrial revolution rapidly changed this condition for the urban family, and, more recently, the introduction of mechanical and specialized types of farming is changing it in rural areas in most Western cultures. Where industrialization has not yet penetrated or has been retarded for political, economic, or religious reasons the older patriarchal patterns are more in evidence. In Western industrial cultures, based primarily on a monetary system, the family is not a unit necessary for the survival of the adult individual in the physical sense, however much it may remain so in a psychological one. The modern marriage does not survive because of fear of starvation but because of the need for companionship. This concept is very economically stated as the subtitle of Burgess and Locke's text, *The Family: From Institution to Companionship*. The belief of many students in the field is that the human need for companionship, for response, is more important than the ancient economic bonds and that monogamous family life will persist in most cultures. The one modern experiment in weakening the family organization of a society on a large scale, that of Soviet Russia from 1917 to 1935, ended with the reestablishment of the family as an institution important to the life of the individual and the nation. The rapid rise of divorce rates in Western European cultures in the last few decades indicates that the adaptation of the family to present conditions is not without its stresses and strains which produce large numbers of failures.

Marital Counseling. The same arguments as were presented for the inclusion of premarital counseling in health department programs can be marshaled for marital counseling. In its simplest terms, the effort to save marriages consists in doing after marriage what is done in courtships preceding happier marriages. It consists in trying to salvage the remnant of what was once a more or less satisfactory response pattern and to build it into a more firm and lasting relationship than it was originally. Judges in divorce courts have supported the thesis that marriages may be saved even in the far-advanced state of dissolution that marks a case for such a court. In some such cases, the marriage does not dissolve even without any special effort being made to preserve it. In about a quarter of the applications for divorce, couples become reconciled before court action can take place.[32] Even where assault and battery are complained of and there is obvious evidence of their actual presence, many warrants are withdrawn before action is taken; presumably a reconciliation has taken place.[33] How many more might be salvaged if counseling were possible earlier in the development of the rift? Figures are not available on the success of this type of work. The techniques used consist in interviews in which a nonjudging, objective third party with some technical training enters the relationship between the partners and enables them to clarify their attitudes, and to change them, so that the marriage becomes tolerable and perhaps even happy.[34,35]

Whether the health department would be justified in operating a special program in marital counseling is extremely difficult to say. It is, however, obvious that a great deal of such counseling will be done in its everyday work involving prenatal, well-baby, venereal-disease, and other types of clinics and in the public health nurse's work particularly. The film "Broken Appointment" illustrates this point very well.[36]

Mental hygiene programs inevitably do marital counseling. If one starts with geriatrics, the relationship between the son and daughter-in-law, or daughter and son-in-law, with whom the old person lives may well become the main issue in the case. If one works at advancing the mental health of children, the marital relation of the parents is of immediate concern. The following case illustrates clearly that to further the mental health of the child the relation between parents must be dealt with:

This case came to attention because the mother complained that her 4-year 2-month-old daughter did not "mind." The mother was pregnant at the time of the first visit and was referred by the nurse who was following her in the prenatal clinic. Very early in the interview it became apparent that the mother was more concerned with her own problems than the child's. The handling of the case dealt almost entirely in the field of the relationship of the parents.

N., the daughter, had been born prematurely because the mother was eclamptic. During the pregnancy, which was greatly desired, the mother was irritable and suffered a great deal with varicose veins. Following delivery, which was itself uneventful, she developed phlebitis and was hospitalized 6 weeks and was kept in bed at home 2 weeks longer. The baby was breast fed for 10 days, but after a bout of vomiting and diarrhea was changed to bottle feeding. She was weaned from the bottle at 18 months. The mother gave a normal developmental history, but considered the child was "slow," particularly in learning to talk. Actually the child used simple sentences at 18 months, the usual age. Toilet training was first attempted when the child was a year old, but the mother did not persist in the effort. When the child was 28 months old, she spent 2 or 3 months with a "pleasant but firm" aunt, and when she returned home she was completely trained. At times the child was constipated. The mother gave her a weekly dose of milk of magnesia and occasionally threatened her with an enema. Rather than take an enema, the child moved her bowels.

Recently there had been some inflammation of the vulva, which the mother attributed to the fact that the father avoided the genitals when he bathed the child. This was successfully treated by the application of petroleum jelly. The child had been noted to handle the vulva. In punishment for this her hands were slapped severely by the mother.

From the age of about 3 until a few months before the initial interview, the child had had severe temper tantrams, usually occurring when she had to be refused some demanded attention. A typical situation was that she would come in from playing, stand at the foot of the stairs, and demand to be carried up. This her mother could not do since she had been medically advised not to climb steps unnecessarily. In the subsequent tantrum, N. lay on the floor and kicked and screamed. Early in the series of tantrums, the mother "beat" the child. Later she sat her on a chair for punishment, but finally she discovered that ignoring the child during the tantrum and reaccepting her as soon as it was over gave the best results with less strain on all concerned. Earlier there was a period of negativism, but it was short and not severe. The tantrums had been replaced to some extent by a tendency to whine and beg a good deal, followed by a period in which the child sulked and sobbed quietly.

The child liked to be petted and showed great affection for her father. She tried to sit very close to him at table, and she talked much about him during the day when he was at work. The mother quoted a typical sample of her talk. "Let's scrub the floor and make things look nice, and then maybe Daddy will stay home tonight." She got on well with playmates and liked them, though she retired easily to play by herself if a child became aggressive in play. She often preferred to play alone.

The father, 33, is of German and Irish background. He is a very sociable person, well liked by "everybody." He does not flare up easily and shows no open resentment if hurt. He stores up his hurts for some time, then, when a little tight on beer, he will bring all his accumulated hurts to the surface. His wife says, "Then he will really grind the organ." He was a dependable workman, considerate of his wife, and had been very generous in providing for her medical care in her severe illnesses. The wife considered that he understood her personality very well—"he can read me like a book"—but that he was a mystery to her—"I never know what he's thinking."

The mother comes from a Bohemian family, her father having immigrated as a mature man. The family has been fairly successful financially, and she is proud of the fact that her father has a successful business. She was 10 years older than her husband. She described herself as frank, impulsive, and quick tempered.

The family lived in the home of the maternal grandparents. The husband frequently suggested that they get out on their own, but debts due to the wife's illness and the husband's gambling had made the move financially impossible and, ostensibly because of her health, the wife resisted moving out anyway. The maternal family was very interested in the conduct of the husband and commented when his way of living varied from theirs.

The wife says that when first married she and her husband were very happy together. She devoted all her thinking to arranging things for his approval and considered his reactions to a situation before her own. He was considerate and thoughtful of her and was particularly kind when she was sick. She says that she "dropped him flat" when she returned from the hospital with her baby; he became "just the man who brought in the money." Although the pregnancy was wanted, it was not planned but occurred when the couple was using "rhythm" as a contraceptive. Following the pregnancy, the physician advised her to avoid pregnancy for 6 to 8 months. No contraceptive advice was given, however, and the wife feared to trust the rhythm method again, so she insisted that there be no intercourse. The period of continence extended to 19 months. The husband did not object openly to this except when he "ground the organ," but he began to go out nights, spending his time at the corner saloon. He played the races and eventually lost several thousand dollars. He borrowed the money from his mother whom he paid back in installments. His remorse was very great, and he dressed quite shabbily in order to save money. Unlike his brother-in-law, whom his wife greatly admired, he refused to give his pay envelope to his wife unopened. He would not even tell her how much he made, though he supplied her with a regular and sufficient amount of money each month. The wife bitterly resented this secrecy. The husband had a "nervous stomach" and had been rejected by the Army because of nervousness.

The management of the relatively unimportant problems presented by the child was along the lines detailed in the chapter on the preschool child. The situation between the parents was acute; the mother was trying to decide whether she wished to sue for divorce, though in the interview she consistently stressed her husband's good as well as his bad points. Being a frank person and quite honest with herself, she could discuss this question quite freely. She was advised that neither she nor her husband could be very happy while she argued this question with herself and that a decision one way or the other seemed indicated. If she decided to remain married, certain changes in her marital practices seemed indicated, and she was encouraged to define what these changes should be. She thought first that she ought to insist that her family quit making comments about her husband's actions. She ought to pay more attention to the fact that he had for more than a year been repaying his gambling debts regularly and managing to care for the family comfortably as well. She thought that perhaps she ought to praise him because of these good things and stress them to the family rather than report his faults for their comment. At this first interview the sex adjustment was touched upon only as a part of the setting for the child's problem. It was not taken up therapeutically in any direct way. The case was discussed with the nurse, but there is no record of whether she attempted any specific work on the problems in the case. Her appreciation of the situation probably affected her general handling of the mother, however.

The next interview came when the new baby was 7 months old. There had been a remarkable change in the mother, who was cheerful and very pleasant. She had not permitted sex relations since the birth of the baby, but had set up a dilemma for her husband to solve in this regard. She would permit intercourse if he would use some other method of birth control than rhythm. He prefers this method, and so things were at a standstill in the sexual adjustment. He was going out rarely and drinking less. He is extremely fond of his son and was thrilled the other day when he said "da-da." The couple had talked over the possibility that N. had felt displaced and had made special efforts to give her affection so that she would not feel neglected. There were no complaints about her behavior at this interview.

The wife had put into effect her conclusions about her family's criticizing her husband. She had seen little of the previously adored brother because he continued to criticize her husband, to which she replied, "I used to do that and it didn't do me nor him any good so I don't do it any more." She added, "When I remember how I used to notice every little thing and make something of it, I don't know how I got along." It should be recalled that during the first pregnancy the wife was irritable; it may be that the situation at first interview seemed more severe than it actually was because of the wife's mood in the pregnancy and that this visit saw her in what is her more usual mood.

Four months later the situation was still in a good state. The husband always stayed home week nights and even on Saturday sometimes. The wife's mother had remarked that few husbands would take from a woman what Ken had from her daughter, indicating a definite shift of attitude on the part of the maternal family. Sex relations were still suspended. The husband had said that he could wait until his wife was ready, and he congratulated himself that he had not "jumped the fence," i.e., had extramarital intercourse. For the first time this problem was discussed in detail; the mother clearly saw the time relationships between the husband's beginning drinking and gambling and her replacement of interest in him by interest in the first baby though the idea seemed entirely new to her. She believed she was ready to invite intercourse, particularly since she no longer needed to fear pregnancy as she did after the first difficult pregnancy. The next interview, 1 year and 8 months after the first contact with the case, showed the family relations to be going smoothly. The wife was again pregnant, and although there was a recurrence of varicose veins, she seemed to welcome the pregnancy. N., through whom the original contact had been made, was ill with Perthes' disease and was about to enter a hospital for the treatment of chronic orthopedic conditions in children.

The case illustrates (1) that counseling, even when it consists of a very few interviews, may be effective in furthering the marital adjustment of partners and preventing divorce; (2) that this field of mental hygiene work may become pertinent from whatever quarter the case first comes to attention. The case also illustrates several points of technique. First, the mother was capable of rapid and honest self-evaluation. This personality trait made it possible for her to see factors that otherwise might have required a much longer time to bring to conscious realization. Secondly, the case illustrates the wisdom of not dealing with obvious factors just because they are obvious. The sexual activity of this couple was unusual and was closely related to the husband's abandonment of the home after the first baby was born. But the exclusion of sex relations by the mother was actually symptomatic of the replacement of the husband in her affection by the child. For this husband, denial of sex relations with his wife was not the central issue. The outcome of the case indicates that he could be satisfied for long periods without sex relations if his wife were willing to respond to him in the other spheres of their life together. To have boldly attacked the wife's sexual rejection of the husband might well have made impossible the broadening of the husband-wife response pattern that is the backbone of this marriage. In this particular case, attacking the wife's insistence on continence would have introduced a series of new and difficult problems since both partners were Catholic. Eventually the wife came to see her rejection of the husband and to understand his reaction to it. This insight came very rapidly because of her personality assets, and it came without arousing the galaxy of sentiments that might well have interrupted the clinic contact had the symptomatic but obvious sexual maladjustment been attacked first.

Sexual Adjustment in Marriage. The sexual relationship of a man and his wife is an important part of marriage, but it is not the only important part. In the case quoted above, it was obviously less important than acceptance and response on the part of the wife. If the husband were granted his share of his wife's thoughts and attention, he was willing to wait until she was ready to accept him in the sexual sphere. Sexual adjustment in marriage ideally would be a situation in which husband and wife had about the same frequency of desire for intercourse and in which both reached orgasm about the same time. The female frequently approaches marriage with her erotic feeling still very generalized. It has not become genitally centered as completely as has the male eroticism, but, after satisfactory intercourse, a degree of genitalization occurs. It is on the basis of this observation that much of the writing about the importance of sexual technique, the technique of love-making, is based. The idea is that the woman requires a great deal of general stimulation before she is ready to accept intercourse and that she is more likely to reach the state of sexual excitement followed by relaxation that is the typical male pattern if she is prepared for intercourse by love-making. To some extent the orgasm pattern is a learned art for the woman, whereas the male appears rather to have to learn that there is an art to sex play and to delaying orgasm. The extent of premarital experience in petting and in masturbation, as well as many cultural and social factors, markedly affect the frequency and dependability of the female's capacity to have orgasm.[11] That these concepts are important numerically as well as to a particular individual is borne out in Davis's findings. She asked 1,000 women "Were you attracted or repelled by the way in which married sex relations came into your experience?" Of the 925 women who reported (75 did not answer the question at all), 223 answered "neither;" of these 173 said they took it "as a matter of fact." The other 50 gave the following answers: astonished, indifferent, frightened were each used by 8 women to describe their reaction; 7 said they were disappointed, 5 that they were interested in the contact, 3 were bewildered. Two said they were resigned, and each of the following words was used by one woman: relieved (that it was no worse), stunned, indignant, sorry, and amused. There were 237 other women who were repelled by their initial sex contact and whose further comments are not reported, and 431 who reported that they were attracted by their initial marital sex relations. The women who were initially attracted were more happy in their marriages than those who were repelled.[37] Terman found that of his 658 women, 24.5 per cent experienced orgasm at first intercourse, 26.6 per cent after days or weeks, 25.7 per cent after 1 to 11 months, 16.0 per cent after one or more years, and 7.1 per cent had never experienced orgasm with intercourse. The capacity of the women to experience orgasm showed no correlation with marital happiness unless more than a year of marriage elapsed before orgasm appeared.[10] The capacity for orgasm seems to be a process of development in many women, while for men it appears in adolescence or before as a mature function in the great majority of cases. Wives generally consider that they have less desire for sex relations than their husbands, and the initiation of the act is generally by the husband.

The sexual act, when both partners invite it and reach orgasm, is regarded as the acme of their mutual relationship by most couples. However, it is but a part of the marital response situation. Davis quotes a few comments of women on this point. ". . . in general they emphasized the spiritual or emotional agreement—the 'mental unity,' as one puts it—which accompanied physical pleasure. Over and over again in this group are stressed the unselfishness, consideration, and self-control of the husband." [37] Orgasm is not an absolutely necessary concomitant of marital happiness. The wife of a psychiatric patient was greatly concerned over the fact that, although she had several children, she had never achieved orgasm. She liked the intimacy with her husband and did not in any sense object to his satisfaction with her, but she did not feel that, even though she "acted" an orgasm for his sake, she fully satisfied him. She blamed herself for his illness on this ground. She explained that any sort of violent emotional reaction seemed beyond her capability. She attributed her rather calm emotional set to her Scotch ancestry. Whatever its cause, she appeared to be a healthy woman and her concern that she had caused her husband's illness by her lack of orgasm seemed quite unfounded. There was no indication that her husband had ever been concerned about it or that he had ever realized that she did not actually experience orgasm.

In contrast to this woman, who actively wished that she could achieve sexual excitement, there are many marital partners who bring sentiments into marriage that make the sexual adjustment difficult. Many such cases are complex and require psychiatric knowledge for their understanding, psychiatric treatment for their relief. They are common enough, however, to be discussed since they illustrate some of the factors to be taken into consideration in programs of sex education. The tendency of the male to put women on a pedestal during adolescence has been discussed earlier. This attitude of "knight errantry" is a part of the ritual of many fraternities and clubs. The acme of womanhood is motherhood, and devotion to and glorification of the mother figure is a part of a normal pattern in many adolescents. The extreme of this is found in the religious devotion to the Virgin Mother, one whose purity is beyond reproach. The resolution of the fantasy of the ideal woman sometimes presents difficulties to the male who finds that his wife or fiancée has sexual urges that are distinctly sensual. If he has accumulated many guilt feelings about illicit intercourse or masturbation and has developed a sentiment that the sex feelings he experiences are identical with sex guilt, he falls into a quandary. How can this beautiful, pure maiden have these feelings if she is as pure as he thought her? How can she be the ideal mother he has fantasied and get sensual pleasure from sex contacts also? Such thinking may lead to the occasional situation in which the male is impotent with his wife but potent with other women. Such a situation might well be prevented by premarital counseling or adequate education in sex and love concepts. Sex education in which classes contain both boys and girls might lead to avoidance of this type of misunderstanding.

On the part of the woman, sentiments may be established that make sexual adjustment difficult and probably contribute to the delay in experiencing orgasm. Some of these are suggested in the initial reactions to sex relations quoted from Davis. To find his wife so uninvolved that she would be amused by his ardor would obviously be a blow to a husband. The intensifying of consciousness of the possibility of genital odors by advertisers of "articles of feminine hygiene" may contribute to sentiments that interfere with uninhibited enjoyment of sexual contact. As in the male, guilt feelings may interfere with sexual pleasure and function. Another sentiment that interferes with the sexual pleasure of women is the feeling that abandonment to any overwhelming passion is not ladylike, a matter of greater significance in the Victorian period than at present. On the other hand, the fact that the male usually leads in initiating the sex act is not acceptable to some aggressive and domineering women. The fact that, to some extent for anatomical and physiological reasons, the female is more passive than the male in the sex act is unacceptable to some women.[38] Much is made of these points by authors who attribute many of the troubles of the age to the inability of modern women to accept the limits imposed upon them by the act that places them in an accepting, passive position rather than an active, aggressive one.[39] These sentiments are brought out here not as an invitation to the unpracticed health officer to put them immediately to test in a public clinic, but as a means of indicating the kind of facts that are to be considered if we are to deal with the whole person in the prophylaxis of the human diseases of unhappiness and maladjustment and of frank mental illness.

The Psychology of Pregnancy. Pregnancy carries with it psychological as well as physiological changes for the woman. Some of these changes are completely shared by her husband, and some he may or may not understand and appreciate. Pregnancy demands changes in the distribution of affection within the family. It imposes restraints on the members of the family within which a *modus vivendi* must be worked out. It may be a welcome or an unwelcome event. Its occurrence can be controlled only within limits. Even recognizing all the modern knowledge of contraception and of the treatment of sterility, there is still an element of chance about this tremendously important life event that places it, like falling in love, not entirely within the scope of understanding and explanation and control. To a certain extent, pregnancy has an element of spontaneity about it that makes both partners passive toward its occurrence. This situation is, in itself, difficult of acceptance by those who need always to be in the driver's seat in life events. The interest of public health in maternity care and in reducing infant mortality has resulted in the development of clinical and prophylactic services in these fields that are available to a large proportion of the population. In most such clinics, the concern is mainly obstetric in the narrow sense of the anatomical and physiological problems involved. This would appear to be the case not because the importance of psychological factors in connection with pregnancy has been overlooked or considered ineffectual, but because no satisfactory techniques have been developed for adding services that can deal with these factors. Some obstetricians feel that mental hygiene efforts may well avoid such difficulties as pernicious vomiting of pregnancy. Some feel that eclampsia might be influenced in some cases by proper psychological guidance. No one has been able to demonstrate that this result will actually occur. It might be said that the mental hygienist would hesitate to include such an aim as the objective for any program now conceivable, although he would like to see a carefully controlled experiment designed to test the possibility. He has a more immediately obtainable goal in view, that of smoothing the family life and making it happier during the pregnancy by alleviating anxieties and resentments and by preparing the family for the reallocation of affection when the new personality enters the home.

The psychology of pregnancy has received far too little systematic study, though the literature on the subject has been expanding in the last few years. The frequency of occurrence of many of the traits of pregnant women recognized in folklore everywhere is not known. Dietary longings of pregnant women are the subject of stories and joking but not of scientific study. Little research has been done on the physiological or psychological needs these cravings represent, other than the exhaustive study of a few cases under psychoanalysis.[13] Yet the occurrence of such longing has been recognized in the medical literature from a wide variety of cultures since earliest times.[40] The lack of knowledge and of research in this field is shocking and the need for investigation most pressing.

Pregnancy is regularly accompanied by certain fears on the part of the mother, anxieties that vary in severity from case to case. Gardiner studied a series of normal pregnant women and found the following common fears: [41]

1. Fear of death during delivery.

2. Fear of not being strong enough to withstand the strain of pregnancy and delivery.

3. Fear of invalidism from infection or laceration at delivery.

4. Fear of being too small to have a baby.

5. Fear of having an abnormal child.

6. Fear of the baby's inheriting familial diseases.

7. Fear of domestic happiness being thwarted by the child.

Other fears concern the possibility of disturbing the relationship with the husband; embarrassment, disgust, or resentment over the bodily changes entailed by the pregnancy; and the need to stretch a budget frequently already strained to what seems to be the limit.

Thompson investigated 100 cases of pregnancy in a hospital outpatient service. Of these but 17 were of planned pregnancy, 79 were unplanned, and the status of 4 was unclear on this point. He found that fears and concerns were present in a large proportion of his cases and came to the conclusion that these were severe enough to merit the inclusion of persons trained to deal with emotional problems in the personnel of prenatal clinics. The following are taken from the case reports included in his publication:

> She was ashamed to go out from her home because of her modesty. She was ashamed to tell doctors of her worries.
>
> A 21-year-old woman who dreaded coming to the clinic because she was so modest.
>
> The husband had contracted gonorrhea from a prostitute, and the couple feared that the baby would be blind or an idiot.

While waiting in the clinic, she heard someone cry during the examination, and she is afraid she will be hurt.

Thompson found many examples of "fears, superstitions, misbeliefs, feelings of guilt, reasons for postponing the first clinic visit, reasons for rejecting the pregnancy," in his survey. Many of these he believed open to beneficial influence by the personnel of the clinic, provided, as he put it, they do not "focus all attention on the lower half of the torso." [42]

Both Thompson and Gardiner worked with patients of the lower-income groups where an addition to the family is frequently not wanted simply because of the financial strain. Furthermore, the mothers they dealt with had unresponsive husbands in rather larger proportion than one might expect in a typical population. In their cases the fears and concerns expressed were quite likely statements in more or less symbolic terms of a wish to "get rid of the baby," of guilt about the conception of the child, and about the conscious or unconscious wish not to submit passively to the inevitably growing fetus within them. Such fears occur in all income classes, however, as evidenced by the questions asked by patients in a private practice.[43] The extent to which they go unrecognized is indicated in a case recorded by Wootten in which the fact that the pregnancy was being concealed by the patient from the family was not considered pertinent by the obstetrician.[44] Many of the fears and anxieties will be relieved if the patient is allowed to vent them. Many can profit by simple recognition of their fears and by honest reassurance by a medical authority who gives them opportunity to talk freely.[45] In some cases, before the patient can be made tolerably comfortable, there will have to be a deeper type of therapy taking into consideration the background out of which the anxieties grow. Some cases will require expert handling and psychiatric treatment, but these will, in all probability, be few compared with the number that can be relieved by a sympathetic and not too rushed physician or nurse. There are no experiments to indicate that it would be true, but it is suspected that the prenatal clinic that pays attention to the pregnant woman's attitudes and emotions will have a more regular attendance than one in which these factors are neglected. G. D. Read has demonstrated beyond doubt the effectiveness of the mother's attitude in influencing the delivery.[46] Zimmerman,[47] Wootten,[44] and Caplan [48] have pointed out the opportunities of clinic and nurse for relieving discomfort through counseling during pregnancy.

In addition to the fears and anxieties occurring during the course of a pregnancy, there may also be mood changes. These may include depression, with the feeling that the world presents more problems than can possibly be met, as well as feelings of high physical capacity and energy. These moods may last weeks or months and are probably related to the stage of the pregnancy. There is frequently a mild degree of depression early in the pregnancy. This may be a reaction to the discomforts of nausea and vomiting, but it may also be a result of the vast physiological reorganization taking place at this time. It may be the reaction of the person to the realization that a pregnancy exists and that the woman and the family now are definitely committed to the series of changes that pregnancy and a new baby entail. The growing fetus takes the leadship; they must surrender to its domination. Following this period, beginning about the time the nausea and vomiting cease to be a concern, there appears in many cases a feeling of well-being. The woman frequently feels better than ever before, and she feels that she can take care of her housework with less fatigue than ever before. It is at this period that the obstetrician generally has to lay down restrictions on activity. He has to worry about weight gain, since the appetite is usually excellent. The change in mood is probably the result of a series of factors. The fact of the pregnancy has been adjusted to. The physiological changes have taken place, and the body has become adjusted at a different level. The physical discomforts are largely gone, and the awkwardness of the latter months of pregnancy has not yet appeared. The woman can enjoy the knowledge of being pregnant and not be bothered by the physical discomforts it entails. The fact of the pregnancy obviates any worry about becoming pregnant. This and the mood frequently make sexual relations more satisfactory during this period for both partners. As the period of gestation draws to an end, the feeling of energy that invites each day's problems to conquer them tends to dissipate in the face of the increasing difficulty of movement, the annoyances of difficulty in balancing, and the fatigue of muscles which makes frequent changes of position necessary. The anxieties about delivery, which is now so near, tend to increase. The power of the unborn fetus to cramp movement and activity in a purely physical sense is frequently added to modesty which cramps the mother and the family socially. The woman begins to hope actively that the whole business will soon be over with. "Delivery" becomes not only giving birth to a baby, but deliverance from a burden becoming more and more irksome. It is well recognized that attitudes toward pregnancy change during gestation. A pregnancy distinctly unwanted when first discovered may be tolerated later but by the time delivery comes the baby may be greatly desired.[44]

Following delivery, there is frequently a glow of good feeling. The expansive good will of the family is seen in the fact that interns and nurses on obstetric services receive many gifts from patients. The father gives away cigars to his friends. Following this period, there comes a letdown to a more realistic facing of real problems. There may be a dip into mild depression, with again, probably, both physiological and psychological bases. In this mood, household tasks loom very large for the woman, and the fatigue seems more than she can bear. It has been suggested that rooming-in of the baby with the mother, discussed on page 178, and the early ambulation of obstetrical patients may meliorate the severity of this change, since the mother will begin the active care of her baby while still in the postdelivery glow. She cannot learn to enjoy the invalidism of a long bed rest with others taking full responsibility for the baby during hospital stay and does not, consequently, have to adjust to such marked variation of circumstance.

These moods do not accompany every pregnancy. There are no data to show that this description is even typical. It is presented simply as a clinical impression to be refined by research, a research that might easily take place in the prenatal service of a health department. It indicates that different evaluations of patients' complaints must be made depending on the stage of the pregnancy. A depressed woman who feels beaten by the adjustments before her has a much lower threshold of complaining than the woman who feels in control of the situation, with ample reserves emotionally and physically.

The family and social situation, as well as the state of physical health of the mother, influence the occurrence of the moods. These influences may be so severe as to pervert the normal sufficiently so that the patient becomes actually mentally ill and requires psychiatric treatment, either in or out of hospital. Sensitivity to this situation is expected of the prenatal clinic physician and nurse.[49]

The husband's reaction to pregnancy is not driven by the physiological changes that pervade the period of gestation for the wife, but the equilibrium of the response pattern between the two is disturbed and he is affected by this variation. Like his wife, he is committed to a series of events by the advent of the pregnancy. If he is a person who needs to be aggressively and domineeringly in charge of situations, he may rebel against the passivity into which he is thrown. This may lead to cruelty to the family or neglect of it. Or it may lead to guilt-driven overcompensation in which he coddles and nurses his wife, enlarging on her fears and anxieties until the home is fear-ridden and the wife made a near invalid. Or he may recognize the facts and face them and treat his wife with reasonable understanding. Possibly because he feels rather proud of his accomplishment, he is often an antidote to the wife's socially inhibiting modesty in the latter months of pregnancy. The end of pregnancy and the first part of the puerperium, when intercourse is usually proscribed, may be a period of stress for the male who has set up a regular sex pattern. One can see some almost ludicrously direct sublimations in men during this period; the nonathletic person, for example, suddenly taking great interest in baseball or golf.

Sterility and Contraception. Sterility in women has not become a public health problem. It is rare enough, involving perhaps 10 per cent of all marriages, so that it probably will not, in any foreseeable future, come to be a problem for the public health officer unless full medical care falls on his shoulders. There are extremely interesting psychological factors in the study of sterility, however, one of the most remarkable being the occasional pregnancy in women previously sterile soon after they have adopted a child. Deutsch discusses this problem fully and interestingly.[13]

The expansion of the population of the world has brought the balance between the number of mouths to feed and the amount of food to feed them into focus as a public health problem. There are areas of the world in which population pressures are very great, so great that undernutrition is commonplace. So long as international relations are such as to make free trade impossible, regulation of the population seems the only way to reduce undernutrition and the consequent ill-health in these areas. There are those who believe the world's population is likely to outrun its food supply, regardless of distribution; these believe there exists a need for population control everywhere.[50] For these reasons, as well as for those discussed in the chapter on heredity, contraception is considered to be a public health problem of great importance.

While this may be true, its inclusion in the field is surrounded with thorny administrative difficulties. Some segments of the population have religious beliefs opposing the use of any mechanical or chemical means of contraception. It is difficult to administer a public health program when one segment of the population must be excluded from its services for nonmedical reasons. Because of this, cases desiring contraceptive advice or needing it for medical reasons are more frequently not dealt with directly by the health department, but, if it is advisable, by reference to some nonpublic agency. The indications for contraception are the subject of wide disagreement. Some would have us believe that no baby should be born which is not deliberately planned for, that "accidental" pregnancy frequently means that the resulting child will be ill-cared for by a mother who was reluctant to conceive it in the first place. They would have birth-control information widely disseminated among both sexes and all social groups to prevent the birth of unwanted babies as conclusively as possible. Others would have contraception available to all in order to make the spacing of babies possible, on the basis that too many babies in too short a time places an intolerable load on the energy and health of the mother. Others would make contraception available when the prospects of the family in question are such that if there is too large a number of children, they all will suffer from the effects of poverty as well as of neglect if the mother tries to work to supplement income. Still others would have it that contraception is proper only when the mother's life would be destroyed by a pregnancy.

Public health can hardly take a stand and develop a program for general application in such a controversial area. In a non-Catholic community with highly developed social consciousness of one type, a public health-sponsored program might be carried out. In an area with a high percentage of Catholics in the population, such a program would invite disaster for all other parts of the department's service. So far as the mental hygiene concepts of contraception are concerned, it may be said definitely that the not wanting of a baby is not always real. An originally unwanted pregnancy may result in a child who is genuinely loved. On the other hand, patterns of rejection of the child, both by neglect and by overcompensation, showering of the child with an outward show of affection, are common enough to be somewhat alarming. Spacing of children may be highly desirable in some situations where the only conceivable medical opinion is that a mother will show mental and physical collapse if loaded with another pregnancy at a particular time. It seems reasonable and sound to limit families known to have produced several children who do not have the physical and mental resources to carry any part of the work of the world. These considerations must obviously be weighed for the individual case, taking into consideration the attitude of the patient as well as that of the physician. Although the variety of techniques of birth control is unknown to most people, some method of control is generally known. Most people can practice birth control if they wish, and a very high percentage of the population actually does so. When it is discovered that birth control is being used, there would appear to be little excuse for not advising as to the most suitable method available, since at least one method, abortion, is definitely a menace to health except when performed under the most rigid medical supervision.[51] Caplan has pointed out the detrimental psychological effects of attempted abortion.[52]

Because of the social and, frequently, economic problems involved, public health departments will frequently deal with the illegitimately pregnant mother. Clinical studies seem to indicate that hyperfertility may exist in many illegitimately pregnant women and that this may depend upon psychological factors.[53] Careful studies show that in many cases pregnancies of this type are not accidental but are psychologically determined by the situation and background of the man and woman concerned. The factors involved can be discovered by sympathetic interviewing and are frequently subject to adjustment. This may prevent recurrence as well as give relief to the parents, who are usually under great stress. Public health agencies may be called upon also in helping other departments of government to deal with the adoption of children, both in the design of laws and in the clinical evaluation of children available for adoption, as well as the evaluation of parents seeking children for adoption. Leontine Young, in "Out of Wedlock," deals with the clinical problems excellently.[53]

Adding Children to the Home. With the advent of the child there comes the necessity for the realignment of affections within the family. The situation presented in the case report on page 320 is an illustration of a not unusual maladjustment in this sphere and of its gradual readjustment with increasing insight on the part of the wife. The husband's becoming jealous of the child, of dynamic importance in this case, is perhaps the most frequent type of maladjustment. The child's demands on the mother set up a situation that facilitates this development if the interparental relationship has not been one of mutual satisfaction before the arrival of the child. The opposite condition is also seen, however, perhaps more commonly in those cultural groups in which the first male child is highly valued, the husband feeling that his wife's service to him has been finished now that she has produced a son. In such a situation the wife may feel neglected and react by developing a dislike for the child. If there are other children, jealousy reactions in them toward the interloper are so usual as to be called quite within the range of normal.

INDUSTRIAL MENTAL HYGIENE

In the young-adult period—indeed, in the emancipation of the adolescent from his home—the work adjustment is an important consideration. Work for pay occupies half the waking time of most men and many women at least 5 days in the week. It has been adequately demonstrated that, while the primary purpose of work is to earn a livelihood, this is not the only aim. Work also serves a social function, and it is a means of expression for the individual. It is a means to achieve the satisfactions of producing something, of feeling that he has a place in the world as well as in his family and in smaller social groups. The history of the industrial revolution is marked by a progressive restriction of the creative satisfactions to be gained from work. When manufacturing centered in the home and each production represented the work of a family led by one craftsman, the opportunities for creative satisfaction were more easily available. A great deal of the concern of mental hygiene in industry is directed toward restoring to labor the dignity of being creative to some degree. The problem is most difficult; the dilemma presented by the need of the human personality for status as an individual making an individual contribution and the economic need for efficient production of goods by modern manufacturing methods is far from resolved.

Selection. The first approach to the problem is to select the job for the person applying, although in this pragmatic age this turns out to be selecting the person for the job. If a man and a job are suited to each other there is likely to be less acute dissatisfaction and underproductivity, more feeling of status and of creative contribution to society. This has already been discussed in connection with the vocational guidance of adolescents. The problem of selecting the round peg for the round hole is not too difficult in terms of general intelligence and specific aptitude. It is much more difficult when it comes to placing the individual where he will fit personally and be able to achieve satisfaction in his work. It does not pay to put a fastidious person in a dirty job just because he can do it, nor will an intellectual genius do well if his job does not to some extent use his assets.

The technical means of selection for job placement that will result in satisfaction to the person are not so clear-cut as the measurement of capacities. Usually the judgment is made following an interview that takes into consideration the length of time the individual has held various types of jobs in the past and the type of work he is asking for. With this history as a background a judgment is made as to his assignment. Frequently, provision is made for trial in one job, and if this shows that a change is necessary, the employee is shifted before he becomes discouraged and fed up. It is obvious that the essence of the placement is that it is a collaborative effort by the personnel official and the worker. The human being is not treated like a part of a machine bound to do as the gears of personnel policy dictate. In plants where such efforts are made, morale of employees is likely to be high. These considerations are fully discussed by Mayo.[54]

Selection practices never achieve perfect prediction. The uninitiated seem often to expect that the selective procedure should be able to say that this man will succeed and this one fail at a particular assignment. No system achieves this, but it can be said that a group making a certain score will produce more successes than a group making a lower score on the same tests. It cannot be stated that the low-scoring group will all be failures, at least in most jobs and positions. Figure 9 indicates the type of prediction that can be made. For the highest-scoring group, 14 per cent failures could be expected; for the lowest-scoring

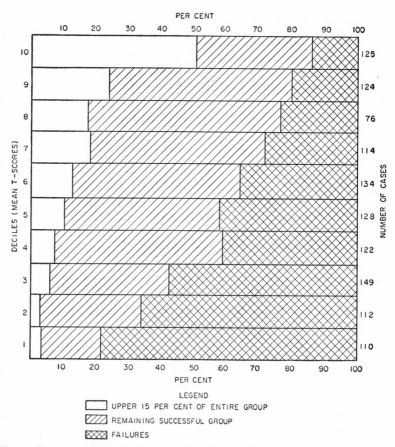

Fig. 9. Success and failure in Coast Guard officers' educational program, compared with scores based on battery of intelligence and aptitude tests and interview evaluation. Selective processes cannot absolutely predict success or failure, but can yield estimate of the chances of success or failure for a given test score. [*Adapted from R. H. Felix, D. C. Cameron, J. M. Bobbitt, and S. H. Newman, "An Integrated Medico-psychological Program at the United States Coast Guard Academy," Am. J. Psychiat.* **101**:635–642 (1945).]

group, 22 per cent of successes. But both failures and successes occur with every score. When selection processes are refined to the highest possible degree, there remains the policy decision to be made of how many failures one wishes to tolerate for every success. It is clear that if many candidates are available for the jobs to be done, few failures need be risked; if there are many jobs to be filled, many failures may have to be risked to get enough satisfactory people to get the work done.[55]

Maintaining Adjustment. The second approach to industrial mental health lies in efforts to maintain the individual's adjustment after he is on the job. In one of the classic experiments of adjustment in industry, a group of industrial psychologists recapitulated the history of the theory of interpersonal relations in a few years. The experiment began with an attempt to evaluate the effect of the physical conditions of work on productiveness. It was found that the factors of competition and of group morale controlled production far more than did lighting, ventilation, and the number, length, and frequency of rest periods. Following this lead, individual productivity was investigated. This varied widely with the individual's attitude toward his job and with his personality adjustment not only at the plant but at home. The conclusion was that productiveness of the individual and his emotional adjustment and satisfaction were dependent one on the other; that industrial productiveness fell when the patient was disturbed either at the plant or in life in the family or other social group.

This conclusion led to the adoption of a program to maintain the adjustment of personnel both at the plant and at home. This consisted in (1) making better known the general welfare policies of the company, such as loan funds; (2) more important, setting up a counseling system whereby each employee was interviewed at intervals by a trained person. He had opportunity to clarify his thinking through catharsis to another person who could be more objective toward the problem than the employee involved, yet at the same time be noncritical. Apparently the fact that the counselors were employed by management did not adversely affect the relationship to employees in most cases. This scheme was found to relieve tensions among workers and to contribute to maintaining production at high levels. Coupled with this effort was the training of company executives and foremen in human relations.[56]

This latter effort was simplified and reduced to an easily duplicated program by the Training within Industry Service of the War Manpower Commission during World War II. The vast increase of the labor force during the war made the training of adequate supervisors an important element in obtaining the high production the nation's needs made imperative. The significance of the TWI effort was that it attempted to make, and succeeded to a considerable extent in making, the fundamental hygiene of supervisor-workman relations so simple and direct that it would be immediately useful. For example, the fundamentals of good supervision were outlined as follows:

> Everyday recognition of people as individuals.
> Letting people know how they are getting along.
> Giving people a chance to talk over in advance the things that affect them.
> Giving credit when due.
> Making the best use of people's ability.

Four steps were necessary for the supervisor to achieve good handling of the employees under him: (1) get the facts, (2) weigh and decide, (3) take action, and (4) check results.[57] With a training program for supervisors based on these principles, employee-management relations improved and production was maintained or increased. Although there is the general impression founded on long experience that such efforts are financially rewarding to industry, the difficulties of assessing the programs are so great and some of the values are so difficult to express in dollars and cents that there is no clear-cut experiment that can be said to prove the financial desirability of such a program.

Direct psychiatric service to employees, including executives of large industries, is now an established practice, though still not widely enough used. In the narrowest sense, this service consists of treatment and rehabilitation of individual employees when they become psychiatrically ill. Services usually begin at this level, but, as the psychiatrist adaptable to the industrial situation becomes a familiar person in the organization, all types of personality clashes and difficulties begin to reach him.[58] Eventually he becomes a consultant in supervisory relationships within the industry as well as a therapist for individual patients. The psychiatrist in industry sees, perhaps more clearly than any other group in mental hygiene, that there is an epidemiology of mental disease.[59] When many employees from a particular department present themselves or are sent for psychiatric consultation, that department becomes the subject for study to see what—or who—is the common etiological agent. The elimination or treatment of the causative agent, be it foreman or vice-president, is found to reduce the discomforts in the department and cause a recession of the flow of patients from it. This is one of the clearest examples of prophylaxis in psychiatry that is now available.[60]

MILITARY MENTAL HYGIENE

Military mental hygiene has been the subject of an enormous literature in the last two wars. Aside from the tremendous size and complexity of the industry set up to make war, military psychiatry and mental hygiene are simply special cases in industrial hygiene. The problem of selection of where a man ought to work for maximal effectiveness cannot be completely solved in the military service, since few people can be made to like the job of enduring the hazards of being on the firing line. The killing of human beings is not an attractive vocation to the average man. The problems of training are enormous. The officer–enlisted man relationship, except for the fact that it is made legally rather than socially and economically coercive, is not unlike the executive-workman relationship. The noncommissioned officer is like a foreman so far as his routine relationships with his men are concerned. The prophylactic problems of the military psychiatrist are much like those of the industrial psychiatrist; in practice, the methods used for solving them are similar. Both are privileged to see cases early in the course of illness, since effectiveness at work is, in general, a more sensitive screening device for illness than is available in other spheres of living. The problem of the extremes of stress placed on the soldier in combat constitutes a special problem, touched upon in Chap. 1.[61,62,63,64]

THE HOME AS INDUSTRY

Setting up and running the home is the industry in which most married women work. The vocational education for this industry is obtained from two agencies—the woman's own parental home, which is probably the more important of the two, and the schools. The influence of the emotional atmosphere of the home on the maturation of the child has been repeatedly stressed. The home also teaches how to cook and sets up habits of what to cook. It teaches how to make the money stretch to cover the bills. It teaches how to select clothing and household furnishings and to a large extent determines taste in these spheres. It sets up habits of living within a certain income which are difficult to change if family circumstances change. There is a great deal of wisdom in the concern about "Can you support my daughter in the style to which she is accustomed?" The home is also the most effective teacher of baby and child care and determines the level from which the public health nurse and physician must begin teaching in these areas.

School courses in home economics are likely to teach refined tech-

niques that do not closely enough resemble the actual practice to influence the ordinary life of the individual. This was more true in the
past than at present, when practice homes may be a part of schools.
Budget-making and the care of children, and even how to get along
with a husband, are being included in these courses. As one sees the
practice homes, however, and compares them with the average American home, there is a great contrast. The school home seems to be far
above what we can hope for for many of our population in any near
future. It is rare to find a course in child care in which actual babies
are used in the training of girls. Home economics courses, if they are
to be most effective as an effort at anticipatory guidance, ought to present life more realistically.

The public health nurse and, through her, the physician are less
likely to make this mistake since their work is constantly controlled
by contact in the home. They are not likely to advise sterilizing bottles
in a pressure cooker where no pressure cooker is owned and there is
no money to buy one. The education of the mother in caring for the
baby will automatically adjust itself to the tools at hand or those the
family is capable of getting or of being stimulated to try to get. The
nurse who knows that a fancy bathtub for the baby cannot be bought
will help improvise so that as good a job can be done as possible with
the materials available.[65] She will have the mother feeling that the job
is satisfying and worth doing. She will know that the child needs affection and care from both parents, and will try to attain this goal
when possible, but she will also realize when the goal is not attainable
and then will seek for substitutes to supply the needs of the child as
fully as possible. She will know when the social case-work agencies in
the community can contribute to the stability of the home. She will
grasp the opportunities for education and recreation that child-study
classes, either privately sponsored or as a part of a public adult education program, can offer to the mother.

RELIGIOUS PRACTICES

For a large portion of the population the church and its activities
afford the means of satisfying not only the need of the human being
to be religious and to have altruistic aims, but also a portion of the
need for social outlet. To some, religious services seem to afford a place
where emotional outbursts are possible; probably they need this sort
of release now and then to maintain even a modicum of stability in
their daily lives. For others, this type of emotionalism is neither necessary nor wanted; they obtain their satisfaction in more ritualistic serv-

ices and in work in the regular and continuing organizations within the church. Religious publications are increasing their space devoted to the general emotional adjustment to life, both of children and adults and, because of their added influence stemming from their origin, are probably effective educational mediums for a considerable segment of the population. For many, the church will satisfy the need for beauty in art and music and offer outlets for the use of leadership skills and talents.

SUMMARY

The young-adult period begins when the late adolescent is able to emancipate himself emotionally, spatially, and financially from the parental home. It includes falling in love and courtship for most people and marriage for the vast majority. For those who do not marry it includes the establishment of a way of life and adjustment that is satisfactory to the individual. For those who marry, the period includes adjustments first to a marital partner and then the amalgamation of two backgrounds into a pattern of family living. Later, this pattern includes children in the family circle, a circumstance that necessitates living through the stresses and strains of pregnancy as well as reallocating affection within the family. During this period the individual is at his peak of physical strength and endurance. Illness may be a severe blow because it is unexpected and entails inability to carry the heavy family responsibilities to be borne during the period.

Almost all the major events of the young-adult period have some health significance and are related to the official public health agency. The fostering of family solidarity is a goal of public health and will in the future undoubtedly receive even more attention in the promotion of all health, including mental health. Education of the family about pregnancy and child care is already fairly well developed, but industrial mental health and premarital and marital counseling are fields needing further development as public health extends its horizons. At present, there are opportunities for the health agency to cooperate with private organizations working in these fields toward the promotion of the emotional health of the population.

REFERENCES

1. *Age at First Marriage,* Bureau of the Census, Population, Special Reports, ser. P-45 (no. 7), May 28, 1940.
2. Dublin, L. F., and A. J. Lotka: *The Money Value of a Man,* The Ronald Press Company, New York, 1946.
3. Tobey, J. A.: *Public Health Law,* The Commonwealth Fund, New York, 1947.

4. Halliday, J. L.: "Principles of Aetiology," *Brit. J. M. Psychol.* **19**:367–380 (1943).
5. Halliday, J. L.: "Concept of Psychosomatic Affection," *Lancet.* **2**:692–696 (1943).
6. Hartz, J.: "Tuberculosis and Personality Conflicts," *Psychosom. Med.* **6**:17–22 (1944).
7. Weber, F. J.: "Mental Hygiene in the Prevention of Irregular Discharge of Tuberculosis Patients," *Dis. of Chest.* **24**:1–20 (1953).
8. Wittkower, E.: *A Psychiatrist Looks at Tuberculosis,* National Association for the Prevention of Tuberculosis, London, 1949.
9. Burgess, E. W., and H. S. Locke: *The Family,* American Book Company, New York, 1945.
10. Terman, L. M.: *Psychological Factors in Marital Happiness,* McGraw-Hill Book Company, Inc., New York, 1938.
11. Kinsey, A. C., W. B. Pomeroy, C. E. Martin, and P. H. Gebhard: *Sexual Behavior in the Human Female,* W. B. Saunders Company, Philadelphia, 1953.
12. Rockwood, L. D., and M. E. Ford: *Youth, Marriage and Parenthood,* John Wiley & Sons, Inc., New York, 1945.
13. Deutsch, H.: *Psychology of Women,* Grune & Stratton, Inc., New York, 1944.
14. Leiby, G. M., and G. W. Larimore: *A Study of Factors Allied with Venereal Disease,* Headquarters, Third Service Command, Baltimore, August, 1945.
15. Kinsey, A. C., W. B. Pomeroy, and C. E. Martin: *Sexual Behavior in the Human Male,* W. B. Saunders Company, Philadelphia, 1948.
16. Cowper, H. H., and E. G. Clark: "Studies in the Epidemiology of Syphilis: IV. The Value of Patient Education," *Ven. Dis. Inform.* **22**:7–11 (1941).
17. Lumpkin, M. K.: *The Individual and Venereal Disease: An Analysis of the Literature Dealing with the Psycho-social Characteristics of Patients,* Cooperative Studies in the Social and Educational Aspects of Venereal Disease Control, Venereal Disease Division, U.S. Public Health Service, Federal Security Agency, Washington, 1948.
18. Buell, B., and Associates: *Community Planning for Human Services,* Columbia University Press, New York, 1952.
19. Carlson, R. O.: *Case Finding and Patient Management through an Understanding of Known Syphilitic Patients: A Study of Non-white Patients in Mississippi,* vol. I, Mississippi State Board of Health, Jackson, Miss., 1950.
20. Lion, E. G., H. M. Jambor, H. G. Corrigan, and K. D. Bradway: *An Experiment in the Psychiatric Treatment of Promiscuous Girls,* City and County of San Francisco Department of Health, San Francisco, 1945.
21. Rappaport, M. F.: "The Possibility of Help for the Prostitute through Functional Case Work in an Authoritative Setting," in Rosa Wessell (ed.), *A Case Work Approach to Sex Delinquents,* Pennsylvania School of Social Work, Publications Division, Philadelphia, 1947.
22. Bossard, J. H. S.: "Residential Propinquity as a Factor in Marriage Selection," *Am. J. Sociol.* **38**:219–234 (1933).

23. Marvin, O. M.: "Occupational Propinquity as a Factor in Marriage Selection," *J. Am. Statistical A.* **16**:131–150 (1919).

24. Burgess and Locke, Ref. 9, p. 469.

25. Mowrer, H. R.: *Personality Adjustment and Domestic Discord*, American Book Company, New York, 1935.

26. Bossard, J. H. S., and E. Ball: *Ritual in Family Living: A Contemporary Study*, University of Pennsylvania Press, Philadelphia, 1950.

27. Groves, E. R., and C. Groves: *Dynamic Mental Hygiene, with Special Emphasis on Family Counselling*, The Stackpole Company, Harrisburg, Pa., 1946.

28. Cooper, R. M., P. Popenoe, J. T. Landis, H. Bowman, R. G. Eckert, L. D. Rockwood, N. Keys, and L. A. Kirkendall: "Teaching College Marriage Courses: A Symposium," *Marriage & Family Living* **8**:32–42 (1946).

29. Mace, D. R.: "What Is a Marriage Counselor?," *Marriage & Family Living* **16**:135–138 (1954).

30. Mudd, E. H.: "Marriage Counseling as Afforded by Recently Developed Marriage and Family Counseling Clinics," *Family* **18**:310–314 (1938).

31. Lindeman, E., and I. M. Greer: "Early Stresses and Strains of Marriage," *Pastoral Psychol.* **2** (24):10–13 1952.

32. Marshall, L. C., and G. May: *The Divorce Court*, Johns Hopkins Press, Baltimore, 1933.

33. Thirty-ninth Annual Report of the Municipal Court of Philadelphia, 1952.

34. Foster, R. G.: "How a Marriage Counselor Handles a Case," *Marriage & Family Living* **16**:139–142 (1954).

35. Mudd, E. H.: "Counseling, A Philosophy and Method," in *Cyclopedia of Medicine, Survey and Specialties*, F. A. Davis Company, Philadelphia, 1945.

36. "Broken Appointment" (film), Mental Health Film Board, New York, 1952.

37. Davis, K. B.: *Factors in the Sex Life of 2200 Women*, Harper & Brothers, New York, 1929.

38. Bonaparte, M.: *Female Sexuality*, International Universities Press, Inc., New York, 1953.

39. Lundberg, F., and M. F. Farnham: *Modern Woman: The Lost Sex*, Harper & Brothers, 1947.

40. Cooper, M. M.: Studies on pica in progress at the School of Hygiene and Public Health, The Johns Hopkins University, Baltimore, to be published.

41. Gardiner, S.: "The Study of Personal and Situational Factors in Obstetrics," unpublished manuscript, used by permission of the author.

42. Thompson, L. J.: "Attitudes of Primiparae as Observed in a Prenatal Clinic," *Ment. Hyg.* **26**:243–256 (1942).

43. Bishkind, L. H.: "Alleviation of Anxiety during Pregnancy," *Ohio State M. J.* **41**:239–242 (1942).

44. Wootten, B. G.: "The Emotional Status of 56 Prenatal Patients: Correlation with Obstetrical Experience," thesis, The School of Hygiene and

Public Health, The Johns Hopkins University, Baltimore, 1951.

45. Klein, H. R., H. W. Potter, and R. B. Dyk: *Anxiety in Pregnancy and Childbirth,* Paul B. Hoeber, Inc., New York, 1950.

46. Read, G. D.: *Childbirth without Fear; the Principles and Practices of Natural Childbirth,* Harper & Brothers, New York, 1944.

47. Zimmerman, K. A.: "The Public Health Nurse and the Emotions of Pregnancy," *Pub. Health Nursing* 39:63–67 (1947).

48. Caplan, G.: "The Mental Hygiene Role of the Nurse in Maternal and Child Care," *Nursing Outlook* 2:14–19 (1954).

49. Skotowe, I.: "*Clinical Psychiatry,*" McGraw-Hill Book Company, Inc., New York, 1954.

50. Notestein, F. W.: "Population: The Long View," in T. W. Schultz (ed.), *Food for the World,* University of Chicago Press, Chicago, 1945.

51. Stix, R. K.: "The Place of Fertility Control in Public Health," *Am. J. Pub. Health* 36:209–218 (1946).

52. Caplan, G.: "The Disturbance of the Mother-Child Relationship by Unsuccessful Attempts of Abortion," *Ment. Hyg.* 38:67–80 (1954).

53. Young, L.: *Out of Wedlock: A Study of the Problems of the Unmarried Mother and Her Child,* McGraw-Hill Book Company, Inc., New York, 1954.

54. Mayo, E.: *The Human Problems of an Industrial Civilization,* The Macmillan Company, New York, 1933.

55. Felix, R. H., D. C. Cameron, J. M. Bobbit, and S. H. Newman: "An Integrated Medico-psychological Program at the United States Coast Guard Academy," *Am. J. Psychiat.* 101:635–642 (1945).

56. Roethlisberger, F. J., and W. J. Dickson: *Management and the Worker,* Harvard University Press, Cambridge, 1942.

57. *The Training within Industry Report,* War Manpower Commission, Bureau of Training within Industry Services, Washington, D.C., September, 1945.

58. Dersheimer, F. W.: "Psychiatry in Industry," *Am. J. Psychiat.* 103:145–148, (1946).

59. Giberson, L. G.: "The Technic of Listening to Worried Employees," *Indust. Med.* 9:414–417 (1940).

60. *The Application of Psychiatry to Industry,* Group for the Advancement of Psychiatry, Report 20, Topeka, Kans., 1951.

61. Glass, A. J.: "Psychotherapy in the Combat Zone," *Am. J. Psychiat.* 110: 725–731 (1954).

62. Bartemeier, L. H., L. S. Kubie, K. A. Menninger, J. Romano, and J. C. Whitehorn: "Combat Exhaustion," *J. Nerv. & Ment. Dis.* 104:358–525 (1946).

63. Edwards, R. M., and D. B. Peterson, "Psychotherapy in the Combat Zone," *Am. J. Psychiat.* 110:721–724 (1954).

64. Menninger, W. C.: *Psychiatry in a Troubled World: Yesterday's War and Today's Challenge,* The Macmillan Company, New York, 1948.

65. Wolf, L. K.: *Nursing,* Appleton-Century-Crofts, Inc., New York, 1947.

CHAPTER SIXTEEN

The Period of Middle Age

Families have a natural history, just as do individuals. The young-adult period usually sees the individual involved in the birth of a new family and sees that family grow in pattern of response between the marital partners as well as in numbers as the children are added to it. Like the children themselves, the family gradually matures. When the children reach late adolescence and have achieved emancipation from the parents and the parental home, the family moves on to a new and quieter level of maturity.

This change marks the beginning of the period of middle age for the purposes of this discussion. The family again contains but two people, but they are very different from the two who originally formed it. They have lived through the joys and anxieties of pregnancy and childbirth. They have known the shared anxiety of having sick children. Possibly they have endured grief together when their parents or perhaps a child has died. They have shared the pleasures of sexual relations for many years. They have struggled to make ends meet financially and usually have seen the family income gradually increase. They have aged some and have increased in judgment. They may have matured and deepened; or they, unhappily, may have shown simply the continued shallowness of youth and only physical evidence of increased age. In any case, they are not the same people who started out together. The family is not the same either.

The end of the period of middle age is marked by the husband's retirement from his usual work. The period of middle age will obviously vary in length and timing for different couples. By the definition employed here, couples who marry young and have their children early will enter middle age early and spend a longer time in it than will those who marry late. Age at retirement varies according to the type of work done and is largely controlled by financial security.

The menopause is frequently used as the event marking the beginning of middle age. An easily datable phenomenon, it has much to recommend it. It is, however, an event occurring in but one individual. It is the group of individuals organized as a family and as a unit in society and a culture that is of primary concern in mental hygiene.

The period of middle age sees the family again reduced to two members. Frequently, the individual has become a grandparent. He realizes that the peak of physical efficiency has passed. Judgment and seniority are likely to be the bases of further job advancement; adventurous new schemes are no longer likely to appear attractive. In the female, there will be the physiological upheaval of the menopause, and, possibly, a similar period in the male. Health concerns rise as chronic disease begins to take its toll. Arteriosclerosis and cancer are no longer diseases that may someday attack; they are at their highest incidence. Death itself must be faced; the average age of death lies within this period for those who retire at 70. Many women will live as widows for a part of the period of middle age.

LOSS OF PHYSICAL EFFICIENCY

The curve of physical efficiency reaches its zenith about the age of 25, then gradually falls. The fall is somewhat accelerated after the age of about 50, though there is, of course, no acute change in the curves to mark the onset of middle age.[1] The loss of efficiency is in both speed and strength of movement. There is a similar decline in sensory functions. A man in late middle age loved to play the piano, but the piano seemed to be standing the years less well than the man. Its upper tones particularly had lost their resonance compared with the middle and bass notes. So the man got a new piano. In a few months its upper tones also seemed weak and thin. This time he had an audiometer test which showed the typical reduction in hearing of tones in the upper registers. He was a well-adjusted man and concluded with rueful humor, "But I have a new piano."

Other senses also lose their acuity and responsiveness. Presbyopia due to loss of "agility" in the lens of the eye is almost universal in middle age. The sense of pain becomes less acute, as do taste and vibration sense, following curves probably not unlike those in Fig. 10. These changes are due to a loss of sensory elements as well as to a reduction in the efficiency of those that remain.[2,3] The age of retirement for professional athletes is sufficient evidence for these statements. Tremors may become very bothersome, particularly in males, during the period of middle age. These are secondary to changes taking place in the basal ganglia of the brain. Sexual prowess follows a declining curve for both men and women.[4]

The changes in appearance of the individual begin before middle age but continue during it and beyond. Probably primarily for physiological and endrocrinological reasons, there is frequently a gain in weight. This is probably contributed to by a tendency toward lowered physical activity due, perhaps, to recognition of lowered efficiency. The

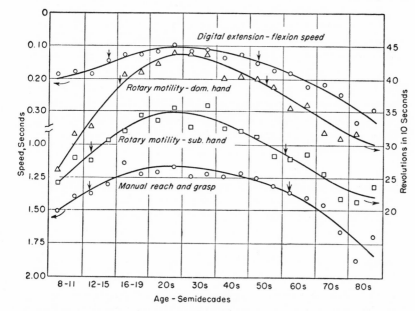

Fig. 10. Curves illustrating the change of speed of various movements with advancing age. (*From W. R. Miles, Measures of Certain Abilities throughout the Life Span, Proc. Nat. Acad. Sc., Vol.* 17, *pp.* 627–633.)

fat is not generally distributed, but shows the waistline deposition known popularly as the "middle-aged spread." The loss of efficiency of the connective tissue causes the fat to have a lumpy appearance under the skin, which itself begins the thinning and loss of elasticity that allow wrinkling of the face and looseness of the skin elsewhere on the body. The graying of the hair is conspicuous during the middle-aged period also. In both sexes there is a loss of hair on the head and body, more severe, of course, in the head hair of the male.

HEALTH AND DISEASE

These physical changes are paralleled by increases in illness and disability. Disability due to accidents does not increase with increasing age, despite the loss of agility. It would appear that although ability to avoid accidents may be reduced, judgment which keeps the individual from taking risks is increased, so that the net result is fewer accidents. Chronic disease is most often discovered during the years of middle age. It is this period more than any other of which the statement, attributed to Osler, was made, "the way to live long is to get a chronic disease and then take care of yourself."

The valuation of physical prowess is at its highest in adolescence but is retained during the young-adult period in many, particularly in men. It is a point of vanity to be physically capable of "anything." Men hate to admit that they are unable to keep up physically any longer, and some make herculean efforts to "stay in shape" by calisthenics and gymnasium work. The age distribution of males buying the equipment for physical development so highly advertised in men's magazines would be very interesting to know. Probably there is a high among adolescents, a fall during the young-adult period, and a rise again as middle age approaches.

In many of the radio and television programs based on family experiences with adolescents, a secondary theme for humor is the attempt of the father to prove that he is as good a man as he ever was. Thorne Smith has used this theme also in his "Topper" novels.[5] The physician whose duty it is to impose a regime of physical restriction after a coronary occlusion or when angina pectoris has appeared frequently finds himself dealing with a person who must be helped to mature beyond the adolescent type of respect for physical perfection.

Anxiety about Sexual Function. Conflict about decreasing physical capacity frequently includes anxiety that sexual prowess may also be failing. Actually the male does begin to decline in total sexual outlet quite early in life, as early as 16 or 20.[6] The decline is gradual, however, and anxiety does not usually arise until middle age approaches with its changes in appearance and, frequently, with rebellion at being thought by others to be an old man. The male at this period also knows that his wife is in the menopausal period. If he shares the common belief that the menopause means the end of her sexual life, he may become panicky that his sexual life is about to end. In this setting of conscious or unconscious panic, some middle-aged men turn aside from established monogamous sexual habits and undertake extramarital liaisons, usually with women much younger than themselves. This situation is capitalized upon by the cartoonist Neher in his "Some Punkins" cartoons.[7] Kinsey points out that, in males who have ever had extramarital intercourse with prostitutes, the amount of such activity increases after the age of 45.[6]

The fact that these changes are made to appear ludicrous probably indicates the depth of anxiety underlying them. Humor is often used as a protective device against anxiety. Perhaps the most typical example is the male's tendency to joke about homosexuality; he strengthens his resistance to these tendencies by making them the subjects of jokes. He does the same in protecting himself against the anxieties of aging. By making ridiculous the man who sets out to prove that he is still young, particularly in amatory performance, he avoids dealing with the fact that he, too, has the fear and at the same time partly relieves his fear by laughing at him who has succumbed to it.

But the affair of the middle-aged man produces a great deal of bitterness on the part of his family. Children of adolescent age see through family situations where the father has temporarily refused to see himself as the husband of an aging woman but continues to think of himself as a virile young adult. The rise in the divorce rate at this age period [8] probably represents the result, to a certain degree at least, of this situation. The most frequent result of such affairs, if they do not end in disintegration of the family through divorce, is a sort of tortured tolerance on the part of the family, which waits until the affair has cooled and then reestablishes the home on the old basis as nearly as possible. Once the affair is past, the man looks back upon it, frequently, as an almost inexplicable episode of infatuation. Whether or not this sort of occurrence deserves a place as a part of normal psychology is questionable, although the fact that a humorous protective device is set up against it suggests that it is not so rare as the lack of literature about it might indicate. Obviously, it is not an inevitable part of the aging process.

There is, in our culture, a great desire to hide the fact of aging. Men and women wear girdles to conceal the middle-aged spread. Women wear cosmetics and dye their hair. How much of this attempt to conceal age is of sexual significance is unknown and depends upon how one interprets the efforts of men and women to make themselves attractive generally. In both sexes there may well be a direct effort to simulate sexual youth they do not possess.

The aging, wealthy widow with her kept young man, frequently one she has convinced herself has talent in one of the arts, is a tragic as well as a ludicrous figure in literature and in life itself. Here again, the culture uses the situation as a subject for humor, from which one may interpret a general anxiety against which some protection is needed by a large proportion of the population.

The Menopause. The menopause, or climacteric, is the physiological change of prime importance to the female at this period. Like the menarche, menopause is an easily observed and dated event. Such events are relatively rare in human development, and they tend to become reference points. Remembered events tend to cluster about such a phenomenon so that it comes to assume more importance in the life of the individual than may actually be justified. A woman may be depressed because her most beloved daughter has left the home for employment or to be married. If she is at this time undergoing the menopause, that event is almost certain to be blamed for the depression.

Although there is a strong tendency to load onto the endocrinological event all the changes, psychic and otherwise, that occur in the middle-age period, the fact remains that there are genuine "nervous" reactions that are due primarily to the physiological alterations taking place. Most symptoms of the menopause are related to vasomotor instability and to general tension. Many of them illustrate beautifully the concept of the unity of psyche and soma. Restlessness, mild or severe depression, fearful choking sensations, anxious feelings with hot flashes represent total reactions, with neural, vascular, and personality components inseparable. All are actually participating in one reaction, the reaction of the person. There has been a decrease in the hormonal activity of the ovaries with a corresponding imbalance in the functioning of the person. In such simple cases, therapeutic test with hormone-replacement therapy rapidly clears the symptoms or alleviates them greatly. Eventually, the replacement is no longer necessary, the economy of the body having become adjusted to the new pattern of secretion.

In practice a physician rarely sees cases in which the hormonal change is so clearly important. Usually the patient shows a long history of the complaints she now attributes to the menopause, and frequently placebos will give as much relief as replacement therapy.[9] No medicine at all will be necessary in the majority of cases if the patient is allowed to pour out her story in detail. Psychotherapy is frequently the treatment of choice for exclusive use, and it may be almost categorically stated that no menopausal patient can be properly treated without recourse to psychotherapy whether or not hormonal treatment is also employed.[10] Such psychotherapy is not to be done by the psychiatric specialist except in the most aggravated cases; it is the responsibility of the general practitioner or the gynecologist.

The proportion of women suffering some symptoms in the climacteric is unknown but is probably large. The severity of symptoms, by any objective evaluation, appears to have little to do with whether the woman presents herself for treatment. Whether she complains and seeks treatment depends on her previous education, including the gathering of superstitious fears about the menopause, on her ability to accept the condition passively rather than aggressively fight it, and on her adjustment in her personal and family life.

There are features of the change of life that are welcomed. It means the end of the possibility of childbearing. This is a relief to many women whose fertility has become a burden to them. To the women who have never enjoyed sex contacts with their husbands it may be a welcome excuse for the further cutting down on sexual intercourse. As Allen points out [11] it is frequently not welcomed as a relief from the bother of the menstrual period itself, possibly because menstruation represents a sign of femininity the woman hates to lose.

Whether the male undergoes a climacteric period homologous to that in the female remains a matter of conjecture. If there is such a condition, it requires treatment much more rarely than does the menopause, and it is much more gradual in onset and, probably, longer in duration. Hamilton finds that men have tended to come to him complaining of failing sexual potency when they were in the age group of 37 to 40.[12] This finding, although admittedly not a statistically valid one, is interesting in the light of Kinsey's discovery that the female reaches the maximum of her total sexual outlet curve around 35, a considerable period after the husband's sex drive has begun to fall off.[6] It is possible that these complaints of failing potency are related to the wife's increase in desire in contrast to his decreasing urge at this age. In other words, the complaint may be the result of a relationship factor rather than an individual endocrinological one. The stresses the male undergoes in realigning his concept of himself as a virile young man to the fact that he is no longer so virile or so young have already been discussed. The "male climacteric" may be related to this and to the other psychological factors noted in the female; an endocrine factor may be present, but is probably less influential. As was the case with the female, treatment must involve the whole person, not only the endocrine factor.

Occasionally pregnancy occurs just before or early in the menopause. There is no evidence of an age-specific rise in fertility at this period, and the frequency of this situation is probably not great, but when it happens, it is of great importance to the family. Pregnancy at this time is particularly disturbing to the woman who has had no children for 10 or 15 years and had considered that her childbearing was over. The adjustment required of her and her husband is very great. The child is likely to be overvalued, in some cases at least, in an attempt to make restitution to it because of guilt due to its being unwanted. In any case, the late and unexpectedly pregnant woman will require special consideration from the mental hygiene standpoint in the prenatal clinic for her sake as well as that of the child.

THE EMANCIPATION OF CHILDREN

That the children grow up and leave home is an event of great importance in the life of the family, second only perhaps to the original setting up of the home as a place to receive and raise children. The leaving breaks up a relationship of perhaps two or more decades' duration—a relationship which the childrens' development has tended to maintain alive and adaptive. The parents are kept flexible by their children's growth-determined changeableness. Contrast the lives of childless couples, which are frequently highly routinized by middle age, with the life of the parents of teen-aged children, which is still varied and adaptable in most instances. When the children leave, this demand for adaptability is relieved. The parents may welcome this surcease, but there are other aspects as well. When the children were actually around the house, there were more affective interactions taking place; these bonds are now unsatisfied. For the first time in many years, there is more time to do things than there are things to do. This is particularly true for the woman, since the leaving of the children from the home marks her "retirement" from her full-time job of household duties and raising the children.

This situation is seen most nearly in pure culture not in the home from which children leave, but in another, less healthy situation. A daughter has remained at home to care for her parents as they grow older, passing up marriage when she was most attractive as a marital partner because of what she considered her duty. She may or may not support the parents financially as well as care for them physically. Their care becomes the principal interest of her life. She tends to shower on them all the interest she would have spent on her children. She may resent the restrictions on her life her parents demand, but she may, on the other hand, love them dearly and completely submerge her other desires in their service. The parents grow older, frequently requiring even more complete care as they suffer from the chronic illnesses of aged people. Then they die. Once the funeral is over and all the affairs have been taken care of, the daughter is faced with a tremendous vacuum in her life. The contacts with her parents, lacking though they were in breadth and adult satisfactions, were at least personal contacts. Now there are none. In such situations depression of pathological magnitude is frequently seen. The guilt about conscious or unconscious wishes that the parents would die perhaps explains the kind of reaction experienced. One cannot help feeling that the emptiness of existence following the removal of the justified and perhaps justifiable duties, and even the loss of chronic irritations inherent in the care of the parents, left fertile ground for the development of a major mental illness.

In the home from which children are leaving, this reaction is rarely seen in such an uncomplicated form. There remains the husband as a personal contact, as a person for whom the wife is still responsible, and there remains the business of caring for the house. Children do not leave all at once, and the relationship is rarely broken as completely as in death. The boys leave home first to go to work and only later to set up homes of their own. Also, their going is accompanied by factors that make the separation easier, as when they go into the Army and everyone else is in a similar position, or take a job of which they and the family are proud. The daughter frequently leaves home later than the son, and her leaving is more usually final in the sense that she goes into her own home directly and with less of a transition. The jokes about the mother of the bride weeping at the wedding illustrate the concern people feel in this sphere. They protect themselves from it with a pathetic type of humor. There is a particular danger that the last child at home will not be allowed to go, the parents making an attempt to hold him or her as the last remnant of a phase of life that is past.

The inability to let children go from home is likely to be greater for parents whose relationship has been allowed to deteriorate through the years of married life. Suppose that the case recorded on page 320 had resulted in the husband's continuing to spend his time in taverns and that he had not succeeded in reviving his wife's interest in him as a person as well as a breadwinner. The mother, adjusted through her all-enveloping interest in the child, might well have attempted, consciously and unconsciously, to keep her child, the principal object of her love, with her. She would perhaps have instilled in the daughter an impossible ideal for a husband, in the hope that she then would be unable to find him. The mother would have devalued the sexual satisfactions of marriage, since she herself had not learned to enjoy them. She would have retarded the child's development by overprotecting her from any possible contaminating but stimulating companionships, confining her to a small group of approved acquaintances. Were the daughter to escape all these precautions of the mother, she would have to rebel, and even then she would face the world inadequately equipped. A similar situation is sometimes seen in the widowed mother who refuses to release her only son. Prophylaxis in such situations is obviously a matter of the general attitude of parents toward children. It is a part of mental hygiene in the child health station and in school health programs.

THE UNMARRIED

There are in the American population about 10 per cent unmarried persons who have never been married by age 65.[13] At any time, from 25 to 35 per cent of the population over 15 will be unmarried, this number including the divorced, the widowed, and those who have never been married. A woman can expect 3 or 4 years of widowhood at the end of her life, since females have a longer life expectancy than males by about that much.[14]

Life expectancy for the married is higher than for the unmarried in both sexes.[14] Some consider this to mean that the marital state is a healthier one than the unmarried; others point out that the selective processes of marrying tend to leave the unhealthy single. Mental disease is considerably more prevalent in the unmarried than the married.[15] Again, there is difficulty of interpretation; some persons are removed from the marriage mart by the fact of their illnesses, and some are not attractive as marital partners because of personality problems that may presage mental illnesses in the future. Physical unattractiveness or disease in itself may act as a stress to warp personalities into patterns that are not attractive to prospective marital partners. The weighting of these various factors inhibiting marriage is impossible at the present state of knowledge, but they do not account for all the unmarried in the population.

It appears that a considerable group of persons are unmarried either through deliberate choice or because opportunity to marry has not come to them. As they approach middle age, the expectancy of marriage has fallen from the 85 chances in 100 that it was at 20 to about 10 chances in 100 at 45.[16] For these people, a possible direction of maturing is closing at middle age. Women have no possibility any longer of becoming mothers. For these reasons, the unmarried are discussed as a part of this chapter.

The distribution of the unmarried population is not spread evenly throughout the social classes but is concentrated in the educated group to a considerable extent. In other words, a considerable proportion of women who become highly educated—more than half of physicians and lawyers, for example—apparently are withdrawn from marriage possibility by the choice of their profession. To a greater or lesser extent the same situation applies to teachers, nurses, and other professional women.[17] Men and women are removed from the population free to marry by the decision to join the celibate religious orders also.

Many students of the family feel that the low marriage and reproduction rates of educated men and women are to be deplored in an age when, to some, it appears that the least able in the population are producing a disproportionate number of children. It has been suggested that perhaps we should establish the custom of marriage brokerage in our society or revert to customs in which mate selection is not left so much to the individual but is settled by the families concerned. While this might reduce the number of persons left unmarried because of lack of opportunity to marry, it would probably not, in democratic societies, do much to change the minds of those who deliberately decide not to marry. How many of these there are among the unmarried is unknown.

Generally speaking the unmarried person denies himself or is denied the pattern of response to another personality with whom he lives continuously. It seems likely that this sort of isolation has some relationship to the folk characterizations of "old-maid" and "bachelor" types of personality. Whether these traits were present and prevented marriage, or whether they resulted from the isolated pattern of living, is unknown; the necessary research remains to be done. Often two or more unmarried women live together, setting up a household that may be permanent, as though they were attempting to mimic the complete homes of their married contemporaries. Men are less likely to adopt this pattern, apparently preferring to live by themselves in rooming houses or clubs. Unmarried women are, of course, more common in cities, both because of concentration of educated women where careers are possible and also because in some cities there are more employment opportunities for women in various clerical positions.

There is a considerable excess of women in the older age groups, since men die earlier than women. It is as sensible for a married woman to prepare for years of widowhood as it is for the male to prepare for retirement. The problem is almost identical and the opportunities for anticipatory preparation much the same. Of course, preparation for widowhood while the spouse is still living would hardly be countenanced in most cultures. Nevertheless, it does seem reasonable that in middle age the wife should build interests that are her own and not dependent upon her husband, to have as a resource in the event of widowhood.

CHANGES IN INTERESTS

Decreasing physical agility and sensory acuteness, and reduction in size of the family group, tend to narrow the range of activities of the middle-aged person. These restrictions are not so onerous as might be expected, however, because there has been growing with the passage of the years a tendency to restrict interests.

The nature of aging itself prepares the person to be satisfied with less variety than in the earlier, lustier years of life. Strong showed that as age increases, interests not only change but become narrower. Interest in physical activity, exploring, aviation, and automobile driving becomes less with increasing age, while interest in home, art galleries, detective stories, and contributing to charities increases.[18] Obviously, with such changes occurring, the leaving of adventurous adolescents from the home might be a relief for the middle-aged person. Strong also found that older people prefer amusements that do not involve large groups. New interests can be taken up by middle-aged persons, but there appears to be less drive for change and more tendency to retain the existing conditions. It is quite possible for the middle-aged mother to go through college with her son, but when she has the drive to do so, it is a matter unusual enough to attract the attention of the news reporter.

One of the interests that appears to expand in middle age is that in health. The saying that young men boast of their sexual adventures, while old men boast of their bowel movements, has a good deal of truth about it. This increased interest in bodily function is probably secondary to anxiety connected with the realization that physical resources are not so great as they were. Undoubtedly one of the reasons the menopause and the male climacteric are so much talked about is the fact that the interest in the body has grown and feelings in the body are given more attention at this age. The protective value of this increased attention to the body must not be underestimated. Bodily concern is entirely reasonable in the age group where angina, coronary thrombosis, and cancer are real threats to life. Public health programs for cancer prevention are based on the fact that this body concern can be mobilized so that it will lead the male with vague discomfort in the epigastrium and the woman who has a lump in her breast to come for examination and, if necessary, early treatment.

Of course, body concern, valuable though it is in the protection of life, may become exaggerated until it itself is disabling. The person who presents himself for examination at the cancer-prevention clinic and does not have cancer deserves more than being sent away with some superficial reassurance given by a busy physician who is a little provoked because "there is nothing wrong with you." There may be a good deal wrong in the life pattern of the individual. To be sure, he may have simply responded to the invitation for a semiyearly examination. On the other hand, he may need reassurance based on a much broader knowledge of his life and life patterns than can be gained from viewing barium studies or endometrial biopsies. The man who needs a restrictive physical regime because of cardiovascular disease may well need help in selecting new interests to replace his golf or gardening and in finding the drive to take them up. The middle-aged diabetic may need help to prevent him from becoming enslaved by his diet and his needle and by his anxiety about his threatening disease. Slavery to the readings of a blood-pressure apparatus is easy to build up in many middle-aged people, and the restoration of a satisfying "freedom within limits" is difficult.

As public health programs directed toward prophylaxis of the diseases of increasing age develop, such factors as these will become a greater concern of the clinician carrying them out. The aim must be not only to prevent death but also to keep living satisfying and productive, even though restrictions may be necessary. It should not be lightly assumed that the techniques for accomplishing this end are now available. They are not, and what ideas are available have not been rigorously evaluated. There is a great deal of research to be done, and this mental hygiene research can hardly be done in other than the public health setting.

The gap left in the life of the couple when their children leave home may be filled by the development of greater dependence on each other and by the expansion of their response patterns. There are many difficulties in the way of this which must be recognized, although many couples achieve the adjustment. In the first place, the male is less at a loose end than his wife; he has not reached the age of retirement whereas her major work is done. His day is still full—full of jobs to be done and full of brushing shoulders with his fellow workers. He may have difficulty in understanding why his wife is so restless. He may wonder why she is always wanting to go places and see people when he is tired and would rather stay at home. He will probably blame it on the menopause, where some blame may actually rest. There are some areas where they can expand their communal life. The church and its organizations is one of these, though here as elsewhere the husband, even if he has the interest, frequently finds himself at a loss for time and energy to attend meetings after his day's work is done.

In this setting the wife tends to expand her own interests. Her bridge club may become a fetish, so great is her need for companionship. Afternoon movie audiences are made up to a considerable degree of middle-aged women who are trying to obtain the stimulation their husbands receive at work and yet be at home in the evening to maintain the response pattern of the marriage. Others throw themselves into political or charitable enterprises, sometimes with a fervor that indicates the depth of the dissatisfaction they feel with their lives in other spheres. Still others, unable to find satisfaction or unable to realize that they have been unwilling to let their children grow to the stature of independent adults, become meddling mothers-in-law.

An aspect of the settling down of middle age is the realization that the youthful ambitions are probably not all going to be realized. The clerk who had always dreamed of a business of his own sees that he will never be able to accumulate the capital he needs. The wife who dreamed of a future president of the firm realizes that her man probably is not going to get out of the bookkeeping department. The foreman sees that he will probably never be able to build and sell that house he has dreamed of. To some, this realization may come as a relief from the driving forces that have made them dissatisfied, and they welcome the prospect of the greater peace offered with the dying of frustrated ambitions. Others resent their "failure" and bitterly criticize the world that undervalued them. Still others transfer their own ambitions, usually in an enlarged edition, to the children.

This problem is probably most frequently faced by the guidance teacher in the schools. In a particular case he may know from his study of the child that the parents' ambitions are beyond the capabilities of the child. He realizes that it is cruel to burden the child with impossible goals; that if the child strives to attain the objectives set for him only disappointment and failure can result, or at least that the probability of success is extremely small. He knows that frustration of this sort will strain the personality before him beyond its limit, that some sort of emotional breakdown is likely to occur unless the parentally induced ambition can be more reasonably directed. This the counselor attempts to accomplish by understanding the need of the parents which drove them to instill the perverted ambition in the adolescent. By presenting the facts he has collected to the parents in a carefully conducted interview, he may be able to bring their ambitions for the child more into alignment with the child's capacity. He is doing a job of prophylaxis against unhappiness, perhaps against mental disease itself. Conversely, he may have to deal with parents who have been crushed by the thwarting of their ambitions and the fixity of social stratification so that they discourage a highly endowed child from aiming as high as his capabilities justify. Surprisingly enough, this attitude may be as difficult to change as the former. Both these circumstances tend to interfere with social mobility in most cultures.

THE ROLE OF GRANDPARENT

Many parents become grandparents during the period of middle age. While many praise this state as a happy one, in which they can enjoy "their" children without being burdened with direct responsibility for them, there is also usually ambivalence present. The very presence of the child attests the grandparents' greater age, and the loss of responsibility for the child implies that they are no longer able to bear such responsibility. Typically, grandparents are very interested in their grandchildren and tend to see them as often as possible. They tend to transfer all their exaggerated hopes for their children, some of which have inevitably resulted in disappointment, to the grandchild, endowing him with attributes his parents, who live with him all the time, quite reasonably fail to see. The grandparents are concerned over the child's care and training and may try to take a hand in it. Frequently, they forget that methods have changed since their children were small, and also that there is another set of grandparents whose standards are probably somewhat different. Many cultures have developed rather rigid patterns which tend to keep such issues from arising. In Hopi culture, for example, the husband leaves his family and joins that of his wife; [19] the reverse is true in Japan, where the wife of a son enters the home of her mother-in-law and lives by her standards.[20] In Western European–type cultures, particularly in highly industrialized countries, such rigid customs have not appeared and the problems must still be dealt with on their individual merits. Perhaps this is more just and reasonable in a world of individual differences, but it is, at times, costly in terms of stress on the parents, grandparents, and grandchildren.

When there are only a few grandchildren, the grandparents may give them gifts, particularly of clothing, which are beyond the standard of living of the parents, thus producing feelings of inadequacy and irritation on the part of the parents. While these tendencies may well be "normal," it is quite apparent that when the grandparents are maladjusted in their own home life, their interference in their children's living, particularly with regard to the care and management of grandchildren, will be more likely to reach the level of unwelcome meddling. This is especially true if they have been unable to fill the activity and emotional gap left when their own children departed.

Problems may become particularly severe if one grandparent, usually the grandmother, is widowed. Faced with a vacuum in her own emotional life, she may unwisely try to fill it through the use of her grandchildren. It is not unusual to find a young mother in a quandary as to how such a situation should be handled. Dare she sacrifice the gifts that may be necessary in the family economy by angering the grandparent in an attempt to gain freedom of action for herself? If the grandparent is her husband's parent, will her objection cause a rift in her relations with her husband? Young mothers are frequently insecure and anxious in handling their children, particularly the first child, and they wonder if perhaps they are wrong and the grandparent right. There are severe emotional tangles over the problem of ambivalent feelings. The grandparent is and should be loved; yet he or she presents aspects that are certainly not lovable and are even hateful. Realization of this precipitates a moral question difficult of solution for many people, particularly so soon after the period of adolescent idealization of motherhood.

The following case illustrates the difficulties that a determined grandparent can make in a family relationship. It also illustrates the ways in which housing, income, emotional attitudes, and the growth of the various personalities concerned interact in the life history of a family.

R.E. was referred to the Mothers' Advisory Service at the age of 11 by the school nurse because of shaking spells occurring when the child played. These spells were never very clearly described, but they were probably similar to what was observed in the clinic. This was a general attitude of tension which led to clenched-fist, rapid flexion and extension of the bent elbows as the child jumped up and down and tried to talk so rapidly that her words "fell over each other." At times she seemed almost to be stammering. The mother added that the child refused vegetables, that she had violent temper tantrums, that it was difficult to get her to go to bed at the proper time, that she seemed jealous of her younger brother and sisters, that she refused to help about the house, and that the paternal grandmother spoiled her and encouraged her to refuse to help. The mother also remarked that the child did most things with her right hand, though she ate with the left.

This girl was the product of the marriage of Catholic parents, one of Irish and one of German extraction. Both families had been in America long enough so that there was no significant clash between the cultures from which they originated. The father was the first of two children. His sister continued to live with the mother and, like her, took a special interest in R. This paternal aunt was, according to R.'s mother, more or less a streetwalker who spent her time with many different men and drank a good deal in taverns. She had no children. R. was the only child and only grandchild in the family for 5 years, and during this period the grandmother doted on her. She kept her in her home a good deal, gave her excellent clothing and a lot of it, waited on her a great deal, treated her as a "princess." R.'s mother was preoccupied during these years with an alcoholic husband. He was rather improvident and somewhat adulterous. The mother did not object to the grandmother's attention to the child during this period. It is probable that she welcomed contacts with her husband's family because she felt lonely, her husband having more or less "cut her off" because of what they both considered an unsuccessful marriage.

The father was a salesman and collection agent with a rather unstable work record. Early in the marriage he drank a great deal, but after a crisis in which his wife says "I scared him," this had not been a severe problem. When R. was first seen, the father was infatuated with another woman whose business partner he later became. The mother, 33 at first contact, considered that she had a moderate temper. She told how angry she had got while bathing her four younger children the night before. She ended by spanking them all and sending them to bed, but later when the house was quiet she became remorseful and kissed them all in their sleep. She had been under strain almost throughout her married life because of the difficulties with her husband and, more recently, the problems R. presents. She had refused to sleep with her husband when she knew him to be unfaithful, but had not otherwise tried to punish him for his unfaithfulness. She had always been appreciative of the regular though small support he supplied for the family. The mother had brought her husband before the Domestic Relations Court on two occasions in the first 5 years of marriage, once alleging that he did not support and was "running with" another woman. She later requested that the charges be dropped. The cause of the second appearance is unknown.

Since R. passed the age of 5, four other children had been born into the family. As the family grew, it became apparent to the mother that R. held a special position with the grandmother to which the other children were not to be admitted. R. remained her favorite; the others were called "brats." R. had fine clothes and four pairs of shoes from the grandmother, whereas the parental family had all they could manage to supply one pair apiece for the other children. When she visited her grandmother and told of how her mother insisted that she do dishes, R. was commiserated with and told it was a shame that she was treated so. The mother felt that this was a purposive attempt to place an emotional wedge between herself and her daughter, and that the grandmother was trying to appropriate the child as her own. The facts available seemed to support this conclusion, though there was no opportunity at any time to observe the grandmother directly. It was quite apparent in the first interview that this was the central problem in the case so far as the mother was concerned.

The family lived in a small house with insufficient room. R. slept in the same bed with her 6-year-old brother.

At 11, R. had learned to play the mother and grandmother against each other. Although she had more things than the younger children, she was jealous of them and demanded even more. She vied for the attention of her mother and had tantrums when she didn't get it. The "shaking spells" and some "twitching" had been present for about 2 years. The mother remarked that at no time had they prevented doing "anything she wanted to do." She was in the sixth grade in a parochial school and made good grades. Stanford revision of Binet-Simon test (1937) showed an M.A. of 12 years 10 months, C.A. 11 years 6 months, I.Q. 111.

The advice at the first interview was aimed at avoiding making an issue of the "shaking spells," the "twitching," and the tantrums. The latter, it was thought, could be reduced in number if a regular schedule of duties could be set up so that they could be completed and done regularly and not ordered arbitrarily by the mother whenever they occurred to her. It seemed that the mother had a tendency to punish R. for the privileges the grandmother gave her and at home brought her more to the level of the younger children than was justifiable in the light of her age. For example, R. had to go to bed at the same time her 6-year-old brother did, yet was expected to do household duties commensurate with her actual age. This was not discussed with the mother completely, though she was advised to set a bedtime for R. rather later than for the younger children. It was suggested that the mother praise R. when she completed a task, being careful to avoid a sarcastic note in her praise. An attempt was to be made by the mother to get the grandmother's confidence and cooperation, though this seemed a vain hope and proved to be impossible.

The second contact came 6 months later. R. was now 12. Things were little better. Time for going to bed had not been changed, and R. was still sleeping with the brother, though the father now opposed this. The parents were sleeping apart because of the father's continuing affair. R. had had a tantrum, not wishing to come to the clinic with her mother, but she came. She had begun to show interest in boys, "on parties she wants to play only kissing games." She spent a good deal of time with the paternal aunt, who took R. with her into taverns. The "shaking" had continued, perhaps not so severe as before: "She twitches her mouth and shakes her hands like she is excited over her game." Handedness had become completely settled, the right definitely dominant. The grandmother babied her still, even washed her face and hands for her in contrast to the busy mother's insistence that she help with the household duties. The sleeping arrangements were gone into again, and a plan was evolved whereby R. and the younger brother could be separated. The relationship of the parents in the light of R.'s tension and her interest in sex was brought out. The mother was asked to think about giving the child some instruction concerning menstruation. The mother's chief comment at this visit was that R. was very obstinate, though at times she would be cooperative. Once when asked to go to the store, she had dressed in a sweater and skirt; in the sweater she had stuffed a towel to mimic enlarged breasts. The mother had handled this incident with a rather delicate combination of sympathy and humor. There is still the problem of the mother treating R. like the rest, neglecting the fact that so much older a child should be treated differently, though not in the same way the grandmother treated her differently. The conversation with R. showed her to be quite sensitive. She felt her mother "hollered" at her all the time. Her eyes filled with tears as she described the living arrangements of the family and her relationships with her father, mother, and siblings.

Six months later, the mother came alone. She said the shaking and the twitching had disappeared. Active tantrums had been replaced by sulking. R. had assumed authority over the younger children and occasionally had to be reprimanded for punishing them physically. The mother had finally been able to allow R. to go to bed later than the other children, though there was still an acute argument about the time quite often. The situation with the grandmother remained unchanged. Although the mother had been able to give no instruction concerning menstruation as yet, the relationship between mother and daughter was such that R. had been able to tell her mother that she was experiencing some tenderness in the breasts. The points previously covered were made again. The mother was congratulated on her progress in the bedtime problem and was again impressed with the urgency of some pre-menstrual education. It was arranged that R. come to the clinic alone the following week. At this interview R. spoke freely of her attitude toward her mother. She said she "felt mad" at her mother much of the time: "I just stand there and let her talk. I don't listen to it, and don't tell her what I think. I don't let my temper out, I try to control it—after school I always have to go home and watch the baby. My mother doesn't like me to go to my grandmother's because she likes me better than her other children." Aside from appreciative listening no therapeutic attempt was made with R. on this first visit to the clinic alone.

The next contact in the case was when R. was 13 years 9 months old, 1 year and 3 months following the previous visit. R. had refused to come, so the mother came alone. There had been quite a change in the girl according to the mother. She now had an "inferiority complex." She wouldn't attend Girl Scouts, saying that they want her only because of her mother anyway. The interest in the home and chores was as little as ever. A repetitive habit of rubbing the wrists together had appeared but was not as severe as the earlier "shaking." The sulking was less, but she was listless. The relationship between the grandmother and the mother was reported improved. This came about after the mother and father had talked the situation over and had come to the conclusion that he would ask his mother to interfere less. The mother had come to the conclusion that the small house which made the sleeping problem so acute and threw all the members of the family so closely together was responsible for much of her trouble. She hoped for a larger place soon. The mother had been able to teach R. about menstruation.

The next visit came when R. was 14 years and 4 months old. The girl was still sensitive about the interest shown in her by the clinic, and the mother did not force the issue. It was quite apparent that a change for the better had occurred. They had succeeded in getting a good seven-room house so that the space pressure was relieved. The relationship between the father and children had improved. He had begun to give his wife a regular weekly sum for the running of the house, a much more generous payment than he could previously have afforded, or had been willing to give. The parents still never go out together, considering that the children are too small to leave alone. R. had showed a change of attitude toward her aunt whom she previously admired and mimicked in her flirtations. She was now critical of the aunt's actions and no longer associated with her. The grandmother was not mentioned in this interview.

By the next visit, when R. was 15 years 4 months old, there had been another radical change in the girl. She had got over the "inferiority complex," had become interested in her school life, and had made two exceptionally close friends whose names the mother had to speak with reverence, so important were they to R. At the same time there had been an upsurge of interest in the house. She wanted to rearrange it and decorate it, sometimes not agreeing with the mother as to how it should be done. The mother handled this by letting R. do as she wanted with her own room, but insisting that the mother's taste be depended upon for final decision in the rest of the house. This brought the allegation that she would be ashamed to have her friends come unless some different curtains were used, but the mother was firm and the friends came anyway. When angry, R. said that she was just waiting until she was 18 to leave home and that her parents meant nothing to her. To a certain extent, R. and her mother conspired to protect her from the father, who tended to be rather strict. The mother concluded that R. is "hard-headed like all the E.'s" and that she would learn. The parents were getting on better, and finances were still improving. They are looking forward to getting an even better house, perhaps in the suburbs.

The next contact with the case was almost 2 years later, when R. was 17 years and 2 months old. Again the mother came alone. There had been a crisis in the family which demonstrated that there was a united front between the parents and that R. was actually more attached to her parents than to the grandmother. The mother said that she, R., was still rebellious and that she had "to learn the hard way," but she felt she was making progress. The mother had left R. with the younger children while she went to the movies one afternoon, and when she returned the girl was not there. She had packed her clothes and left, leaving word that she intended to live with her grandmother. The precipitating cause was the fact that the parents had refused to buy a high school class ring during her junior year. Most students got this ring in the senior year, and the parents had planned it as a graduation gift. In spite of the fact that not giving the ring had precipitated R.'s leaving, the mother felt they had made the proper decision. The parents were hurt rather rather than angry, but the father insisted that the girl could no longer vacillate and that since she had closed the door on herself, "she must give up her key to the house." The grandmother had taken the girl in, an action the mother felt was not proper. Two days of separation brought the girl to her mother saying she would like to come back but didn't feel she could because of the father's attitude. The mother told her that the home was still her home, and that she was welcome, but that she did owe her father an apology. The next day she did apologize to her father who tried to be stern. Finally she was reinstated, everyone with tears in his eyes. Soon there was grumbling again, but the mother managed it by allowing R. to decide between two alternatives: she could help at home or get an after-school job and contribute so that the mother could have some outside help. She chose the latter, and for some months has earned $10 a week and given her mother $3. She is saving money for her last year in high school. After this arrangement got under way she actually did things about the house without being specifically asked.

Meanwhile very important things had happened in the relationship between the parents. The husband had begun to take the wife out, and they had learned again to enjoy each other socially. The first occasion was quite unexpected by the wife. The husband called from a tavern and said he was with some old friends and asked if she could join them. She did, though it meant some hurry on her part to make the date. His friends complimented him on her appearance and teased him because he had not been letting them see more of her. They began a custom of having regular Saturday night and Sunday dates, and the wife seemed as happy as a young bride as she told about it. Their twentieth wedding anniversary had been a great occasion spent in a club where the orchestra leader, at the husband's request, played a melody sung at their wedding. The wife is proud of and in love with her husband now. She says that she can appreciate his kindnesses more because of the trouble she had in her earlier marital relations. Apparently the relationship with the grand-mother is no longer an issue. Again it did not appear in the interview.

R. was 18 years 9 months old at the time of the last report in the records. She had been graduated from high school and was working as a bookkeeper in a bank. The mother insists that she pay a moderate room and board and that, in addition, she save some money. In six months she has managed to save $50 from her small salary. R. has a "regular boy friend," 5 years older than her-self, a member of a family of old friends. He is approved by the parents, but criticized and "lied about" by the grandmother and aunt; as a result, R. sees her grandmother very little.

The grandmother has tried to replace R. with another grandchild. She first attempted to entice one of the boys to her, but he would have none of it. Then she chose R.'s 11-year-old sister. This worries the mother, for this child is "easily influenced." Since a conference with the priest, who knows the whole family well, the mother tries to keep this child apart from the grandmother and aunt except at family affairs when all members are present.

R. retains her temper. On one occasion she swore at her mother before the other children when the mother was late getting home and R.'s date was delayed. On a later occasion, the mother did a job for R., but took the occasion to point out that such helping out was a necessary part of family living for all members.

On Christmas Eve, 2 weeks before this interview, R. impulsively hugged her parents and told them she had the best father and mother in the world. The mother said she thought R. was gradually coming to a more friendly point of view toward her parents, a reasonable interpretation that takes satisfaction from a happy event but recognizes that there will probably be other storms in the future.

This case demonstrates again the principle that mental hygiene efforts cannot be directed at only one segment of a problem, that the family relationships are almost invariably dealt with, and that one is confronted with the mental hygiene of all age groups in most cases. The case showed an interfering grandmother, but to understand it fully, the development of an adolescent, the maturing of a marital relationship, housing, family income, an adulterous husband, and many other factors had to be considered. Assets had to be worked with, and liabilities had to be recognized. Either the liabilities had to be overcome, or methods of helpfulness had to be devised which could function within the limits imposed by the situation. Movement in the case had to be adjusted to the pace of the individuals involved, so that it did not interfere with the fundamental tool that made any influence possible, the relationship of the mother with the mental hygienist.

Children may interfere in the lives of their parents when they have become grandparents, also. They may expect them always to be available as baby-sitters and always to sacrifice their plans for those of the younger couple. In this situation it may be as difficult for the grandparent to speak out in defense of his freedom and individuality as it was for the young mother referred to above. In some subcultures in which most women work, the grandmother may virtually be asked to raise a second family. It is not unusual, in areas in which illegitimate pregnancy is prevalent, for the grandparents to be left with the children of their daughter who were born before the daughter married. Some of these invasions of the life of the elderly person by the younger will be further discussed in the next chapter.

SUMMARY

The period of middle age marks the passing of the zenith of physical agility and of speed of intellectual reaction, although the acquisition of experience over the years and other maturing factors make for the peak of an attribute that is difficult of definition, judgment. The recognition of the recession of physical powers, including sexual ones, is a blow to which some personalities react with anxiety that results in irrational types of behavior of various degree. The female climacteric commonly presents symptoms the severity of which depends upon other factors as well as endocrinological ones—notably personality type as regards passivity and aggressiveness—and upon the relationships within the family. The narrowing of the family circle by the departure of the children leaves some women's lives empty. Various means are taken to fill this gap, such as club activities, movies, or interest in grandchildren. The leaving of the children from the home places the middle-aged wife in the position of a person who has retired, at a time when the husband is still stimulated by his work associations. The increasing prevalence of physical disease during this period is a real threat to the individual which deserves attention in public health programs against cardiovascular disease, cancer, or diabetes since the increasing interest of the middle-aged person in the body and its functions predisposes to hypochondriacal concern. The blow that the admission of physical disease constitutes against the pride of the individual deserves attention and adjustment whenever a restrictive physical regime has to be imposed on a middle-aged patient.

Public health has no programs particularly designed to serve middle-aged people as a class. The problems of this age period will be encountered directly in case-finding and treatment programs for those diseases of high prevalence during this period. Such services should include consideration of the personality and life situation as well as of the particular disease sought for or discovered. Indirectly, the problems of this period will be encountered whenever a program requires the understanding and cooperation of the family as a prerequisite to success.

REFERENCES

1. Miles, W. R.: "Psychological Aspects of Ageing," in E. V. Cowdry (ed.), *Problems of Ageing,* The Williams & Wilkins Company, Baltimore, 1942.
2. Miles, W. R.: "Measures of Certain Abilities through the Life Span," *Proc. Nat. Acad. Sc.* 17:627–633 (1931).
3. Critchley, M.: "Ageing of the Nervous System," in Cowdry, Ref. 1.
4. Kinsey, A. C., W. B. Pomeroy, C. E. Martin, and P. H. Gebhard: *Sexual Behavior in the Human Female,* W. B. Saunders Company, Philadelphia, 1953.
5. Smith, T.: *Topper, An Improbable Adventure,* The McBride Company, Inc., New York, 1926. The other two books of this series are published by Grosset & Dunlap, Inc., New York, 1933, and by Doubleday & Company, Inc., New York, 1932.
6. Kinsey, A. C., W. B. Pomeroy, and C. E. Martin: *Sexual Behavior in the Human Male,* W. B. Saunders Company, Philadelphia, 1948.
7. Neher, F.: Cartoons released by Consolidated News Features.
8. Statistics on Divorces and Annulments, Reporting Areas, 1951, Vital Statistics—Special Reports, National Summaries, vol. 38, no. 3, Mar. 19, 1954, U.S. Department of Health, Education, and Welfare, National Office of Vital Statistics, Public Health Service, Washington.
9. Donovan, J. C.: "The Menopausal Syndrome: A Study of Case Histories," *Am. J. Obst. & Gynec.* 62:1281–1291 (1951).
10. Hoskins, R. G.: "The Psychological Treatment of the Menopause," *J. Clin. Endocrinol.* 4:605–612 (1944).
11. Allen, E.: "Female Reproductive System," in Cowdry, Ref. 1.
12. Hamilton, G. V.: "Changes in Personality and Psychosexual Phenomena with Age," in Cowdry, Ref. 1.

13. Folsom, J. K.: *The Family and Democratic Society*, John Wiley & Sons, Inc., New York, 1943.
14. Dublin, L. I.: *The Facts of Life from Birth to Death*, The Macmillan Company, New York, 1951.
15. Landis, C., and J. D. Page: *Modern Society and Mental Disease*, Farrar and Rinehart, Inc., New York, 1938.
16. *Statistical Bulletin, Metropolitan Life Insurance Company* 23:(5) 5 (1942).
17. Tharpe, B. B.: "Relation of Education to the Success of Eminent Women," *Scient. Monthly* 37:134–138 (1933).
18. Strong, E. K.: *Vocational Interests of Men and Women*, Stanford University Press, Stanford, Calif., 1943.
19. Thompson, L., and A. Joseph: *The Hopi Way*, University of Chicago Press, Chicago, 1944.
20. Benedict, R.: *The Chrysanthemum and the Sword*, Houghton Mifflin Company, Boston, 1946.

CHAPTER SEVENTEEN

The Period of Old Age

There is no point or particular age at which old age may be said to begin in any individual. Events in the life of the individual concerned, birth and the beginning of walking, were used in defining infancy. In other epochs, the event was determined not by the individual himself but by cultural factors; an example is the ending of the preschool period. In middle age, the marking event concerned a small sociological organism, the family, and the event was the departure of the children. The event chosen to mark the onset of the period of old age is the retirement of the male from active, regular work in the professions or in industry—again a factor determined more by the larger social setting than by the individual in many instances. The end of the period of old age is, of course, the death of the individual.

PROBLEMS OF AN AGING POPULATION

The proportion of older people in the population is rising as the effect of the control of infant and child mortality becomes apparent in many parts of the world. In 1850 the proportion of the population over 65 was 2.6 per cent,[1] whereas by 1950 it had increased very markedly to 8.0 per cent, representing almost 13 million people.[2] Even though the proportion of people reaching old age has greatly increased and will probably continue to increase, there has been but a small change in the length of life once the age of 65 has been reached. The economic problems inherent in an increase of nonproductive persons have been pointed out as an increasing burden to be borne by the productive portion of the population. In addition, there is the increasing cost of disabling illness which demands larger numbers of beds in nursing homes, chronic-disease hospitals, and general and psychiatric hospitals.[3] In all this anxious counting and prognosticating, the older person appears as a threat—a danger to the stability of the social order. Such great pessimism does not seem completely justified. Much productive

369

power in older people is wasted at present because of unjustified prejudice against their employment. Also, pride of achieved status prevents many older people from taking jobs below the highest level they achieved during their productive years. Both these problems are subject to change, and undoubtedly will change, partly through the education of those concerned. Furthermore, proper nutritional and, perhaps especially, social care will prevent many illnesses and shorten others. There is no side-stepping the public health, economic, and social problems inherent in the increase of our aging population; neither is there any reason to regard these problems as hopeless of reasonably satisfactory solution. It is obviously unfair to act as though the problem were the responsibility of the older people themselves. Strictly speaking, the problem is rather one of the cultural changes that have made longer life possible. The scientific discipline of public health is to a large extent responsible for these changes, and it must accept a large share of responsibility in minimizing the problem for the culture and for the individual aged person.

PHYSICAL AND PERSONALITY CHANGES

The period of old age involves rather rapid physical deterioration and an increase in the prevalence of chronic disease and disability. It involves, for the male, stopping work and thereby losing the stimulus offered by regular responsibility. He is thrown on his own resources to fill his time. The family income is usually lowered, which may precipitate housing and other problems. The period involves facing its inevitable end, death.

The curves of physical agility tend to fall more rapidly during the sixties and seventies than during middle age. Physical movement is slower, speed of perception is less, and the losses are more rapidly progressive (see Fig. 10). The personality tends to lose its power of originality and inventiveness as age increases, technical ability being maintained longer. This capacity of older people to continue in technical, repetitive work into old age was demonstrated during World War II, when the expanded labor force included more elderly individuals than had been kept employed in a less rushed period. A special case of this retention of a skill is found in intelligence testing, where capacities represented by vocabulary, general information, comprehension, and other tests are found to decrease less rapidly than the ability to solve arithmetic problems, for example.[4] The change of interests noted in the preceding section continues, but there is a decrease in the number of interests and a narrowing of outlook.[5] With this, there is, of course, a loss of appreciation of the interests of others and possibly a tendency to become touchy and irritable because of being left out of things in which there is little real interest anyway.

Research on the changes in personality function of aged persons has shown that the extent of these changes does not correlate closely with the extent of senile degeneration of the brain. This is the case in other brain affections as well; e.g., the brain pathology in paresis may in some cases be extreme while behavior changes are mild, while in other cases pathology is mild but behavior disorder very severe. It has not been possible to relate behavior change with location of damage except in certain rather specific situations, as in central paralysis and speech disorders. These facts have led to the conclusion that the prevention of brain damage, while essential, is not the only method available for the prevention of senile behavior disorders.[6]

The other preventive measures lie in the maintenance of function by adequate stimulation so that disuse atrophy does not occur. This involves keeping the older person functioning, not allowing him to "go to seed." This, in turn, requires, in addition to opportunity, the maintenance or the creation of attitudes of interest and cooperation which are too often lost as older persons are restricted in range of activity through stopping work, because of poverty or through physical infirmity. The major mental hygiene challenge in old age is to keep before older people the opportunity to be mentally and socially active and as active physically as their condition will allow.

Prophylaxis against the diseases of old age at the present state of knowledge is usually not directed toward preventing the onset of a disease, but toward preventing or minimizing the disability it produces. This process has a great deal to do with the social and emotional situation of the individual. If he has no stimulation or is continuously frustrated in his attempts to do things, or if he has no audience for his talking and thinking, his disability is likely to be much greater than the extent of his disease justifies. On the other hand, with proper stimulation and outlet, his disability may be very small in the light of the existing organic pathology. Prophylaxis against an unhappy old age, like prophylaxis against dissatisfactions in middle age, is a lifetime proposition. Wendell Muncie has said that every man should be preparing for his retirement during the active productive years so that there will be a fund of undone tasks and unsatisfied interests inviting the older person to their leisurely fulfillment in old age.[7] Throughout this book, treatment and rehabilitation have been neglected in favor of prophylactic techniques in mental hygiene. In old age, however, it appears justified to point out some of the experiments in rehabilitation as a means of indicating a prophylactic program. Dr. Lillien Martin was a pioneer in the rehabilitation of the aged, insisting and proving that the assumption that old people cannot become interested in new tasks is false. She showed, in her own life and in the lives of others, that respect for the elderly person and the fuller development of his faculties can result in happiness for him and in a contribution to society.[8] Social agencies are active in providing places where old people may meet, talk, play, and learn together with their contemporaries, avoiding the mental dilapidation that seems closely related to the factor of isolation in old people.[9] The force of this factor and the need to avoid it—a need that the elderly recognize—is well illustrated by the fact that programs which bring old people together result not infrequently in marriages, sometimes to the embarrassment of the children. These marriages represent an attempt to rebuild for themselves a pattern of shared response that will keep them from the personality dissolution which is, to some extent at least, secondary to isolation.

Gruenberg has showed that the factor of isolation is correlated with behavior disorders requiring hospitalization and that this factor operates, at least to some extent, independently of the financial situation of elderly persons.[10] Nevertheless, poverty is a major factor in imposing isolation on older people, restricting recreational activity. Transportation, which is likely to be more expensive for the older, somewhat infirm person than for more agile people, is made more difficult by poverty.[11]

RETIREMENT

Retirement of the male from active, regular employment is, for many, a tragedy. The emptiness of a life completely relieved of its usual responsibilities has been stressed previously in the case of the unmarried person who has devoted his or her life to the care of aged parents. This situation has also been seen in the middle-aged woman much of whose life work is ended by the fact that her children leave home. A striking example of the same type of situation, though the setting is far more complicated, is the suicide of the war hero when the war is over and he is reduced to humdrum civilian existence again. In the same vein, it is perhaps appropriate to point out that suicide rates are higher in elderly males than for any other group.[12]

For many men their work is an extremely important part of their total life. In the first place, it requires a large segment of their time. They may work a 40-hour week. When traveling to and from work and other preparatory activities are added, the amount of time in which the job is the primary interest is actually much higher. For men who own and run their own businesses or who are executives or professional men, the time spent with the job in the forefront of their thinking usually amounts to even a greater proportion of their lives. In mere time spent the job is enormously important. Social relationships are, furthermore, frequently built around the job associations. His cronies, the men he plays poker with regularly or meets for bridge games with his wife, are likely to be fellow workmen. The social bond may be more dependent upon the work relationship than on personal friendship. For some men the productive activity of work is their only creative outlet. It channels not only their intellect and their social drive, but also what artistic, creative urges they may have. Furthermore, their work may be an outlet for a need to show their power—power over men if they are supervisory personnel, over things if they are not at that level. For many the work relationships give a status, a position in the eyes of others, that is a source of satisfaction. The union relationship may be of great importance to the individual as an outlet for his feelings of social or community responsibility. A large part of the man's intellectual and emotional life may be all in one basket, his job.

When he retires from the job, this large segment of his life is lost. Lawton remarks, ". . . the sudden stoppage of work is one of the most important explanations for the fact that men, in the post-retirement years at least, are.apt to exhibit more symptoms of aging, both psychic and somatic, than do women." [13] The blow of retirement is somewhat lessened by the fact that the male tends to restrict the range of his social contacts as old age approaches and that the range of interests tends to contract so that, to some extent, the loss of the multiplicity of contacts may be a relief to him. If, at retirement, there is some physical blow, such as coronary disease, which restricts physical activity at the same time as regular work responsibilities drop out, the life of the old man may be empty indeed. He may become preoccupied with his physical ills, become crotchety and complaining and irritable or even seriously depressed. Such a case was seen a few years ago:

The man was 67 when he appeared for consultation. His life had been an adventurous one in business, and he had made a lot of money. He sold the first talking machine in his state and was the first Ford agent when the model T came out. He was influential in service organizations and his church. When a new church was built, he had donated the organ—characteristically to the memory of his mother. His son showed little evidence of his dominating type of personality, being self-effacing and not, in his father's eyes, quite up to running the prosperous family business. Because of this opinion, the father had stayed on as the active director of the business longer than he had meant to. This seemed largely to be a rationalization, the fact being that he vaguely realized that if he stopped work and responsibility, his existence would be bare indeed. Then came a mild coronary occlusion and the physician's order to stop work. There was no financial hardship whatever. A trip to Florida was flat, and he made no friends. He spent most of his time sitting about, worrying about when the next coronary occlusion would strike. He became depressed and suicidal and eventually was hospitalized for psychiatric treatment. The treatment was relatively simple, and hospitalization would probably not have been required had there been a more understanding general practitioner handling the case. The physician, however, stood in awe of the patient's wealth and his dominating personality and could not bring himself to deal with the patient in terms other than those concerned with the cardiac blood supply and its revelation in the electrocardiogram. Treatment in the hospital consisted in giving the patient a way of looking at his place in life a little more objectively. His son had proved to be reasonably reliable, and, in any case, he "was a big boy now" and no longer his father's responsibility.

The father was found to be able to use a concept of himself that gave him courage as well as status. He learned to look upon himself as a man somewhat in the position of a soldier about to go into battle. There was a chance that life would end at any time, but the soldier cannot stop his fighting because of this chance. To be sure, he takes precautions against death, but he lives on, and lustily, within the limits reasonable precaution allows. When he became able to entertain this philosophy, the patient was able to look for opportunities for activity and expression that remained within his capacities. His club activities had not been interdicted, and he could revive them. Cards offered a competitive interest that had previously been considered below the dignity of so busy a man, but were now found actually to be fascinating. Books had never appealed to him for much the same reason, but now he found them pleasurable. It was discovered that he had business interests which he did not control but which would welcome his advice though not his domination, a trait he recognized and could give up with almost a feeling of relief. During the course of the discussions and planning and practice in living described above, the anxious depression subsided and a more comfortable, less driving, somewhat more agreeable person emerged with less need to lead and to dominate.*

Old age in women does not involve the sudden loss of so large a part of life's interests, even though the woman may be employed. She usually maintains a home or apartment and does her own cooking or a part of it, takes care of her own clothing, etc., even though employed. She does these things to a much larger extent than the male, who tends to rely on others for much of his physical care. The need for the skills of the home does not disappear when outside employment stops, and the interest in the home arts may continue unchanged into quite advanced years. A woman who has a husband and children and grand-

* This case was treated by Dr. Adolf Meyer, to whom the writer was an assistant at the time.

children never need feel that she is not needed by society and that there is no place for her in the world, feelings common among retired men. There are still meals to be cooked, clothes to be cared for, and a house to be cleaned. Her skills are always necessary and are usually welcomed. She fits in better in the homes of her children if she goes to live with them, since she is able to contribute directly to the work of the home. She can even support herself to some extent by baby-sitting for the neighbors, a task her contemporary male may feel below his dignity. Perhaps the woman has had less need to dominate, or her skill in controlling situations is more subtle than the male's, thus allowing her to get along with less difficulty in another's home. Possibly because she is able to contribute more to homes she lives in which results in a feeling of usefulness, and because of her social skills, and also because the older female is perhaps more resistant to disease in general, the rate of admissions to mental hospitals for women over 65 is definitely lower than that for men of the same age group.[14]

In industrial cultures, retirement from active work, whether because retirement age has been reached or because of failing health, is apt to bring with it a reduction in income, frequently amounting to great hardship. In societies based more on nonmechanized agriculture, activity can frequently be progressively modified from heavy to lighter work as physical strength and agility are reduced, other members of the family replacing the older ones in the physically exacting tasks. In patriarchal societies, the children support the parents in the parental home, which is owned by the father. He retains his leadership of the family until it passes on to his eldest son at his death. In industrial cultures, particularly with highly mobile populations as in the United States, this usually is not the case. The children do not stay in the home, which is not now the place where the livelihood is gained and upon which they are economically dependent. They leave, and home ties and dependencies are likely to be ruptured completely. The "homestead" may be a house with no productive land about it, or perhaps an apartment to which there can be no emotional attachment for the children, however much the elderly parent may like the place. Many families nowadays tend to be migratory, however, so that even the parents may have no real attachment to the place where they live. Under such circumstances, the parents may move to a smaller place, a change that may symbolize a loss of prestige and intensify the male's feeling of loss of personal status in his retirement.

Or the parents may move in with their children. This involves the reduction of the parents from a position of authority in their own home, to a lesser position subject to the decisions of others. This is the case even if the parents are contributing to their own support. Usually they are conscious of the change of position and tend to be overcautious in asserting themselves at all. They do not fit in well with the friends of their children; frequently both generations are embarrassed about this, even though both wish it were otherwise.[15] The situation is apparently a greater strain on the male than the female. It probably accounts for the fact that older men tend to live alone more often than older women.[11]

There may come a point at which the factor of the late-maturing trait of judgment becomes less effective in the personality than the increasing factor of narrowing of interests and growing rigidity. It is difficult to judge this point in a practical sense, and it is precisely this difficulty that has led to the setting of definite retirement ages in many fields. The humiliation of removing a man from office because he is no longer competent is avoided by setting an age limit on his holding a position. The conclusion is that it is better to waste a few years of remaining good judgment than to risk having men refuse to vacate jobs they are no longer fit to fill. In some settings the change is made from an executive position to a policy-making one dealing in long-term trends. Corporations tend to move the president of the company, who must be physically active and mentally decisive and adaptable, to the position of chairman of the board where his influence and experience are assets, but his loss of physical and mental agility is not so likely to interfere. In universities, professors become emeritus professors, perhaps with some remaining teaching load but with no administrative responsibility. From the mental hygiene viewpoint, these practices have a great deal to recommend them, since they preserve the values of the aged person while relieving him of the strains on his declining abilities. Business executives and college professors make up a very small segment of the population, however, and many members of both groups feel ill-used when retired. Some corporations have evolved definite plans for gradual retirement of executives so that the work stoppage will not come as so severe a shock, and so that replacement interests can be developed for fuller use after retirement. For skilled and unskilled workers such elaborate plans have not been developed. Members of this much larger group, when faced with an absolute retirement age, are frequently at a loss as to how to fill up weary hours. Such a tragic situation is shown in the moving picture "Steps of Age," [16] a film so realistic that many find it uncomfortable to see. The building of leisure-time activities during the young-adult and middle-aged periods can help solve this problem, but for many in the population at present the only solution appears to lie in continued work, either at the lifetime job or in one less exacting physically. There are many problems in this area to be solved only by intensive community planning and education, a large share of the responsibility for which falls on public health agencies.

DISABILITIES IN THE AGED

Geriatrics is rapidly becoming a recognized public health responsibility, particularly in those areas where medical care and chronic hospitals are included in programs. Most health departments have at least the minimal responsibility of licensing of nursing homes and similar institutions. Public health licensing has, in the past, been mainly concerned with the basic requirements for sanitation and for safety. Studies have shown that, in Maryland, only 40 per cent of private nursing home patients are without gross mental deviations and that 40 per cent of all patients are "confused" most of the time.[17] Clearly the licensing authority should expand its basis for inspection if the public is to be able to feel secure that a license means that the institution concerned is able to carry its responsibilities at least on a minimal level.

In addition to the diagnosis and treatment of chronic disease in mental hygiene of old age, the individuality and responsibility of the person must be more carefully protected. There is a tendency to accept uncritically the idea that old age tends to make people "childish" and to assume that they can be treated like children in the sense that they can be regarded as the responsibility of someone other than themselves. In dealing with older people the dignity of the individual, the recognition of his fundamental worth—not as a productive person necessarily, but as one whose very survival marks him as unusually worthy of respect—is most important. So much of the treatment of the ills of old age requires the active cooperation of the patient that he becomes a respected collaborator rather than someone on whom treatment is imposed. As a matter of fact, he will probably not follow any treatment imposed upon him; he will rebel and do as he sees fit unless the responsibility of his care is shared with him.

Old age brings a reduction of memory for recent events. There is little evidence to indicate whether this is due to organic loss or to the fact that the interest and attention of the older person tend to veer away from things over which he has increasingly less control. In any case, there is a loss that makes living with others somewhat difficult at times. Glasses get mislaid, and there is a tendency to feel that mislaid things have been deliberately taken away. The older person tends to think upon events long past. Again there is a question of whether this is due to loss of brain tissue or whether it represents the older person thinking back to days when he was more powerful and influential in life than he finds himself in old age. A trait that often appears is unwillingness to part with things, possibly representing a tendency to hold onto the past in which there was better and more complete control of the environment. The thwarting of these tendencies may bring out suspiciousness and irritability and development of a stubborn rigidity that defends the person's place in life. There seems little doubt that if there were understanding of these traits, fewer older people would have to be hospitalized for the psychoses of old age. These psychoses often seem to be as much the result of failure to understand by the family as they are of failure of the patient to react normally. This conclusion is borne out by the fact that many old people whose actions cannot be tolerated in the homes of their relatives are easily cared for in families not their own.[18] The hangover of difficulties of parent-child relationships, unadjusted during earlier years, and the factor of difficulties in the in-law relationship make the understanding care of the aged in the homes of their own children more of a problem than is justified from the condition of the patient himself.[19]

A frequent expression of the suspiciousness of old people is the feeling that the children are simply waiting for them to die so that property may be inherited. Here again, the liability of the patient to entertain such ruminations may be dependent upon organic factors, but the fact that the ideas actually appear is likely to be due to the situation under which the older person is living. Investigation frequently leads to the conclusion that such thoughts were actually being entertained in the home responsible for the old person, though perhaps they were not stated in words and were actually but one phase of a genuinely ambivalent attitude. The techniques of adjusting personalities socially and individually apply in old age as well as in other age groups. Their use will result in better treatment of old people and, possibly, in a lowering of the incidence of hospitalization.

Older people are subject to mental illnesses that are quite independent of the aging process itself. There is a tendency to feel that the prognosis of mental illnesses in the aged is uniformly bad. This is not entirely true. Depressions in older people frequently yield to treatment, and many confusional episodes yield to temporary simplification of environment in hospital and to supportive treatment. Nutritional deprivation may be at the basis of some psychoses and prove readily treatable. In addition, many psychoses from which the patient does not completely recover do not prove so disabling that the patient cannot leave hospital to live again in his own family, a foster family, a nursing home,

or a home for the aged. The future will probably see much more movement of old people in and out of hospitals, depending on temporary
variations in mental state. Such movement will undoubtedly lead to
better preservation of personality assets, though it must be recognized
that it will involve the extension of social service work and of the field
of activity of the public health nurse.

ATTITUDES TOWARD AGING

In old age the threat of illness is increased, and death must be faced.
According to Lawton, most old people do not fear death so much as
they fear pain and the isolation that comes with long-continued illness.[13] He is inclined to the belief that, like people of other age groups,
aged people do not recognize the threat of death as applying to themselves until it is actually upon them. This seems doubtful, since many
have written about their attitude toward it. Those who are chronically
ill think much about it. If they are well adjusted and have had satisfactions in life, they do not fear the end that will relieve them of pain and
relieve others of their care, but rather invite it. Some, in better health,
can invite the pleasures of old age, the capacity to review a long past
with memories of struggles won and lost, to contemplate the reasons for
existence, to look at a rushing world from the vantage point of one
about to leave it. For the person who has no fear of death—and Lawton
feels that fear of death indicates mental illness of some degree even in
old age—its approach has a peculiar effect of intensifying the sensual
and philosophical satisfactions of living. Although Hans Zinsser was
not an old man at his death, this attitude of high appreciation of the
world is beautifully illustrated in his revealing book, *As I Remember
Him*. Having just been told of his approaching death, Zinsser reports: [20]

> But in those few minutes, R. S. told me, something took place in his
> mind that he regarded as a sort of compensatory adjustment to the thought
> that he would soon be dead. In the prospect of death, life seemed to be
> given new meaning and fresh poignancy. It seemed, he said, from that
> moment, as though all that his heart felt and his senses perceived were
> taking on a "deep autumnal tone" and an increased vividness. From now
> on, instead of being saddened, he found—to his own delighted astonish-
> ment—that his sensitiveness to the simplest experiences, even for things
> that in other years he might hardly have noticed, was infinitely enhanced.

Stanley Hall, in a much quoted statement, indicates the same feeling
as death approached, "and so I am grateful to senescence which has
brought me at last into the larger light of the new day which the young
could never see and should never be asked to see." [21] These men seem

to achieve a kind of objectivity without rancor. Even so tortured a spirit as Somerset Maugham could quietly evaluate his life and what critics had said of him and be not dissatisfied with it though recognizing its faults. He says: [22]

> I do not care much if people agree with me. Of course I think I am right, otherwise I should not think as I do, and they are wrong, but it does not offend me that they should be wrong nor does it greatly disturb me to discover that my judgment is at variance with that of the majority. I have a certain confidence in my instinct.
>
> I must write on as though I were a person of importance; and indeed, I am—to myself.

Some old people gain an interest in the very process of their physical dissolution. A letter from an older woman recording the onset of symptoms due to arteriosclerosis includes the sentences, "I have always wondered what it would be like when I began to go to pieces. Now I know." Other old people, however, do not see the problem in this light. They may be irritated and humiliated by their increasing infirmities, or frightened by them. Not all old people can behold their own aging from the pinnacles of success and financial security that characterize a Hall, a Zinsser, and a Maugham. They must look at life through the dirty window of a dilapidated room which poverty or their own pride of independence forces upon them, and which physical infirmity bars them from brightening with washing cloth and paintbrush. For people of the lower socioeconomic levels the miseries of old age can frequently be reduced only by the action of community social and health agencies and by the various sorts of volunteer services that are increasingly being developed.

HOUSING AND SOCIALIZATION

Housing for the aged has received a great deal of attention. For the most part it is agreed that institutionalization is unwise unless it is necessary to obtain care not otherwise available. Occasionally, institutions are useful when no other means can be found to supply social contacts for the aging person.[11] Housing for the aged has been of two general types: (1) grouping the aged together in projects, a method frequently used in northern Europe; (2) constructing space for the elderly mixed with dwellings for younger families. The latter pattern appears to be preferred in the United States, though it must be admitted that the problem has received little enough attention in that country thus far. Special architectural planning for the elderly is not generally recommended for the United States, it being contended that safe construction for the elderly is no more than safe construction for all, and this is a particularly important consideration in the reduction of home accidents at all ages.[23]

In addition to housing and official social and health services, many different types of volunteer services have been developed, directed primarily at increasing stimulation for the aged and reducing isolation. For the elderly who are not homebound there are protected workshops in some communities in which the relatively inefficient older person may work. There are also recreational and educational centers to which they may go for stimulation and companionship. Many churches are building such programs for their older parishioners and for the community as a whole. In earlier times and still to a considerable extent, the older woman does handwork to be used as gifts to her children and grandchildren. For the homebound there are plans which make it possible for the older woman to earn some money through needlework; this may also be done as a charitable undertaking if she is not in need. In their plans volunteers usually organize themselves to take the material to the worker and collect the finished product. Other groups simply visit the elderly, bringing the stimulation of the outside world to those who cannot get out. Such ventures frequently bring such improvement that the worker changes to a transportation volunteer, helping the older person get to the recreational center where he can associate with his contemporaries.[11] These various plans have not yet been subjected to strict statistical evaluation, but there is little doubt that they prevent or delay the onset of senile psychoses in some cases.

Gruenberg's Syracuse study indicates that elderly people who live alone are more likely to require psychiatric hospitalization than those living in families.[24] It is possible that the isolation from social intercourse with other people is a cause of mental illness in the elderly. This may be one factor which changes the condition of a somewhat degenerated nervous system in a behaviorally sound personality into a personality showing behavior disorder intolerable to the community. It appears that isolation and lack of stimulation may be as dangerous to the aged as they are to the infant. It has recently been shown experimentally that isolation of adults, if severe, can produce observable changes of personality function within a few days.[25] This factor has been considered to play a part in the personality dulling observed in war prisoners where each man is isolated by reason of his suspicions that the next may be an informer.[26] Data are accumulating that may culminate in the generalization that any environment which tends to isolate an individual from others offers a stress that will lead to distinguishable personality changes, increased susceptibility to pathological

personality functioning, and perhaps psychiatric illness. As in the conclusion of the American Public Health Association regarding housing
for the elderly,[23] what is imperative for the aged would contribute to
the health of all.

At socioeconomic levels that do not themselves restrict socialization,
the elderly form themselves into groups for relief from isolation. There
are clubs exclusively for retired executives, buildings obtained by the
people themselves as places to play checkers, etc.[27] Poverty is a tremendous retarding influence to such spontaneous organizations, however.
The elderly are no less sensitive than others about attending organization functions when their dues are unpaid.[28] The thesis that the public
welfare is best served by mere subsistence grants for persons dependent
upon the state may be reasonable for the young adult, but for the
elderly—and for children as well—there must be something in the
budget for transportation and for recreational activities with groups. In
line with good group social work practice at all ages, for the aged such
services should provide minimal managerial leadership. The agency
should provide stimulation to start the project, then work exclusively
with the group in planning and management.

Death to the older person has a social meaning as well as a personal
one. It means increasing loneliness as his contemporaries disappear
from the scene. This is, of course, most acute when one of a couple dies
after long years of living together, and after they have achieved a response pattern that almost makes them a single biological unit. Edna
Ferber illustrates this pattern and the consequences of its interruption
by death in her story "Old Man Minick." [15] The death of each friend
cuts off another social relationship and tends to reinforce the narrowing of interests that is proceeding anyway, probably on the basis of
physiological and anatomical changes in the body. Ferber's story illustrates the fact that the environment may reinforce the narrowing more
than is comfortable for the individual and that, given opportunity, the
older person may find new friends and interests.

In general, the older person left behind by the death of his contemporaries is a better than average human being in most aspects; he is an
example of the survival of the fittest. It is well known that effectiveness
of personality, intelligence, and physical stamina are correlated rather
highly and in a positive direction.[29,30] This probably accounts for the
number of examples of continuing productiveness into old age. The
examples usually cited, including Justice Holmes, Corot, and Goethe,
cannot be called typical of old age. They represent the old age of highly
exceptional and highly endowed people. It is as unfair to set such men

as these as examples for all old people as it is to set Menuhin or Mozart as the ideal for every child taking up the violin or piano.

Old people are people and have the faults of people. Others tend to expect them all to be acquiescent, reactive to suggestion, thankful for every opportunity, and never carpingly critical. When they are found to be stubborn, resistive to suggestion, captious, quite capable of romance, insistent on making their own decisions, there may be disappointment and feeling of frustration on the part of those attempting to serve and help them. Like all people, they must be accepted as they are, personalities reacting in individual ways.

SUMMARY

Old age is marked by rapid decline in physical and mental agility. There is a decline in judgment and a narrowing of interests, which is difficult to judge as to time of onset. To avoid having people remain in responsible positions after the assets are diminished beyond the point of effectiveness, retirement from positions of active responsibility is the rule in some classes of employment. In other classes, physical disability, either because of disease or infirmity, is the cause of dropping the full work load. Stopping work may leave a gap in the time, the social relationships, the recreations, and the interests of an individual which he may be hard put to it to fill. Reduced income and physical infirmity, as well as the anxieties of children about their elderly parents, make living with the children a common practice in many industrial cultures in contrast to older paternalistic cultures. There is a danger that the elderly will be neglected as responsible individuals and may be treated as someone's dependents, a humiliation that may give rise to adjustment problems. Older people tend to have trouble with recent memory and to recall more vividly the times when they were active and influential. They respond to the means of improving adjustment as do younger people, though more slowly and with greater difficulty. The methods of study of situations and personalities are not different than at other ages. The proper application of these principles may lower the rate of hospitalization in this age group as well as preserve the happiness and productiveness of people beyond middle age.

REFERENCES

1. Burgess, E. W.: The Growing Problem of Aging, in C. Tibbetts (ed.), *Living through the Older Years,* University of Michigan Press, Ann Arbor, 1949.
2. Federal Security Agency: *Man and His Years,* Health Publications Institute, Raleigh, N.C., 1951.

3. Perrott, G. St. J., L. M. Smith, M. Y. Pennell, and M. E. Altenderfer: *Care of the Long-term Patient, Source Book on the Size and Characteristics of the Problem,* National Conference on Care of the Long-term Patient, Commission on Chronic Illness, Baltimore, 1954.

4. Wechsler, D.: *The Measurement of Adult Intelligence,* The Williams & Wilkins Company, Baltimore, 1944.

5. Rorschach, H.: *Psychodiagnostics,* Verlag Hans Huber, Berne, 1942; Grune & Stratton, Inc., New York, American distributors.

6. Lemkau, P. V.: "The Mental Hygiene of Aging," *Pub. Health Rep.* **67:**237–242 (1952).

7. Muncie, W.: Staff conference discussion, Henry Phipps Psychiatric Clinic, Baltimore, unpublished.

8. Martin, L. J., and DeGruchy, C.: *Salvaging Old Age,* The Macmillan Company, New York, 1930.

9. See *Survey,* **82:**105–114, for a series of reports by G. Lawton, M. W. Wagner, A. Stone, and K. Gorrie on such experiments, 1946.

10. Gruenberg, E. M.: "The Syracuse Study of Mental Health Problems of the Aging," paper read at the annual meeting of the American Psychiatric Association, May 5, 1953, Los Angeles, unpublished.

11. Breckinridge, E., H. G. Laue, M. H. Little, and H. Manning: *Community Services for Older People,* Wilcox & Follett Co., Chicago, 1952.

12. Gordon, J. E., E. Lindemann, J. Ipsen, and W. T. Vaughn: "An Epidemiologic Analysis of Suicide," in *Epidemiology of Mental Disorder,* Milbank Memorial Fund, New York, 1950.

13. Lawton, G.: "Psychological Guidance for Older Persons," in E. J. Cowdry (ed.), *Problems of Ageing,* The Williams & Wilkins Company, Baltimore, 1944.

14. Landis, C., and J. D. Page: *Modern Society and Mental Disease,* Farrar & Rinehart, Inc., New York, 1938.

15. Ferber, E.: "Old Man Minick," in J. Strode (ed.), *Social Insight through Short Stories,* Harper & Brothers, New York, 1946.

16. "Steps of Age" (film), Mental Health Film Board, New York, 1950.

17. Unpublished data from survey of patients in nursing care institutions made by the Commission on Chronic Illness in Cooperation with the U.S. Public Health Service and the Maryland State Department of Health, 1952.

18. Pollock, H. M. (ed.): *Family Care of Mental Patients,* State Hospitals Press, Utica, N.Y., 1936.

19. Stern, E. M., and M. Ross: *You and Your Aging Parents,* A. A. Wyn, Inc., New York, 1952.

20. Zinsser, H.: *As I Remember Him: The Biography of R. S.,* Little, Brown & Company, Boston, 1940.

21. Hall, S.: *Senescence,* Appleton-Century-Crofts, Inc., New York, 1932.

22. Maugham, W. S.: *The Summing Up,* Doubleday & Company, Inc., New York, 1938.

23. *Housing an Aging Population,* Committee on the Hygiene of Housing, American Public Health Association, New York, 1953.

24. Gruenberg, E. M.: "The Epidemiology of Mental Disease," *Scient. Am.* **190**:38–42 (1954).

25. Hebb, D. O.: "The Significance of Neurophysiologic Theory for Psychiatry," paper read at the annual meeting of the American Psychiatric Association, May 6, 1954, at St. Louis, to be published.

26. Rioch, D. McK.: *Report on Temporary Duty in Japan and Korea, April 14 to July 17, 1953,* Army Medical Service Graduate School, Walter Reed Army Medical Center, Washington 12, 1954 (restriction removed July 13, 1954).

27. Levine, H. A.: "Community Programs for the Elderly," *Ann. Am. Acad. Polit. & Social Sc.* **279**:164–170 (1952).

28. Tibbitts, C. (ed.): *Living through the Older Years,* University of Michigan Press, Ann Arbor, 1949.

29. Terman, L. M., and M. H. Oden: *The Gifted Child Grows Up,* Stanford University Press, Stanford, Calif., 1947.

30. Allen, G.: *Families Whence High Intelligence Springs,* Bulletin 25, Eugenics Record Office, Carnegie Institution of Washington, Washington, D.C., May, 1926.

CHAPTER EIGHTEEN

Summary and Prospect

THE CONCEPT OF SOCIAL DISTANCE

The experiences that enter the personality structure of any individual and influence it involve other personalities to varying degrees. When there is quantitatively and qualitatively intense relationship between individuals, the social distance is said to be short. If the relationship is evanescent and at a very formal level, it may be said to take place at a greater social distance, e.g., a citizen's relationship to the mayor of a large city. Still more distant relationships exist, such as that between the national governing body and the individual citizen. Impersonal factors also determine experiences that enter personality structure, such as the effect of the absence of recreational space on the incidence of juvenile delinquency, or the effect of crop failures in producing states of mind in which violence is easily set off.

The mother-child relationship is, of course, the one involving the shortest social distance imaginable, and this undoubtedly accounts to some extent for the important place given it in theories of personality formation. The parent-child relationship involves another person, and the addition of siblings in the family still further extends the relationship range. This pageant of broadening relationships has been traced until it reached its maximum complexity and expanse during the middle period of life when it included family, work, religious, political, and many other types of contacts. These vary from the very short social distances involved in the husband-wife relationship to the vastly greater distances involved in concern for the community welfare.

For the most part, the experiences treated in this book are of relatively short social distance. They are usually personal experiences, ones which touch the person so immediately that he can feel, and we can observe, their impact quite directly. It should not be assumed that the experiences at a longer distance are not considered formative. Rather, experiences have been selected from those most effectively dealt with by personnel who meet the population singly or in relatively small groups, rather than in terms of broad political movements, which usually take place under nonmedical leadership. It may well be that these massive movements are of greater importance than the more personal experiences. It is true that the specialties dealing in the greater social distances, such as sociology and social anthropology, political science, and economics, contribute to the understanding of mental hygiene and to its action program. However, medicine as presently conceived is allowed, in most cultures, to deal effectively only with issues involving relatively short social distances.

THE COMMUNITY AS A SOCIAL ORGANISM

The concept of social medicine is, in the minds of most leaders in the field, still at the level of interpreting the effect of the larger community and its patterns of living upon the individual. On the other hand, there is evidence of a tendency for medicine to escape this merely interpretative function and to attempt to study the community as a patient would be studied, to attempt to diagnose and treat the presumably sick community. Thus we find concepts such as the "paranoid" nation appearing, and discussion of "sick societies," and "unhealthy civilizations." Indeed there are some who feel that dealing with the problems implied by these names is the fundamental area of concern of public health, that this specialty has no function in individual diagnosis and treatment at all.

The thinking on which such concepts is based has to do with the progression of levels of integration discussed on page 8. Here, it will be recalled, behavior of the human being was said to rest upon physics and chemistry as they show themselves in metabolism of cells, in the action of forces and elements in varied combinations. Thinking and feeling become possible on the basis of metabolic activity and out of thinking and feeling come speech and symbolic activity. Speech demands socialization; it requires at least two individuals to perform the act of verbal communication. The individual is an integrate made up of billions of cells; is it not conceivable that the community is a sort of colony of "cells" each of which is an integral human being? And, if so, is it not proper to speak of the community in health and disease? By such reasoning the physician may come to make such diagnoses as the "psychotic nation" or the "underprivileged country." Rarely does he offer treatment, and such as is advised is usually in terms of advice about conduct and patterns of thought. The "body politic" can hardly be treated by giving medicine; occasionally one would like to surgically remove individuals from it, and society does this for itself when certain of its integral parts disturb or threaten it too greatly.

It is inviting to dwell on this concept of the "treatment" of the community as a medical or public health issue, but most highly organized cultures do not allow the physician and his helpers this right. Earlier and primitive cultures, in which healing and religion were combined and controlled all the activities of a group, did grant the physician the role of priest and governor. Modern complex societies usually demand that there be a fairly strict separation of these several spheres of activity. Even in an area as closely associated with health as housing, control is not in the hands of the physician. The houses are planned and built in what is essentially a political atmosphere. The idea of medical interference with political leadership is so ludicrous that cartoonists have held the idea up to ridicule, even though the politician was depicted as badly needing some sort of medical care.

The public health official and the physician are, of course, granted the position of technical experts in housing problems, but the ultimate decisions rest on nonmedical grounds, and on these the physician is not asked to testify. It is unlikely that in our day a physician will even be asked to testify as to the health of the decisions of a national leader, except under most extreme conditions in which society has already been outraged. Early case-finding efforts among politicians, so far as mental health is concerned, are unlikely for some time to come. In the light of these interpretations, it is at least doubtful if there is much advantage in thinking of the community as a patient to be treated. It is probably much more remunerative to think of society as a series of individuals each of whom may be dealt with at whatever level of integration may be indicated, resting upon the confidence that healthy integrals will produce as healthy a society as may be possible. Felix tells of a father anxious to read his paper and being pestered by his little boy. Thinking to get some peace and quiet, he tore from the paper a map of the world and reduced it to jigsaw-puzzle pieces, giving them to the boy to put together. The lad returned in a short while to have him come and see the map put together, the world all in its proper arrangement. Astonished, he asked the boy how he had done it so fast. The boy said, "Oh, it was easy. There was a picture of a man on the back, and when I put the man together correctly the world was all right, too." It is this basis of the increase of individual health making for an increase in the total health of the whole world that public health adheres to for the most part at the present time. It is on the basis of this philosophy that greater attention is given in public health mental hygiene to the relatively short social distances of family relationships than to broader community and cultural issues. No brief is held that this is correct; it is at least more feasible and offers more tested ways of operation than in the area of the greater social distances.

This does not mean that public health personnel do not have responsibility for the broadest type of community planning; it does appear to mean that when they enter this field as other than technical consultants they enter as citizens and not as medical personnel. Their function then becomes one of broader community leadership rather than of medical diagnosis and treatment. As a technical consultant, the health professional may insist that there be a rail on every set of steps in a housing project, or a bathtub in every dwelling unit, but it will be as a citizen that he will campaign for appropriations for the project to exist at all. As a technical consultant he may be responsible for the size of the sewer connection, but it will be a judge or council of citizens who will decide whether the community can afford to make the transition from outside to inside toilets. The psychiatrist may see the politician as a dangerous fool, but short of outrage, it will be his vote cast with those of other citizens that removes the man from office.

It is difficult to gauge whether such words are written in frustration, in fear of an impossible task, in honest humility, because of lack of passion for the ideal of the healthiest population, or in the fundamental concept that the health of the people is genuinely the people's responsibility and not that of the profession of medicine and its public health specialists. It can be concluded that most public health activities, including mental hygiene efforts, will, so far as actual manipulation of ideas or instruments is concerned, probably be at relatively short social distances. Those areas of public health not dealing in direct manipulation, such as health education, might escape this stricture, yet this field, too, is concerning itself with specially interested smaller groups within the population rather than addressing itself to the unclassified whole of the community in its most recent developments.

MENTAL HYGIENE IN PUBLIC HEALTH: STATUS

"Health is a state of complete physical, mental, and social well-being." There is no question of the physical aims, nor has there been for centuries. The inclusion of the aim of mental health is relatively more recent in so far as deliberate planning is concerned, but it has achieved some status. The foregoing sections of this chapter not only have indicated the difficulty of distinguishing clearly among the three categories included in the World Health Organization definition, but have pointed up the kinds of problems introduced by the concepts of social and mental health. The conclusion has been drawn, rightly or wrongly, that at the present state of development, planning public health programs in mental hygiene is, to a considerable extent, a matter of influencing human relationships of relatively short social distance with the general aim of promoting the development of the soundest possible personality structure.

Difficult as it is to define just what program will best carry out this aim, the aim itself is rapidly becoming accepted as a legitimate matter of concern of tax-supported and voluntary health agencies. Psychiatrists interested in public health procedures and processes are becoming much more numerous over the world. The mental health nurse consultant appears to be becoming an integral part of the public health nursing division in an increasing number of health departments and agencies.

As in every developing program, there is considerable anxiety as to where and how work shall be done. Psychiatry and psychology have not produced all the facts needed as a basis for action, and public health research in this area has not yet developed fully. Schools of public health, harassed by financial problems, have been unable to enter the field as enthusiastically as they would like now to do, though earlier there was real resistance to entering it at all. Integration of mental hygiene into public health teaching still appears to lag somewhat except in the area of maternal and child health. The integration is proceeding, however, both in the schools and in the field. Workable programs are under way. Evaluation of programs remains a problem for solution in the future, but this pressing problem is also receiving increasing attention.

To go forward with doubts about the essential value of programs seems to be the fate of public health in many instances. Continuing and extending efforts in mental hygiene seem to fall in this sense into line with the historical patterns in this field. And it is impossible to turn back now. Seely, a sociologist, in his paper, Social Values, The Mental Health Movement and Mental Health, comes to the conclusion:

> But it is no longer even a question for policy. No known man or body of men now has the power to arrest the flow or alter the general direction of events, even if, on mental health grounds, that should be indicated. If we, the mental hygienists, should amputate our writing arms and seal our reluctant lips, the field would fall to the quack and charlatan, and the principal difference would be that the self-consciousness would be worse founded and more misleading. There is no choice open in that direction for us, any more than there is a way of abdication for the physicists in the face of the atomic bomb and its more violent variants.

This force of sociological movement has pressed public health into activities in the past, it is pressing it into the attempt to relieve and control the chronic illnesses, and it will continue to be effective in forcing the development of concepts and programs in the area of building sound personality structures.

This marching into the unknown while using all the resources of knowledge presently available makes every mental hygiene program, every effort to control a mental illness or prevent one, or to promote mental health, an on-going experiment, a piece of research that may never be repeatable under the same conditions. The ignorance that casts its shadow over all our work can be dispelled only through carrying out programs in the full consciousness of their research import. There is no place in science for blind belief; when blind faith in one or another principle directs programs, there is bound to be catastrophic friction with other blind beliefs. The aim must be to preserve an attitude of sufficient faith to work, yet sufficient doubt to inquire consistently and carefully about the immediate and the ultimate values of the work in achieving health for the population.

Review of Psychopathological States

The public health officer is frequently responsible to some degree for the legal commitment of patients to psychiatric hospital. In some countries he is expected to be a fairly expert psychiatrist. In the United States it is more generally required of him to decide whether or not there is mental illness present of severe enough degree to require removal of the patient to hospital. He will also wish certain basic knowledge to allow him to work effectively with psychiatric consultants who furnish treatment or consultative service to the health department.

This appendix is merely a brief summary of symptoms of the various illnesses and types of reaction for easy reference. Statistics on the incidence and prevalence of some of the more important groups of diseases have been included where useful figures are available. An attempt has been made to use figures believed to be capable of at least some generalization, though it should be noted that most of the studies quoted have been done on Western European cultures.

The classification of mental illnesses would be much more satisfactory if it could be constructed entirely on the basis of etiology. This is not as yet possible, as will be seen in the outline used here. Some conditions are of known etiology; some are simply descriptions or groupings of symptoms that are generally found together. The American Psychiatric Association issued a revised nomenclature in 1952. The arrangement of diagnostic groupings here conforms to the pattern of that manual in adhering to a basic division into brain disorders and personality disorders not known to involve brain damage or destruction. Beyond this, however, more traditional terminology has been used.

Any of the standard textbooks of psychiatry will serve as references for further reading in this field, and are recommended as necessary adjuncts to the following outlines. The statistical data presented come from a variety of sources, which, along with other references and material for additional reading, are included in the reading list.

CLASSIFICATION OF PSYCHOPATHOLOGICAL STATES

1. Conditions associated with known damage to nervous tissue.
   a. Injury states due to infection.

   b. Injury states due to toxins.
   c. Injury states due to trauma.
   d. Injury states due to nutritional deprivation.
2. Conditions due to degenerative changes in nervous tissue.
   a. Senile conditions.
   b. Conditions associated with cerebral arteriosclerosis.
   c. Conditions associated with other neurological diseases.
3. Mental deficiency.
4. Psychopathic personality.
5. Psychoses "psychogenic" (not known to be associated with brain damage or destruction).
   a. Manic-depressive psychoses and allied states.
   b. Schizophrenia and allied states.
6. Convulsive disorders (epilepsy).
7. Behavior disorders in children.
8. Neuroses (including psychosomatic disorders).

CONDITIONS ASSOCIATED WITH KNOWN DAMAGE TO NERVOUS TISSUE

These conditions are of almost infinite variety, and their diagnosis and treatment frequently defy the expert. This section touches only a few of the most prominent problems in the group.

Injury States Due to Infection. *General Paresis (General Paralysis of the Insane, Meningoencephalitic Syphilis).* In neurosyphilis there is a periarteritis that eventually causes damage of brain tissue by deprivation of blood supply. There is also direct damage to brain cells due to invasion of the tissues by the spirochete. Prior to the development of the modern treatment of syphilis and neurosyphilis, the psychosis resulting from this invasion was of a reasonably constant type. At that time, clinical diagnosis was apparently not so difficult, the classical signs being seen much more regularly. Modern practice tends to make the diagnosis on the basis of spinal-fluid findings and the clinical history. The diagnosis is made early, and treatment is begun. As a result, the course of the disease is so modified that the classical picture is now almost a rarity.

The history in paresis includes the primary infection which took place years before the patient is seen. Sometimes he has had inadequate treatment; in some cases this seems to speed the appearance of neurosyphilis. Then there appeared some act definitely unusual for the person. The soldier fails to carry out duties he has done faithfully for 20 years; the bookkeeper makes unaccountable errors. There may be attacks of unconsciousness, with or without convulsions. Speech becomes slurred and careless. The patient may show an euphoric mood, or he may become depressed, or he may feel that everyone is against him. He may hear voices of plotters against him, or others that seem to support his exalted opinion of himself. The psychosis may in fact take almost any form, especially when modified by treatment. In every psychosis, regardless of how clearly the symptoms seem to indicate that it falls into some well-recognized group, serological tests on the blood for syphilis should be done, and if positive, spinal-fluid examination should also be carried out. The mental status in paresis will usually show marked defects in both recent and remote memory, accompanied by the development of physical weakness and other signs of deteriorative illness.

Neurosyphilis manifested by positive spinal-fluid findings, with or without evidences of paresis, should be brought under appropriate treatment without delay. For the most part nonsymptomatic neurosyphilis is now treated in general hospitals or by ambulatory treatment, psychiatric hospitals receiving only actively psychotic patients or those in whom treatment has failed or in whom it began only after severe brain destruction had taken place.

Paresis appears in most cultures to be more common in males than in females. Differences in incidence in various ethnic groups are probably more related to economic and other social factors than to differential susceptibility, though the question is not finally settled.

First admissions of paretics to psychiatric hospitals in the United States have decreased from 5,681 in 1933 to 3,641 in 1949, or from 4.7 to 2.4 per 100,000 population. There can be little doubt that this decrease is due to better prevention or better treatment of syphilis, though some of it was probably also due to the fact that more neurosyphilis received treatment in general hospitals than previously.

Epidemic Encephalitis. The disturbances of behavior in acute encephalitis have received widespread attention; the unusual sleepiness in some cases, the sleep reversals, the hyperactive cases are all well described. The late sequels of the disease are probably less well recognized. Apparently the damage to the brain tissue due to the invasion of the infective agent is not completely reversible. The history usually reveals a sharp change in personality. Before a certain time, the child was easily managed, got along well in school, slept well, and talked no more than the average child. Since a spell of illness, he shows distinctly different reactions, talks all the time, makes sudden, jerky, and apparently uncontrollable movements, is physically hyperactive, has severe tantrums in which he is maliciously destructive, or is cruel toward other children or pets. He shows no response to the methods of correction that were formerly effective in curbing misbehavior. When the health officer sees such a case, a postencephalitic disorder should be suspected, and the child should be referred to some agency prepared to investigate the matter more thoroughly. Such a case will not profit by the usual corrective procedures of a juvenile court, and in some cases hospitalization will be necessary. There have been no large epidemics of encephalitis in the United States for some years. Cases of this sort are likely to be rather rare but do appear sporadically in association with measles or other types of encephalitic involvement.

Parkinsonism is the most common late sequel of encephalitis. This state is hardly to be differentiated from the paralysis agitans of old age. The severe behavior disorders frequently seen in children are rare in cases of parkinsonism. It is characterized by hypertonic muscles, giving a sort of rigidity to the patient that is shown in the stooped posture, the masklike facies, and the exceedingly slow movement. The tremors are constant and interfere with the patient's ordinary movements. Oculogyric crises occur and may be mistaken for epileptic attacks. This group of symptoms may appear at any age following encephalitis. In industry it is important that the picture be recognized early, since the psychic trauma of trying to maintain the usual pace in the face of increasing slowness of movement is a strain that may lead to the greatest despondency and thus further cut down efficiency. The condition is usually progressive and finally leads to complete invalidism, although treatment with certain of the atropine series of drugs as well as the newer relaxing compounds frequently helps to alleviate the symptoms.

Psychopathological States Associated with Other Infections. All the various sorts of meningitis may produce brain damage and leave motor, sensory, and thinking deficits. The tendency to overlook these deficits, in the general satisfaction that the patient's life has been saved, may lead to inaccurate or incomplete evaluation of treatment results. The reported cures of tuberculous meningitis, for example, rarely give accurate data on the psychiatric condition of the patient. Experience in treating postmeningococcal meningitis patients indicates that in many cases the convalescence is much longer than reports usually imply.

Intrauterine infection may also give rise to brain damage, as discussed in Chap. 10. Improved understanding of infectious diseases may well result in better understanding of such problems as long convalescences after viral infections such as Q fever and some forms of influenza, in terms of mild but slowly healing encephalitic processes. While at the moment this group would appear to account for only a small group of cases of mental disorders, further investigation may lead to the identification of a larger proportion of the group of psychiatric illnesses of unknown origin as related to infections.

Injury States Due to Toxins. Nervous tissue may be injured by many different toxins. The most important statistically is ethyl alcohol.

Alcoholism. The use of alcoholic beverages leads to excesses in certain personalities. As yet, there appears to be no distinct personality structure that is more likely than any other to fall into the pattern of alcoholism. The psychological reasons for drinking appear to vary markedly from case to case. Nevertheless, certain generalizations are possible and may be regarded as signposts in the investigation of the individual case, to be looked for though they will not always be found.

The person who indulges in alcohol to excess is likely to be of the hail-fellow-well-met personality type, the salesman who talks easily and seems at home with people. Usually he shows some immaturity of personality, an overdependence on a mother with difficulty of emancipation from her in adult life, and a tendency to feel hurt and self-pity when a defeat is sustained. Sometimes he seems to have more or less "slipped" into excessive indulgence by drinking with friends until he no longer controls alcohol but alcohol controls him. This history, however, is not so common as the superficial statements of drinkers would indicate. Alcoholism may become a symptom of some psychiatric disease, probably most often of depression or elation. In these cases, the alcoholism is obviously not the primary issue and may be expected to clear up when the primary illness improves.

The toxic effects of alcohol may be divided into acute and chronic. The acute alcoholic states include simple intoxication and the so-called "pathological intoxication." The latter is a state of wild and uncontrollable excitement, characterized frequently by belligerency and destructiveness. It is comparatively rare and appears to follow the ingestion of large quantities of alcohol in a short time. The state is of short duration, a few minutes or hours, and is followed by stupor or one of the other simple effects of alcohol. Alcoholism is frequently associated with the question of legal responsibility for criminal acts. In general, alcoholic intoxication is not considered to alter responsibility, inasmuch as the criminal act followed the ingestion of alcohol, which is itself presumed to be a willful act. The laws of the states of the United States vary on this point, and there is also variation from country to country. When the question of responsibility is likely to arise, it is wise to obtain blood-alcohol levels in the patient by one of the recognized laboratory measures. The introduction of such measurements as evidence in courts is often not allowed, but having the data at hand gives the physician considerably more confidence than if he is forced to testify purely on the basis of clinical observation.

Modern work on the vitamins has demonstrated that the more severe and lasting psychoses formerly assumed to be due to the toxic effect of alcohol may well be due to vitamin deficiencies, particularly deficiency of vitamins B_1 and B_6. The heavy drinker pays little attention to food and frequently neglects to eat at all during a bout. After varying lengths of time, from a few days to a few weeks of excessive drinking and neglect of food intake, the signs and symptoms of delirium tremens appear. The patient becomes fearful and shows motor agitation and restlessness. He is suspicious, often fearful that he is to be killed. Frequently he is hallucinated, seeing or feeling bugs or mice crawling on his body, or "pink elephants" may be present. Frequently the delirium mimics the patient's occupation. He frequently does not know the time or date and cannot get himself oriented. Misinterpretations of the environment are frequent.

Delirium tremens usually lasts 3 to 5 days and may be shortened by adequate treatment. The disease is frequently fatal, especially in the third or fourth attack. Heart failure may be a complication. There is a tendency to treat these cases lightly, but fatalities are so frequent that immediate hospitalization is mandatory so that proper treatment may be started. Early hospitalization may often be the responsibility of the health officer. A night in jail while awaiting examination may mean the difference between life and death.

After repeated attacks of delirium tremens, though sometimes without any episodes of delirium at all, the chronic disorders secondary to alcoholism may appear. Vitamin deficiency probably plays a part in the causation of these states.

Chronic hallucinosis is a state in which the patient experiences false impressions from the various sense organs. Usually this is a constant flow of "voices." They call the patient foul names, accuse him of being "yellow" or of being homosexual. Sometimes the voices simply comment, not unpleasantly, on what he is doing. Memory loss, especially loss of recent memory, combined with a silly jocularity or euphoria and the tendency to confabulate to fill in the gaps in memory, are the basic symptoms of the Korsakoff psychosis, a second effect of chronic alcoholism. In this disease there is demonstrable and frequently irreversible damage to the brain with loss of cells in the cortex and other areas. Alcoholic polyneuritis is probably directly due to vitamin deficiency. It may accompany any of this group of toxic disorders.

Improvement in these chronic psychoses extends over many months; the earlier therapy is begun, the better the prognosis. The chronic states are often ushered in by a bout of delirium tremens, the proper treatment of which is the best prophylaxis against their development.

The incidence of simple alcoholic intoxication is very high in most cultures, depending on the definition of the terms. It is said that in the United States there were, in 1952, 3.8 million problem drinkers, giving a prevalence rate of 625 per 100,000. In contrast, the annual admissions to all psychiatric hospitals in the United States because of alcoholism with or without psychosis in 1946 were 15,524. Discharges in that year were about 100 less than admissions, which would not result in too large a figure for prevalence of hospitalized alcoholics over the annual admissions. The incidence figures indicate that many alcoholics are hospitalized in general hospitals, a well-known fact, and that probably a still larger number are not hospitalized at all. The Alcoholics Anonymous movement and other voluntary organizations are endeavoring to increase the early hospitalization and active treatment of alcoholics in the hope of reducing personality deterioration.

Alcoholism is four to five times as common in males as in females in most cultures. The difference is probably due to morals and customs, which are more tolerant of the use and abuse of alcohol by men than by women. Folkways are clearly reflected in the following data for the State of New York. During the years 1929 to 1931 the age-adjusted rates of first admissions with alcoholic psychosis to all mental hospitals were for the male: Irish, 44.4 per 1,000 corresponding population aged 15 and over; Negroes, 29.5; Scandinavians, 13.4; Italians, 7.6; native whites of native parentage, 6.8; Germans, 6.2; English, 4.8; and eastern Jews, 1.0. Another example of the sociological relationships of alcoholic psychoses is afforded by the drop in admissions during the early part of the prohibition era in the United States. Toward the end of the thirties, preprohibition rates were again generally found.

Toxins Secondary to Infectious Diseases. There is no more startling example of the prevention of mental diseases than the tremendous reduction of toxic deliriums secondary to infectious diseases since the introduction of sulfonamides and the antibiotic drugs and the earlier control of infectious diseases through immunization. There seems to be no documentation for this statement in the literature, though it is an undisputed fact. Deliriums secondary to inadequate physiological support of the brain in heart disease and cerebral arteriosclerosis are, however, still common.

Toxic deliriums secondary to infectious diseases are, of course, best treated by treating the primary disorder. Psychiatric measures include lessening the opportunities of misinterpretation by avoiding dim lights and hazy shadows. Constant reassurance of the patient is necessary. If restraint is needed, it is best supplied by nurses or attendants who not only hold the patient but constantly reassure him that he is being cared for by people who have his welfare at heart and will protect him until he is well. Suicidal risk in delirium is considerable.

Other Toxins. Carbon monoxide poisoning may result from industrial causes or be incidental to suicidal attempts. In treating the acute phases the possible underlying psychosis should not be overlooked, and the patients should be attended constantly to avoid a second suicidal attempt. If anoxemia of the brain proceeds to actual destruction of tissue, the results of carbon monoxide poisoning are similar to the chronic alcoholic psychoses and consist in loss of memory and other personality assets secondary to the destruction of cortical cells.

Certain other industrial poisons leave brain destruction in their wake, but the resulting psychiatric syndromes are not to be distinguished from those already mentioned. Among these are lead, which may produce encephalopathy, and certain industrial solvents.

There is the possibility that the unborn infant may be subject to injury from the presumed toxins of toxemias of pregnancy, though at present damage in intrauterine life is considered more likely to be due to anoxemia related to the clinical condition of the mother.

Injury States Due to Trauma. Severe traumata to the head, particularly blows that violently displace the contents of the cranium, are frequently the cause of damage to the brain. Sometimes this consists in a single large hemorrhage, in which case there are likely to be localizing neurologic signs, but more frequently it consists in multiple small areas of damage throughout the brain. Unconsciousness, followed by a period of confusion and disorientation, which is in its turn followed by recovery, is the most common sequence of events. In some cases the unconsciousness is prolonged and may be followed by delirium and signs of increased intracranial pressure. Violent excitements may ensue following recovery from coma. The late results of trauma provide the greatest difficulty of evaluation. In some cases there is plainly residual brain damage evidenced by loss of memory, of general intelligence, and of ability to care for simple needs of the body.

The most difficult cases are those grouped under the term "posttraumatic constitution." In these cases, signs of damage to the nervous system as determined by the usual neurologic examination may be lacking. There is a set of purely subjective complaints of headache, dizziness, lassitude, emotional instability, decreased tolerance for alcohol, etc. Frequently the cases are complicated by compensation problems that make the persistence of symptoms advantageous to the patient. In the absence of neurologic signs of damage or changes in the spinal fluid the cases must be evaluated on the basis of the patient's honesty before the accident and a careful comparison of personality before and after the trauma. Sudden, uncontrollable outbursts of anger associated with exacerbation of headache and evidences of vasomotor instability in a man who has worked steadily for 20 years as an expert welder and whose brothers still work at steady jobs would seem to indicate that the man suffered from actual brain damage. On the other hand, one would be suspicious of malingering or hysterical reactions in a man whose history indicates multiple changes of jobs and a few court appearances for nonsupport or alcoholism. The electroencephalograph may aid in the solution of the diagnostic problem.

The numerical importance of hospitalized posttraumatic psychoses is not at present very great. In the United States (1946), they represented but 0.4 per cent of all admissions to hospitals or 633 cases. These are, of course, only the most severely damaged cases. The number is considered likely to rise as industrialization and transportation by automobile extend more widely over the world.

Injury States Due to Nutritional Deprivation. The relation between behavior disorders and nutritional deprivation is still not completely worked out. Psychoses with pellagra have in the past constituted a small number of admissions to mental hospitals in the areas of the country where that disease was prevalent. The relation of nutritional deficiency to alcoholic psychoses has already been mentioned. Psychoses associated with the neurologic changes secondary to pernicious anemia exist but are not common. The concept of pregnancy wastage, i.e., that abortion and stillbirth are the lethal extreme of a gradation of damage to the fetus has led to the suggestion, with some experimental confirmation, that nutritional deprivation of the mother during pregnancy may result in the production of infants with maldeveloped brains, who may be mentally deficient or show other defects. There is some evidence that nutritional deprivation is related to certain obstetrical complications and that these, in turn, are significantly more common in the histories of children with mental defects, epilepsy, and behavior disorders than in normal controls. The indication is that nutrition may prove to be important in the prevention of some of these behavioral difficulties.

Nutritional deprivation as a cause of behavior disorders is a matter of concern to the hospital administrator and inspector. It may prolong psychoses that would otherwise recover; it may add complications to psychotic syndromes not originally due to it. Failure to eat is a frequent symptom of mental illness. This failure may occasionally consist in the rejection of specific foods so that a patient will show behavior disorder due to nutritional deficiency even though weight loss does not occur. Furthermore, budgets for mental hospitals are notoriously small, and frequently diets must be hardly more than barely adequate. If a patient does not eat all his food, or if he for some reason requires more of some nutritional element than the average, he may actually develop a deficiency disease while in hospital under treatment. There is need of a great deal of research in the relation of nutritional deprivation to mental disease, some of which will continue to be done in mental hospitals, where it is relatively easy to control dietary intake.

It is frequently difficult to maintain adequate nutrition in older persons because of economic stringencies and because food is neglected when people live alone as many elderly people do. It is possible that adequate diet would prevent the appearance of psychoses in elderly people in some instances, just as restoration of adequate nutritional level ameliorates symptoms in some who must be hospitalized. There is some rather tenuous evidence that minor mental disorders not requiring hospitalization may be related in some cases to nutritional disorders.

Psychosis with pellagra has never been an important cause for mental hospitalization. In 1923 the rate in South Carolina state mental hospitals was 3.35 first admissions per 100,000 population per annum; in 1948, 0.05.

STATES DUE TO DEGENERATIVE CHANGES OF NERVOUS TISSUE

These mental illnesses are, roughly, of three types. Without prejudging the possibilities of clinical differentiation, it seems more realistic to treat senile psychoses and psychosis with cerebral arteriosclerosis as one group for statistical purposes; the group may be called "mental diseases of advanced age."

Admissions to mental hospitals have increased enormously over the last decades. Most of the increase has been in the older age groups, the proportion of those over 65 to total admissions to state hospitals having risen from 19 per cent in 1938 to 24 per cent in 1948, with figures as high as 36 per cent in New York State for later years. Hospitalizations of persons over 65 average 2.4 years, a shorter period than those of younger patients, but even so there is an increase in proportion of resident patients over 65 in hospitals. The prevention of the mental illnesses of the aged is a pressing public health problem. If the preventive efforts do not stem the increase in hospitalizations, better care and new methods of care will have to be developed.

In the psychoses of old age, recent study has shown that hospitalization for a period of "training" of both patient and family often makes it possible to return the senile patient to his own home for care. The public health officer can be a help in such adaptations. By understanding guidance, he may perhaps prevent the breakdown of family ties by avoiding hospitalization completely. Old people are occasionally "railroaded" into hospitals because they are somewhat of a nuisance, or for the financial advantage of an unscrupulous complainant. Caution should be exercised that the committing officer does not become a party to such schemes. On the other hand, an otherwise stable home should not be jeopardized by the dying hand of an older generation. It is also frequently possible for mildly psychotic old people to live in foster homes when living with their own children is impossible. Inspection and supervision of the foster homes is necessary under these circumstances, and there must also be available a counselor, usually a psychiatric social worker, to confer with the "case holder" and the patient about problems which may arise.

Senile Conditions. In senile changes with diffuse loss of brain substance, there is usually marked memory and judgment defect which is frequently "covered up" by an easy confabulation to fill the gaps. Age and birth date are forgotten. There is a tendency to relate circumstantially—and not too accurately—events long past, while more recent events are neglected. The elderly person may feel persecuted; when he misplaces his glasses, he is likely to feel that they have been stolen. Hoarding is a common trait, and irritability is marked when the hoard must be disposed of. Grandiose ideas are not uncommon, especially if the patient is euphoric. Hallucinations befitting the mood are common.

Today's urban housing has made necessary the hospitalization of many old people who previously were cared for in their own homes. Modern electric and gas appliances cause trouble when they are turned on and forgotten and are dangerous in the hands of a somewhat confused person who tends to get up and wander about the house at night—a common presenting symptom in the senile psychoses.

Conditions Associated with Cerebral Arteriosclerosis. These conditions are secondary to destruction of brain tissue due to rupture or thrombosis or other types of blockage of sclerotic blood vessels in the brain. They usually have their onset at earlier ages than the senile group. They are secondary to cerebral arteriosclerosis, best noted by changes in the eye grounds. Frequently there is generalized arteriosclerosis and hypertension. Usually the psychosis is accompanied by neurologic signs of focal damage to the brain—paralysis, aphasia, reflex changes, etc. There are likely to be violent deliroid periods, and these may be followed by periods of relatively complete recovery. When the cortical damage is severe or widespread, memory and judgment deficits appear, frequently with paranoid and hallucinatory overtones. Death is the result of the intracranial hemorrhage or thrombosis or of some intercurrent infection.

Conditions Associated with Other Neurological Diseases. Psychopathic states due to other neurological degenerations are difficult to discuss in terms of a single grouping. Multiple sclerosis, while in general confined to the spinal cord, may affect the brain and give rise to focal signs such as the silly, empty wittiness of the frontal-lobe syndrome. Huntington's chorea ends in a state of idiocy. The presenile types of degeneration give pictures approaching that of senile psychosis, but the course is more rapid and the dilapidation of the personality even more profound. While these states are very distressing to the families and to the patients concerned, they are numerically not very important.

MENTAL DEFICIENCY

Intelligence varies according to a bell-shaped distribution curve. Those individuals falling on the lowest part of this scale are found to be unable to care for their simple wants, unable "to guard themselves against common physical danger." By intelligence tests, the members of this group, technically called "idiots," are unable to perform as well as an average 3-year-old child, or have an I.Q. of less than 25. Higher on the curve are those called "imbeciles," defined as having a mental defect not so great as in idiots, "yet so pronounced that they are incapable of managing themselves or their affairs, or, in the case of children, of being taught to do so." These have an M.A. of more than 3 but less than 8 years, or an I.Q. of 25 to 49. Extending above the imbeciles on the distribution curve is the group called "morons," with an I.Q. from 49 to 70, and defined as "persons in whose case there exists from birth or from an early age mental defectiveness not amounting to imbecility, yet so pronounced that they require care, supervision, and control for their own protection, and for the protection of others, or, in the case of children, that they, by reason of such defectiveness, appear to be permanently incapable of receiving proper benefit from instruction in ordinary schools." *

The causes of mental deficiency are many, and further research will probably bring even more to light. Gross malformations of the central nervous system are almost always accompanied by mental deficiency, and it is probable that there is a substrate of brain malformation or defect in almost all cases of simple mental deficiency, although the defect may be so slight as to be undetectable by laboratory methods. Some forms of mental deficiency are accompanied by abnormal excretions, indicating faulty metabolic processes which affect brain function.

Until fairly recently it has been assumed that mental deficiency was usually an inherited condition transmitted according to a recessive pattern. There is little doubt that it is inherited in some instances, but there is doubt at the present time as to what percentage of cases are accounted for by heredity. Some authors give 80 per cent, but the number may be found to be considerably lower in future investigations. Recent work has shown that mental deficiency is much more common in children whose mothers have suffered obstetrical complications than in control groups. It appears likely that brain damage is suffered by the child because of the complication and that this is the cause of the mental deficiency in a considerable number of cases. The implications of these findings for obstetrical research and for programs of prenatal care are obvious.

The history usually shows retardation in the time of learning to hold the head up, to crawl, and to walk and talk. There will be retardation in the development of the ability to make the complicated adjustments necessary for eating and attending to elimination, so that wetting and soiling are problems longer than in the normal child. When the child gets to school, he cannot keep up with the class and frequently fails, so that finally he stands out as the "dummy" of the class, much larger than the rest and a source of difficulty in the school organization. In more modern schools, this individual will be recognized by a test early in his school career, after one or two failures at most, and he will be put into a special class adapted to the slower progress possible for him. After the school years, mental deficients are found in the laboring and unskilled trade groups as a whole, though occasionally traits of character such as faithfulness and meticulousness will help them reach a higher employment level. The more severe mental deficients may, of course, never be able to learn to talk, or to handle any responsibilities whatever, but will continue to have to be cared for as young children. These cases eventually get into the institutions for the feeble-minded.

There would appear to be no direct relationship between criminality and

* Definitions used are from Report of the Mental Deficiency Committee, Part IV, H. M. Stationery Office, London, 1929.

mental deficiency. Deficients are likely to be easily led either for good or for bad, and it is possible that there are more chronic bad actors among the group than there would be found in the general population, but this is not to say that mental deficiency is responsible for the bad traits of character. A mental deficient may fall into bad company and be induced to commit a crime, but he is not likely to be the more dangerous person who designed the crime.

In general, mental deficiency will show itself by a deficiency in ability to plan or to reason from past experience. Emotionally, deficients are likely to be less stable than normals, and outbursts of rage—tantrums—with accompanying uncontrollable motor excitement are not unusual. Occasionally emotional disturbances may become so great and so lasting that continued existence in the community becomes impossible, and the patient has to be hospitalized until the episode quiets down in a few weeks or months. It should not be forgotten that mental deficiency does not confer immunity to other types of mental illness. Judgment is poor because of the inability to draw proper conclusions from facts presented and because of easy suggestibility. The patient may realize his deficiency. In some cases, this leads to exquisite pain; in others, it is simply accepted without much feeling.

The less severely defective may not be recognized, adjusting themselves, particularly in adult life, without attracting any attention. However, modern educational systems screen all pupils with group intelligence tests, discovering many mental defectives who otherwise would not be recognized. The health officer will have to recognize the grosser grades of deficiency and will have to judge which cases can be maintained in the community and for which institutionalization should be advised. He should be able to recognize mental deficiency as a cause for slow development and be able to advise the anxious mother that patience and repetition will be necessary in the training of the defective child. He should know to whom he can apply to have psychological tests made when he feels the need for support for the clinical judgment of mental deficiency in a given case. He should be aware of the hereditary factor in some cases of mental deficiency and feel free to advise psychiatric consultation with a view to sterilization for the prevention of the production of further defective children. Finally, he should be able to respect this large group of citizens as being of great value to society in that they perform the hard and monotonous tasks that make up so large a part of unskilled occupations.

In specific cases the public health officer may be required to recognize mental deficiency as a barrier to his health education program. It should always be remembered that language used in pamphlets, posters, and talks will have to be simple and direct if its meaning is to reach any of this large group of the population.

Statistics on mental deficiency must always be presented with special attention to age, since, especially in our culture, children's mental ages are determined by tests, while for adults the definition is usually in terms of social competency (see p. 256). It is impossible to apply the prevalence rates found for school children to older age groups. The largest and most thorough investigation into the prevalence of mental deficiency was that conducted by the

Mental Deficiency Committee in England in 1925–1927. It covered three urban and three rural areas with a total population of 623,000. The age-specific rate for children was 14.07 per 1,000, while for adults the corresponding rate was but 6.10. In all age groups mental deficiency was found to be more common in rural than in urban areas. Mild conditions of mental deficiency are much more frequent than severe ones. By and large, about 5 per cent of the total are classified as idiots, 20 per cent as imbeciles, and the rest as morons. Morons are more prevalent in the lower socioeconomic groups than in more favored sections of the community. Idiots and imbeciles, on the other hand, appear to be fairly evenly distributed through all classes. Likewise, morons often have parents of low intelligence (though not necessarily defective themselves), whereas the idiots and imbeciles are frequently the product of normal parents. These findings seem to indicate that to a large extent moderate mental deficiency is merely a continuation of the normal distribution curve of intelligence as determined by genetic and environmental factors. In the cases of severe defectives, however, and in particular of idiots, we often deal with gross pathological deviations caused by "special" hereditary factors or by brain damage. The prevalence of severe mental deficiency is definitely higher among males than among females. No satisfactory explanation has been offered for this phenomenon.

Most mental defectives are cared for in the community; only a relatively small number are in institutions. The number of institutional cases in the United States is about 100,000, or approximately 62 per 100,000 of the population. The figures are not exact because reporting practices make it impossible to segregate epileptics from mental defective patients and from other diagnostic groups, and because of the frequency of multiple diagnoses. Of the hospitalized defectives, approximately 20 per cent are classified as idiots, 40 per cent as imbeciles, and 40 per cent as morons. The idiots are four times, and the imbeciles twice, overrepresented against the estimated distribution among all defectives.

PSYCHOPATHIC PERSONALITY (PATHOLOGICAL PERSONALITY)

The concept of mental deficiency has furnished a basis for the classification of other personality deficiencies, the theory being that various sorts of characterological deficiencies exist and are, like mental deficiency, relatively stable features of the personality not amenable to much change, i.e., are "constitutional." This theory answers a need that all workers feel in explaining those difficult people who fail to respond to the usual types of appeal and who repeatedly commit the same types of antisocial acts, never seeming to learn from past experience what actions society will tolerate and what things invariably lead to trouble. There is also the group of "weak" or "soft" personalities who seem constitutionally inferior in determination and in ability to withstand the normal buffetings of living.

The classification of this group is under constant study and revision to sharpen the definitions and include various theories of etiology. How inclusive the group should be depends to a large extent upon the theory of the psychiatrist. In general, the group of psychiatrists who believe mental illnesses are to be explained on the basis of inborn weaknesses and basic organic difficulties tend to diagnose psychopathy frequently. They consider many neurotic and psychotic cases to be secondary to inherent personality weaknesses rather than to experienced-determined conflict and its effect on personality structure. On the other hand, there is a large group who hold to the psychogenic theory of the causation of the psychopathic personality as well as of many other illnesses. These tend to diagnose few cases of this condition; in general, contending that fixed constitutional determination of personality rarely occurs and that many cases so diagnosed are actually experience-determined. The classification used here is one that is entirely descriptive. Until about 1944 it was the official classification used by the U.S. Army. The discussion is the author's.

1. *Criminalism.* Recidivist criminals who are "case-hardened" and respond neither to good treatment nor to severe punishment, and who frequently maintain a cynical and unrepentant attitude even when it is profitable for them to do otherwise. Also included here are the smooth confidence man and the swindler types, with their excellent social veneer which they use to good advantage.

2. *Emotionally Immature.* The group who are easily influenced because of emotional dependency on others, unable to stand on their own feet, often showing mood swings into superficial elation and depression, leading to the exercise of bad judgment in the direction of squandering money when elated, and to spiteful as well as depressive suicidal attempts when disappointed.

3. *Inadequate Personalities.* Those easily beaten in any situation that would, in a more normal type of personality, serve to bring out features of determination.

4. *Paranoid Personalities.* Suspicious eccentrics who feel that they do not get a fair chance in life, that others are robbing them of opportunities, are stealing their ideas, and are otherwise making their lives difficult. Frequently the suspicions appear to be used as excuses for the person's failure to perform well.

5. *Pathological-liar Type.* Personalities who seem to lie for the joy of lying, even when the lie saves them no trouble and furnishes no excuse for failure.

6. *Sexual Psychopaths.* Confirmed homosexuals and those apparently wedded to other sexual perversions such as masochism, sadism, or fetishism.

7. *Unqualified.* All other sorts of incorrigible personalities. This group includes most cases of drug addiction, including chronic alcoholism as well as addiction to the narcotic drugs.

No grouping of this sort furnishes mutually exclusive categories, since all we have is a description of symptoms with no reference to possible etiology except the rather inadequate and unsatisfying concept of "constitutional" determination. Many thinkers in psychiatry are entirely unsatisfied with this idea, and feel that at least some personalities in this group act as they do because of conditioning in early life (see page 191), and that since a life experience made them as they are, a therapeutic experience can and will so adjust the person to his experiences that his personality pattern will change to something within the range of normal. A great deal of work is done with these people with discouragingly poor results. Investigation with the electroencephalograph has shown that some cases exhibiting the symptoms of constitutional psychopathic personality have brain waves indicating abnormal cortical activity. These findings tend to link the psychopaths with the epileptics and have led to interesting therapeutic experiments using drugs known to influence the frequency of epileptic attacks or to affect cortical functioning, in some cases with gratifying results.

The mental status of the psychopath is much less helpful than the history; indeed, psychopathy is sometimes described as a sociological state rather than a medical one. Occasionally, these unstable personalities will exceed what the culture will tolerate in life outside hospital and, under pressure, they may become depressed, or even hallucinated, and require hospitalization for a period. In these cases, the psychopathy is of secondary importance, and the health officer will be required primarily to act as the committing officer because of the gross behavior disorder. It is always wisest to let a psychiatrist in a mental hospital decide whether a suicidal attempt was only a gesture to bring another person to terms and not to end life. In the case of prisoners, it is generally assumed that the recognition of the presence of psychopathic personality is not a reason for stopping the prosecution of the criminal. The justice of this view has been questioned, since the assumption is that the patient is suffering from a psychiatric condition that makes his rejection of socialized and circumspect living inevitable and that he no longer has the "free will" to decide to choose the "right." Most psychiatrists and criminologists agree that criminals of the group are best handled by the use of indeterminate sentences under which society can be protected from their depredations for as long as possible.

The U.S. Public Health Service has set up hospitals for the treatment of drug addiction, and the public health officer should learn how to admit cases to these hospitals when necessary. Drug addiction is not a hopeless state, and with the active research programs in these hospitals, it bids fair to become even more amenable to treatment. Its victims are usually public charges in all parts of the world, though special provisions for their treatment may not be provided. The tremendous variation in prevalence of drug addiction in different cultures, the capacity this deviation has for arousing epidemics of furor in the press, and the association of addiction with petty and major crime make it a subject for continued research. Public arousal about drug addiction often leads to pressures to set up local treatment services. The condition, in the United States at least, is usually found to be so infrequent that such services are both very expensive and very difficult to staff with well-trained personnel. The clinical demand is not great enough to have given rise to training of personnel in numbers large enough to supply facilities in more than a few of the largest cities and states. It would appear that provisions for temporary care in the local community and maximal use of the Federal facilities would be the most economical way to deal with drug addiction problems in the United States. Perhaps the warning should be added that drug addiction does not automatically carry with it the diagnosis of psychopathic personality.

The public health officer should also be aware that sex crimes are frequently associated with a mental illness of the type of psychopathic personality and with even more severe and disorganizing disorders. He should lend his influence to having these cases examined by a psychiatrist, preferably employed and called by the court, before the frequently useless and often definitely harmful jail sentence is passed.

The definition of the term "psychopathic personality" is so extremely difficult and varies so widely in usage, depending on the particular observer, that statistics concerning the group are of almost no value. The social situation at the time of the observation is also of importance in interpreting statistics in this field. Thus a survey in Baltimore in 1933 indicated that the psychopathic personality occurred at the rate of 13 per 10,000 of the population studied, but 3 years later a resurvey, using similar methods and personnel, obtained a rate of 5.2. The difference lay, apparently, in the fact that early in the depression years there was a tendency for the sources on which the survey was dependent to interpret inability to earn a satisfactory living as an evidence of psychopathic personality. By 1936, the seriousness of the world financial depression had been more clearly recognized, familiarity with unemployment had made it less a mark of defective character. In World War II, the rate of diagnosis of psychopathic personality among draft registrants reaching physical examination was 8.2 per 1,000. Rejections by reason of psychopathic personality made up more than a quarter of all rejections because of mental disease.

PSYCHOSES ("PSYCHOGENIC")

Two groups of psychotic illnesses are "psychogenic," not known to be associated with brain damage or destruction. These represent the major research challenges in the mental health field today. Both attack people during their productive years, and both—but particularly schizophrenia—produce tremendous morbidity. The etiology of neither is clearly understood, and treatment is still to a considerable extent empirical.

Manic-Depressive Psychoses and Allied States. Manic-depressive psychosis represents an exaggeration of normal mood alternation. Depression or elation becomes fixed, extending beyond the normal emotional swing, and the return to normal mood is delayed. There are depressed moods lasting months or years, and elations equally long. The fact that prolonged and profound depression tends in some cases to alternate with prolonged states of elation and excitement early attracted medical attention and led to the diagnostic grouping "manic-depressive psychosis." The name is still used, though it is recognized that it describes only the cases with alternating moods, whereas the more common finding is to see but one of the phases of the "complete" mood cycle.

Depression represents a deep-going physiological change. This appears in the general metabolism as a loss of weight; in the gastrointestinal tract, as loss of appetite and constipation. Sleep rhythms are disturbed, with the pattern of early-morning awakening appearing. There is a general loss of muscular tone. Concentration is slowed, and the patient complains that he finds himself reading the same words over and over without grasping their meaning. Speech is slowed along with thinking. With the deep sadness come feelings of guilt and personal worthlessness. Freedom of emotional reaction is constricted so that the patient complains that long-standing affections are no longer moving, and this becomes a fruitful source for guilt feelings. The patient feels lonesome, deserted, worthless; time passes slowly and painfully; he is utterly miserable. The idea that life is not worth living appears so frequently that suicide must always be considered a hazard. After weeks, months, or even years, the mood generally gradually disappears, and the patient finally recovers.

In elation, the same pattern of early-morning awakening is manifest. The mood, however, is elated. Instead of feeling worthless, the patient feels powerful, capable of performing almost anything he sets his mind to. He is "sitting on top of the world." His thinking he believes to be crystal clear, and he is angered when others find him unable to carry an issue to a logical conclusion. He is witty in his own conceit and angered when others find his puns and rhymes more forced than humorous. Numberless projects are begun only to be replaced by others before they are fairly under way. The distractibility may become so great that feeding is a problem, and this and the immense physical activity cause marked losses in weight. In spite of this the patient feels physically strong.

The symptom complexes are rarely as clear as they have been pictured here. The depression may deepen into actual stupor. Confusion and bewilderment are frequently observed in depressed cases. The man who feels himself worthless and guilty of breach of good faith in having become ill is likely to feel that others recognize his guilt and accuse him. Panics and fear states may arise on this basis, especially when the projection goes on to actual hallucination of voices stating his guilt and worthlessness. On the other hand, the manic when thwarted is likely to become very angry and convinced that he is persecuted. His ideas of self-aggrandizement may go on to definite delusions that he is the Messiah, or some powerful person.

This illness is likely to appear in more or less stable personalities. The disease in definite enough form to be clearly recognized rarely appears until emotional maturity is reached. Frequently the patient has a good work record of years' standing and is a stable member of the community when well. In general, patients of this group tend to be gregarious, to enjoy companionship with others. It has been suggested that the repression of resentments, anger, distaste, and disgust, which is so necessary for successful social life and which the truly gregarious person hardly notices as he achieves it, eventually becomes impossible any longer and the depression or elation is the result. In the elation the patient relieves himself of all responsibility and "says what he damn pleases" for a while. In the depression, he loads himself with grief over his sins. It is as though when he has repented enough for his own as well as others' faults, he recovers. On the other hand, in some depressions the patient appears to be punishing others for things he has long resented, although at the same time he is full of guilt feeling for the loss of affection for those he appears to be punishing.

Involutional melancholia or agitated depression frequently appears during the age period associated with sexual involution in the female. The motor agitation of these cases stands in contrast to the slowed movement already described. Wringing of the hands, pacing, restless picking of the nails or skin are associated with ideas of poverty, physical disease, malfunction of organs, fears of death and destruction, and all sorts of catastrophes. These cases have a tendency to fall into a rut of thinking and action, and the illness is inclined to be stubborn and slow to recover. This type of depression tends to occur in people of perfectionistic, meticulous personality type. Electroshock therapy is likely to be effective in most psychoses of the manic-depressive group but is particularly successful in this group of cases.

The etiology of manic-depressive psychosis is unclear. It has been grouped here as a "psychogenic" psychosis, but the concept of psychogenesis is to be construed in its broadest sense. Many authors consider the disease to be due to constitutional factors, inborn and but little influenced by life experiences. In Hitlerian Germany, the disease was legally considered hereditary and was a cause for sterilization. Others feel that, although there is probably a basic hereditary factor, its penetrance is low and it produces actual illness only in situations of emotional stress and strain that act as a trigger for reactions as outlined above. The fact that these illnesses tend to recover is basic in their therapy. The depressed patient must be protected from suicide, the elated person from stimuli that would tend to enhance his excitement. Symptomatic treatment, of course, is indicated. It usually includes sedation to overcome the sleep difficulty, control of constipation, etc.

The responsibility of the public health officer is again one of early recognition. Recognition of a depression and proper protection will avoid suicides. Early hospitalization and active psychiatric treatment shorten most elations and depressions and thus save the community productive time that would otherwise be wasted.

Admissions with diagnosis of manic-depressive psychosis and allied states to state mental hospitals were 9,882 in 1948 in the United States, giving an admission rate of approximately 6.1 per 100,000 of the population. Surveys of the prevalence of the disease in the general population indicate a much higher rate, 70 per 100,000. Hospitalization for affective illnesses is probably declining because of the increasing efficiency of treatment on an outpatient basis—not, unfortunately, on any basis of prevention of the psychosis. The illness is much more common in females than males, the ratio in various studies varying from 2:1 to 4:1. Recurrences of the psychosis are frequent, though from 25 to 50 per cent of patients have but one attack. Depressive illnesses are much more frequent than elations and the cyclic form of alternation is even more rare. The median age of admission to hospital (United States, 1948) was 32.8 for manic-depressive psychoses and 52.7 for involutional melancholia. Age of onset is likely to be earlier than age of admission, since many cases are neglected for a considerable period before admission.

Manic-depressive psychosis seems to occur with fairly equal frequency in all socioeconomic strata. If anything, the reaction appears more frequently in the more prosperous groups.

Schizophrenia and Allied States. This group not only is the largest in point of number of cases requiring long-continued care but also constitutes the most difficult problem in the field of psychiatry. It was once considered to represent defective thinking or intellectual function, as opposed to the defective emotional function seen in the manic-depressive group. Such a distinction proves false, however, for intellectual functions are disturbed in manic-depressive illnesses, and disturbances in emotional reaction are present in schizophrenia.

The most striking symptom of schizophrenia (dementia praecox) is likely to be bizarre or unusual behavior. On investigation, this is found to be based on unusual ideas, or on conclusions reached on the basis of misinterpretation of facts or through patterns of logic that do not conform to the ordinary methods of thinking used by normal people. The unusual behavior may be accompanied by an unusual emotional state, apathy, or poorly directed excitement, or stark fear. The behavior may arise because of sounds or visions experienced by the patient but not apparent to others, hallucinations. There may be disturbance of motor activity—impulsive outbreaks of activity, slow halting actions, or complete elimination of action so that the patient is stuporous. Language disturbances range from complete mutism to great push of talk, and from interruptions of the stream of talk because of preoccupation to a constant babbling of jargon that fails to perform the communicative function of language at all. Regard for social living is sometimes lost to the extent of complete isolation in stupor, or the breakdown of the usual habits of cleanliness and decorum. Frequently, the observer notes that there is a loss of fellow feeling; he cannot understand the patient or enter into his emotional state.

Four types of this illness are usually pointed out, but these types are generally thoroughly mixed, or change from time to time, so that the designation of type is frequently a matter of more or less of one or the other rather than a clear picture. Cases with most marked motor disturbance, frequently with a tendency to alternate between excitement and stupor, are called "catatonic." Hallucinations and delusions are common. These cases often show depression and elation to a marked degree. Perhaps related to this, they also tend to recover more frequently than the less emotionally tinged schizophrenic types of illness. The paranoid group is characterized by the predominance of the feeling that "something is wrong in the atmosphere," a feeling of suspicious suspense. Delusions of persecution or, less frequently, of great inflation of personal importance are basic symptoms. The dilapidation of personality, which is so frequent in schizophrenia, appears to be less rapid in this group. This "deterioration" is most pronounced in the vague, silly, preoccupied, frequently hallucinated hebephrenic group and in the simple schizophrenic deteriorations. In the latter, delusions and hallucinations may never be present, but there is a dissolution of personality with vagueness of thinking, paucity of ideas, and emotional apathy as the outstanding symptoms.

The etiology of the schizophrenic group of illnesses is not completely known. Some workers believe the disease to arise from strains in living or struggles with the control of the instincts, masturbation, homosexual, and other sexual conflicts being particularly prominent. To some, the difficulty appears to be the blocking of normal emotional outlet and inability to appreciate and fit into the emotional patterns of others. The result is a frustration pattern that develops into illness when stress arises in the course of living. There is opinion that the reaction is related to emotional isolation in infancy with consequent loss of capacity to relate to others which eventually culminates in schizophrenic symptoms. Still others believe the disease to be due to a fundamental organic change of unknown type. Probably it is most profitable at this time to consider that the disease is the product both of an inherited constitutional vulnerability and of life strains and pressure of adjustment. It is generally recognized that the catatonic type of illness tends to develop in fairly mature personalities. The period of onset is in the third or fourth decades. Paranoid illnesses appear to arise in touchy, sensitive people with a talent in the direction of productiveness or inventiveness. The symptoms are of somewhat later onset. Hebephrenia is likely to appear in adolescence and to be a continuation and caricature of adolescent idealism and mysticism.

All the types appear to be able to revert to normal reaction under certain circumstances. Emotional shocks, and especially physiological ones, tend to bring this about. This forms the basis for the presently popular empiric school of treatment in which the physiological disturbance is produced with insulin or other drugs or through electric current, with or without convulsions. Anoxia may be the common physiological insult in these and is the most important element in carbon dioxide treatment. More recently, brain operations, varying in location and extent of permanent lesion produced, have been introduced for the alleviation of symptoms in schizophrenia. Most psychiatrists believe that the operations, usually called "lobotomy" because the frontal-lobe radiations are severed, should be used with great caution and only when other treatment has failed. In recent years there has been great revival of interest in psychotherapy in schizophrenia, but the treatment is too expensive to be applicable to any large proportion of the population, and its results are not yet proved successful. Supervision in hospital by understanding physicians, nurses, and attendants constantly on the alert to keep the patient stimulated toward social living, and psychotherapy designed to clarify the life situations of psychodynamic importance are still the bulwark of treatment in schizophrenia, however.

The public health officer will find cases falling into this group in any community. He will often be confronted with the problem as an emergency for disposition. Acutely ill patients must, of course, be hospitalized, but many cases can be cared for in the community at large after a period in hospital. Family care for selected cases is recognized as a satisfactory method of treatment and management for this group. The fact that the patient may show motor excitement and bizarre thinking often leads to great fear of him; this fear is rarely justified. Proper familiarity with the disease pictures will form a basis for medical interest and will dispel the common tendency to dispose of the patient and his disquieting ideas as rapidly as possible and with as little direct contact as possible. Sympathetic interest in the patient and a curiosity as to what brought on the attack will often form the basis for rapport. Then hospitalization may be a therapeutic and not a punitive measure in the patient's eyes, and the groundwork for therapy will be laid. It is hardly necessary to add that an interest in the patient and his illness will tend to lower the frequency of the completely reprehensible practice of deceiving the patient as a means of getting him to hospital. Regardless of how ill he may appear to be, or how little he seems to understand of what goes on about him, there is never any excuse for lying to him about the medical decision concerning hospitalization. If force is necessary to see that the patient gets to hospital, it should be available, but proper explanation to the patient will frequently make force unnecessary. Mechanical restraints likewise usually can be replaced by rapport and explanation.

The expectancy for schizophrenia in Western European–type cultures is about 1 per cent of all children born, or 1,000 per 100,000. The proportion ill at any one time is approximately 290 per 100,000, of whom approximately 147 per 100,000 will be in hospitals. In the United States, the average stay in hospitals for schizophrenics is 13.1 years. This tremendous chronicity is responsible for the occupancy of 47 per cent of all mental hospitals beds in the United States, though for only about 22 per cent of all first admissions to hospital. The average age at admission to state mental hospitals is 32.6 years for schizophrenics. Neglect of cases is common, and average age of onset is probably considerably lower. The disease is approximately equally distributed between males and females. It is more common and more severe in the lower socioeconomic groups than in the higher. This does not appear to be due to downhill socioeconomic mobility of persons already ill.

Both manic-depressive psychosis and schizophrenia appear to "run in families." There are those who argue that this does not indicate that these diseases are associated with inherited factors but is, rather, due to the effect on the developing personality of living in association with people having the disease or its premonitory symptoms. Twin studies indicate strongly that the capacity to break down with these diseases is in all likelihood inherited. The mechanism of the pattern of inheritance is not completely known.

EPILEPSY

Acute and chronic brain disorders associated with convulsions, whatever their etiology, constitute so striking a type of abnormal behavior that the person suffering from them always stands out from others. He is barred from many types of activity and is likely to be looked upon with fear by his fellows. He knows his illness is "serious" and that if he tells that he has convulsions, many types of work will be closed to him. Furthermore, he is hopeful always that he has had his last fit and therefore is always ready to try his hand at a new job, only to find it denied him after a recurrence of attacks. In military psychiatry, the epileptics always seem to be the most anxious to get into the service and stay in, and the concealing of a history of epilepsy appears to be much more common than the submission of a false history of fits to avoid service. The epileptic is subjected to great emotional strains, and it is possible that the warped reaction patterns described under the term "epileptic personality" are as much the result of these strains as they are of the causative agent of the epilepsy, whatever that may be in the individual case. The "epileptic personality" is variously described but generally includes epithets such as emotionally unstable, egocentric, fawning and oily, and hyperreligious.

The differential diagnosis of convulsive disorders is a difficult problem. A certain number of cases may be explained on the basis of brain damage by trauma, by infection, and by space-occupying lesions in the cranial cavity. In some cases, the periodic discharges are correlated with maldevelopment of the brain, localized atrophies, porencephaly, etc., being found on investigation. The largest number of convulsive disorders never yield to etiological investigation, however, and remain lumped together under the term "idiopathic" or "cryptogenic" epilepsy.

The history of the epileptic includes investigation as to the time of onset of the attacks and their duration, the circumstances surrounding the first attack, the localization of the symptoms, especially in the first few seconds of the spell, and previous medication and its success. It should also include discussion of the various equivalents for attacks, furors (tremendous outbursts of rage and destructiveness), fugues, and states of unexplainable tension and their relation to the more usual type of attack. The presence of petit mal attacks either alone, as the sole feature of the disease, or along with seizures should be inquired into. These data should not preclude investigation into the social and personal history, for this would appear to be a fruitful field for therapy. How does the patient get on with his parents, brothers, and sisters? Has he friends, or is he "one against the world"? What work has he done and with what success? Does he have a job now, and what sort of work can he do or be trained for? What are his intellectual assets—how is he getting along or did he get along in school?

The ability of the epileptic to live comfortably in the community and to make social contributions through work depends primarily upon the control of his attacks. Education of the community away from prejudice against epileptics and away from fear of them will help, but it will be less necessary if attacks are well controlled. The public health officer should know the number and location of the epileptics in his community and accept some responsibility for seeing that they are as well studied as his situation permits. Programs for the treatment of epilepsy are included in crippled children's programs and operated through consultant services and hospitalization for diagnosis and treatment when necessary. Public health responsibility in connection with epilepsy is becoming more important, for modern methods of treatment result in the rehabilitation of many hitherto uncontrollable cases. Therapeutic advances in the field have been very great in the last two decades, and advances in understanding and therapy of the disease are still being made.

In some cases the fit is preceded or followed by various types of automatic functioning or fugues and by tremendous emotional and motor outbursts. These cases, together with those with frequent fits that make them entirely unadaptable to the social situation, and those in whom there has been such marked dilapidation of the personality that life with them is intolerable, must be hospitalized, frequently permanently. With better treatment it is probable that hospitalization for custodial care will be less frequent in the future. If fits can be controlled, personality dilapidation is likely to be less common also, since the patient can be kept socialized and will not suffer so greatly from the frustration and isolation associated with the disease.

Epileptics in fugue states occasionally commit crimes against persons. In cases of murder or assault marked by unnecessary and gaudy cruelty, the alert medical officer will suspect such a state and will take this possibility into consideration in studying the case to report to the court. This problem is extremely rare though socially of the greatest importance.

Epilepsy is present in about 225 per 100,000 of the general population in the United States and is somewhat more common in males than females. Although it is a little more common in children than in adults, it is fairly evenly spread through all age ranges. There are about 25,000 epileptics in hospitals in the United States, representing, of course, only the most severe cases and those complicated by mental deficiency, psychosis, other neurologic disease, or severe personality dilapidation.

BEHAVIOR DISORDERS IN CHILDREN

The decision as to where "normal" living stops and where the abnormal begins is often extremely difficult. In evaluating the behavior of children the problem is probably more difficult than anywhere else in psychiatry. It makes a difference, for instance, who tells about the child; only in rare instances is it the child himself who reports his problems. Very few clinics are devoted to seeing children about whom no one has complained. Experience in such work, however, shows that the "threshold of complaint" varies extremely widely among parents. Many children whose behavior apparently raises no questions whatever show as much or more extreme behavior as do those who are seen by the psychiatrist at the parents' or the pediatrician's request. Nevertheless, the complaint remains the only practical basis for definition of behavior disorder in children, just as admission to psychiatric hospital remains the most practical definition for severe adult mental disease. The bases of most of childhood behavior disorders will, then, be found in what has been described as "normal" behavior in Part 2. What we deal with here is abnormal prolongation or exaggeration of essentially normal behavior.

Behavior disorders in children present very difficult problems of classification, probably because the relationship of childhood disorders to the homologous disorders in the mature personality are incompletely known. Usually classifications divide the cases into those in which the primary complaint is of conduct disorder, disregard of the accepted patterns of decorum appropriate to the age of the child, and neurotic disorders which comprise symptoms indicating physiologic malfunction usually secondary to anxiety. Conduct disorders are much more common among boys, while neurotic disorders are approximately equally frequent in the two sexes. In many cases the distinction into the two groups is not feasible nor is it therapeutically necessary.

No attempt will be made to do more than list the problems falling into this general group of disorders. Among them are feeding difficulties, constipation, persistent vomiting, car sickness, nonorganic limps, nail biting, bed wetting, stuttering, obsessive behavior, temper tantrums and breath holding, head rolling, rocking on hands and knees during sleep, sleepwalking and talking, general hyperactivity, lying and stealing, excessive masturbation, and extraordinary sex interest and experimentation.

In general, the etiology of such behavior lies in some feeling of insecurity, insecurity being interpreted in its broadest sense.

Insecurity in the child may arise from many sources. The common observation that problems are much more frequent in children of broken homes illustrates one threat. Sibling jealousy, also a common etiological agent, is the result of a threat, real or fancied, to the child's place in the home. Devices for attracting attention of the parent, such as telling tall tales or frequently refusing food, tend to reflect the child's need for acceptance and his need to establish himself in the home as a participator in the affections of its inhabitants. It is obvious that when parental adjustment is not smooth there will be overlaps between the child's and the parents' problems with resulting strains which may show first in disordered functioning in the child. Difficulties in the school situation are not uncommon and are frequently related to unsympathetic teachers who cannot understand the child and his background or have not made the effort to do so.

Insecurity is not the only etiological agent in the production of behavior disorders. Many other factors, such as imitation and disappointment, may be found in particular situations.

Therapy in the severe cases is usually a job for the expert. The health officer's duty will be to recognize the cases and direct them to the proper diagnostic and treatment center. Therapy generally begins with a thorough investigation of the case by the psychiatrist, psychologist, and social worker. The parents are interviewed to get their story, and the home is visited so that an idea of the community and household may be obtained. The child is interviewed so that the story as he gives it to a sympathetic, understanding, and nonjudging listener may be evaluated. After all the facts so gathered are put together, a plan for treatment is made. This may include modification of the home situation physically. It includes increasing the child's understanding and tolerance of his home and the relieving of tensions through telling the story and discussing it frankly with a "neutral" adult. It often includes treatment and adjustment of emotional problems in the parents. It may include foster-home treatment if the home the child came from cannot be salvaged. In some cases, it includes hospitalization for psychiatric therapy, though institutions for such work are not provided adequately by most states and, unfortunately, are costly to operate.

It may also include education of the teacher so that she will appreciate the sore points of the situation and treat them properly. Such therapy is usually effective, both in relieving the immediate problem and probably in increasing the child's resistance to the development of symptoms in later difficult situations.

The difficulties of definition of the limits of "normal" make statistics on the prevalence of behavior disorders in children exceedingly unreliable. Such statistics should be accompanied by full and exact definition of just what constituted the type of behavior included in the counting, since general descriptive terms are likely to vary in meaning depending on who is using them. Figures on delinquency based on juvenile-court action, for instance, are likely to be more a reflection of the activity of the court and the education of the community as regards it, than a measure of delinquency in the community. About 1.2 per cent of all children in the United States between the ages of 7 and 17 appear before juvenile courts. The number of persons receiving care in mental health outpatient clinics in 1952 in the United States was estimated at 200,000; the proportion of children of this group is unknown but is probably at least half. School systems find from 5 to 10 per cent of children are severely disturbed enough or present other problems requiring psychiatric diagnosis and guidance, if not actual treatment. The U.S. Public Health Service, through its National Institute of Mental Health, is attempting to improve reporting practices so that better statistics on the type and frequency of childhood behavior disorders and other psychiatric illnesses treated on an outpatient basis may be available.

NEUROSES

There is good reason for believing that the "neurotic" behavior disorders in children are related to neurotic symptoms in adults. Gillespie has prepared lists of early behavior disorders such as those mentioned above and has come to the conclusion that a verified history of the occurrence of any significant number of these in childhood should be a cause for rejection for certain types of military work, since these traits indicate predisposition to breakdown under the strains of military service. Hadfield found that 69 per cent of his military cases (326) showed a "predisposition" before puberty. Later studies have tended to throw some doubt on the usefulness of these data as predictors of mental instability at adult ages. It appears that some fliers who successfully completed tours of duty had histories not much different from some who broke down under stress.

It has long been taught that the situation conditioning for neurotic symptoms in adults originates early in childhood. The psychoanalytic school is convinced that the situation has to do with the problems of the distribution of love and affection in the home, especially concerning the two parents. This school tends to give the later development of the person less consideration, centering on the very early experiences. Other schools tend to feel that there is a continuous flow of experiences, any or all of which can and probably do contribute to the development of the neuroses of adult life. It is on the basis of this type of thinking that this book has indicated some areas of developmental stress and strain which everyone passes through. In some cases experiences are not properly "built into" the personality structure and may give rise to illness. A corollary includes the theory that the stress playing upon an individual may come from deficiencies within the individual himself. For example, the epileptic suffers frustrations, and the child whose capacity to empathize with others has atrophied from neglect in infancy is under a handicap in dealing with the ordinary problems of living.

If the origin of neurotic symptoms is causally related to life experiences, then therapy will consist in the recall and ventilation of the etiological experiences, the modification of attitudes toward them, and finally, the reorganization of the personality to include these experiences without the "reaction" that gave rise to the symptoms. The aim of prophylaxis becomes promulgation of modes of living all through life, so that problems do not go unsettled to rise up and haunt the patient later in the form of symptoms when a precipitating strain of physical fatigue, emotional conflict, or instinctual conflict arises.

There are varying degrees of vulnerability to neurotic illness among people, and one never deals with the situation alone, but with a situation and an individual. Probably there is a limit of conflict or difficulty for any individual and all will "break" into one or another of the "psychogenic" groups of disorder if the strain is great enough. The factor of resistance is little understood, but it is generally assumed to be inborn or constitutional.

Psychiatric research has not yet been able to discover why one set of symptoms appears in one individual and why another individual shows an entirely different group. Epidemiological studies indicate, however, that the grouping of all the symptom pictures together is sound, since, in general, all the particular types of reaction tend to show the same distribution when broken down by sex and race. The "choice of symptoms" appears at the present state of knowledge to be dependent on individual rather than general considerations, and although thorough study of the individual case often furnishes the explanation for that case, it does not lend itself to any general hypothesis.

Perhaps the most common type of neurotic reaction is anxiety, characterized by the emotion of fear and the physiological changes normally accompanying that emotion. Palpitation, sweating, tension of muscles, diarrhea, and polyuria are acute signs of anxiety; examples of the chronic physiological evidences are insomnia, cardiospasm, and spastic colitis. Hysteria is one of the most gaudy symptom complexes in psychiatry. Paralyses, anesthesias, or paresthesias are frequently seen and are often accompanied by a singular lack of concern about the symptoms on the part of the patient. Chronic fatigue in the absence of physical disease, multiple and chronic physical complaints, useful to the patient as a means of avoiding unpleasant life situations, are often encountered. Depression of spirits which goes beyond a theoretical "normal" reaction to grief or disappointment is often grouped with the neurotic disorders. Obsessive, repetitive thinking, compulsive actions, and phobias of all sorts are found in some cases. Categories are never mutually exclusive, and a careful study almost invariably ends with the diagnosis "psychoneurosis, mixed type." In most cases, the symptomatology is of less importance, once its significance as indicating a psychogenic disorder is grasped, than is the readjustment to the precipitating situation and to the factors in the life history which facilitate the reaction.

The public health officer's interest in the neuroses will be to recognize them when present and to arrange or advise treatment. Such treatment may be obtained from private practitioners of psychiatry or from public clinics (see pages 34 to 131). There are few more challenging public health administrative experiments going forward than the process of working out diagnostic and treatment services for psychiatric patients not needing hospitalization, most of whom will be diagnosed as psychoneurotic.

The public health officer also has the responsibility of not making the neurotic client worse by ridicule or impatience. He should think of the possibility of syphilophobia occasionally when tempted to "scare" a syphilitic into regular treatment visits and when designing his educational program for control of venereal disease. Overcautious advice in suspected heart disease has been the source of much hypochondriasis and body overconcern. The health officer will endeavor, furthermore, to teach good emotional attitudes as well as good formulas in his maternal and child health work as an effort in the direction of prophylaxis against the neuroses.

Statistics on the neuroses are beset with the same difficulty of definition encountered in the discussion of behavior disorders in children. It is the general impression that neurosis of one sort or another is more common than any other type of illness, physical or mental. Yet the reporting of cases is so incomplete that what statistical studies there are present values in which neurosis is indicated as being less common than frank psychosis. A person is not likely to be completely incapacitated by neurotic symptoms, or is incapacitated only a short time, so he is not counted so carefully as the hospitalized psychotic case. There is some evidence that anyone described as "nervous," if he has no more sweeping psychiatric disorder, is likely to be properly called psychoneurotic. It has been estimated that from 1 to 5 per cent of the population suffers from neurotic disease sufficient to reduce efficiency in daily living. Perhaps 30 to 50 per cent of patients treated by private practitioners of medicine and in general hospitals, have varying degrees of neurotic complaint, either as the sole cause for seeking treatment, or as a complication of other disease. Contrary to general opinion, in the United States at least, psychoneuroses are most common in the lowest economic stratum. They are about three times as common in women as in men.

REMARKS ON PLANNING PSYCHIATRIC SERVICES

In the Western European–type cultures it appears that there needs to be supplied about one psychiatric hospital bed for each 200 of the general population. For other cultures the need may be approximately the same, though it is doubtful that any but a highly industrial economy can support so heavy a commitment for hospitalization. There is little evidence that the rise in psychiatric hospitalization observed throughout the world can be reversed by even the complete application of therapeutic knowledge now available, though the speed of the rise certainly can be slowed. The eventual solution of the problem would appear to lie in two directions: (1) new knowledge on the prevention and care of mental diseases; (2) changes in cultural patterns which will allow the absorption of more chronic patients into the social order outside hospitals. Probably the investment of money to provide the best possible treatment of patients is economical in the long pull, but proof of this is extremely difficult to obtain.

Outpatient services are needed in the United States to the extent of one clinic to each 100,000 of the general population. How long this figure will stand will depend eventually on whether the clinic can demonstrate that its value is sufficient in prevention and relief of symptoms to justify its cost to a larger or to a smaller population unit. No community has as yet been saturated with available outpatient services; there are strong indications that the appetite for service at the present time will place the population nearer 50,000 than 100,000. Such a fluid situation presents striking challenges to the public health administrator.

READING LIST

1. Landis, Carney, and James D. Page: *Modern Society and Mental Disease,* Rinehart & Company, Inc., New York, 1938.
2. Dayton, Neil A.: *New Facts on Mental Disorders,* Charles C Thomas, Publisher, Springfield, Ill., 1940.
3. Malzberg, Benjamin: *Social and Biological Aspects of Mental Disease,* State Hospitals Press, Utica, N.Y., 1940.
4. *Epidemiology of Mental Disorder,* Milbank Memorial Fund, New York, 1950 (contains excellent bibliography).
5. Tietze, Christopher: "A Note on the Incidence of Mental Disease in the State of New York," *Am. J. Psychiat.* **100**(1) (1943).
6. Goldhammer, H., and A. W. Marshall: *Psychosis and Civilization,* Free Press, Glencoe, Ill., 1953.
7. Cohen, B. M., and Ruth E. Fairbank: "Statistical Contributions from the Mental Hygiene Study of the Eastern Health District of Baltimore: I. General Account of the 1933 Mental Hygiene Survey of the Eastern Health District," *Am. J. Psychiat.* **94**:1153–1161 (1938). "II. Psychosis in the Eastern Health District," *Am. J. Psychiat.* **94**:1377–1395 (1938). "III. Personality Disorder in the Eastern Health District in 1933 (with Elizabeth Green)," *Human Biol.* **11**:112–129 (1939). "IV. Further Studies on Personality Disorder in the Eastern Health District in 1933 (with Elizabeth Green)," *Human Biol.* **11**:485–512 (1939).
8. Lemkau, P., C. Tietze, and M. Cooper: "Mental Hygiene Problems in an Urban District. I. Description of the Study," *Ment. Hyg.* **25**:624–646 (1941). "II. Psychotics. The Neurotics," *Ment. Hyg.* **26**:100–119 (1942). "III. The Epileptics and Mental Deficients," *Ment. Hyg.* **26**:275–288 (1942). "IV.

Mental Hygiene Problems in Children Seven to Sixteen Years of Age," *Ment. Hyg.* **27**:279–295 (1943).

9. Tietze, C., P. Lemkau, and M. Cooper: "Schizophrenia, Manic-Depressive Psychosis and Social-economic Factors," *Am. J. Sociol.* **47**(2): 167–175 (1941).

10. Lemkau, P., C. Tietze, and M. Cooper: "Complaint of Nervousness and the Psychoneuroses," *Am. J. Orthopsychiat.* **12**:(2): 214–223 (1942).

11. Lemkau, P., C. Tietze, and M. Cooper: "A Survey of Statistical Studies on the Prevalence and Incidence of Mental Disorders in Sample Populations," *Pub. Health Rep.* **58**(53): 1909–1927 (1943).

12. Rowntree, L. G., K. H. McGill, and D. I. Edwards: "Causes of Rejection and Incidence of Defects," *J.A.M.A.* **123**:181–185 (1943).

13. Lilienfeld, A. M., and Pasamanick, B.: "Association of Maternal and Fetal Factors with the Development of Epilepsy, I. Abnormalities in the Prenatal and Paranatal Periods," *J.A.M.A.* **155**:719–724 (1954).

14. Bowlby, J.: *Maternal Care and Mental Health,* World Health Organization, Geneva, 1951.

15. Hollingshead, A. B., and F. C. Redlich: "Schizophrenia and the Social Structure," *Am. J. Psychiat.* **110**:695–701 (1954).

16. Perrott, G. St. J., L. M. Smith, M. Y. Pennell, and M. E. Altenderfer: *Care of the Long-term Patient,* Commission on Chronic Illness, Baltimore, 1954.

17. Lemkau, P. V.: "The Epidemiological Study of Mental Illnesses and Mental Health," *Am. J. Psychiat.,* to be published.

18. *Patients in Mental Institutions,* U.S. Department of Commerce, Bureau of the Census, Washington, D.C., 1943.

19. *Mental Disorders: Diagnostic and Statistical Manual,* American Psychiatric Association, Mental Hospital Service, Washington, 1952.

PSYCHIATRIC TEXTS

1. Henderson, D. K., and R. D. Gillespie: *A Textbook of Psychiatry,* 3d ed., Oxford University Press, New York, 1932.

2. Muncie, Wendell: *Psychobiology and Psychiatry,* The C. V. Mosby Company, St. Louis, 1939.

3. Noyes, A. P.: *Modern Clinical Psychiatry,* W. B. Saunders, Philadelphia, 1953.

4. Cameron, Norman: *The Psychology of Behavior Disorders,* Houghton Mifflin Company, Boston, 1947.

5. Kanner, Leo: *Child Psychiatry,* 2d ed., Charles C Thomas, Publisher, Springfield, Ill., 1948.

Visual Aids

The following motion pictures are recommended for use in illustrating the various concepts discussed in this book and also as a guide to the planning of mental health programs. The health officer interested in awakening his community to its mental hygiene problems and responsibilities can use many of these films to provoke discussion. The health officer or others in his department can use the following bibliography as reference material for community clubs or organizations interested in developing programs in mental hygiene. Use of these films can relate mental hygiene to other public health programs and can aid in planning in-service programs in mental health.

The author has personally reviewed most of the films in this bibliography. Those he has not seen are included on the basis of recommendations by such agencies as the National Institute of Mental Health, the National Association of Mental Health, the U.S. Children's Bureau, the American College of Surgeons, and the Psychological Cinema Register; or upon the basis of the established integrity of the film producers such as the Text-Film Department of the McGraw-Hill Book Co. While the bibliography is reasonably inclusive, no attempt has been made to list all films bearing on the subject. Readers, if interested in locating additional films, should consult the following references:

"Educational Film Guide." H. W. Wilson Co., New York 52, N.Y.

"Mental Health Motion Pictures." National Institute of Mental Health, U.S. Public Health Service, Washington 25, D.C.

"Selected Films for Mental Health Education." National Association for Mental Health, New York 16, N.Y.

"Motion Pictures on Child Life." Children's Bureau, U.S. Department of Health, Education and Welfare, Washington 25, D.C.

"Psychological Cinema Register." Pennsylvania State University, State College, Pa.

"Films in Psychiatry, Psychology, and Mental Health." Health Education Council, New York, N.Y.

"Directory of Professional Medical Motion Picture Films and Authors." Professional Publications, Lawrence, Kansas.

All of the motion pictures in the following bibliography are 16mm films. Unless otherwise indicated, they are sound and black-and-white (b&w) films; those which are color and/or silent are so identified. Immediately following the title of each film is the name of the producer; and if different from the producer, the name of the distributor also. Abbreviations are used for the names of producers and distributors, and these abbreviations are identified in the list of sources at the end of the bibliography. Following the producer-distributor information is the year of production, an important factor in choosing films for public showings.

Each film is listed and described under the chapter heading to which it is most closely related. In some instances, films are listed by titles under other chapters with a reference to the primary chapter heading. Many of the films can be used for various purposes and audiences, and readers are urged to examine the entire bibliography in selecting films for specific programs.

Most of the films may be borrowed or rented from local sources such as public libraries, health departments, universities, or state mental health authorities. A list of these and other film sources is given in "A Directory of 2660 16mm Film Libraries," available for fifty cents from the Government Printing Office, Washington 25, D.C.

PART ONE. THE PLACE OF MENTAL HYGIENE IN PUBLIC HEALTH

Chapter 1. The Field of Mental Hygiene

Mental Health: Keeping Mentally Fit (EBF; 1952; 12min color or b&w). Defines and describes good mental health and discusses its importance to the individual and to society. Illustrates symptoms of various mental disorders.

The Nation's Mental Health (MOT/McGraw; 1951; 18min). Shows facilities for training psychiatric personnel in hospitals, various methods of therapy for psychiatric patients, and the work of the National Association for Mental Health.

Psychiatry in Action (BIS; 1943; 60min). Presentation of the results and treatment of war neuroses in British hospitals by professional workers in the fields of medicine, psychology, psychiatric nursing, neuropsychiatry, social work, and occupational therapy.

Search for Happiness (MOT/McGraw; 1948; 17min). Portrays man's attempts to cope with the complexities of modern living, and his susceptibility to cure-alls and nostrums.

Shades of Gray (USA; 1948; 66min). Portrays through dramatized situations and case histories various mental disorders experienced by soldiers during training and combat ranging from mild anxiety states to severe depressive reactions and paranoid psychoses; traces the life patterns of each affected soldier and relates his early familial and environmental experiences to the circumstances which precipitate his mental breakdown; demonstrates methods of psychotherapy, including emotional catharsis, narcoanalysis, hypnotic suggestions, and group therapy; and makes the point that in terms of mental health, no one is either "black" or "white"; everyone is a "shade of gray."

What's on Your Mind (CNFB; 1947; 11min). Discusses the strain of modern life upon the mental health of individuals, how millions try to find surcease in the advice of quacks, and why psychiatry offers genuine help for many mental ills.

Chapter 2. Mental Hygiene as a Public Health Responsibility

Broken Appointment (MHFB/IFB; 1953; 30min). Story of a public health nurse who learns that in handling a case successfully the understanding of a patient's emotions can be as important as interpreting his physical symptoms.

First as a Child (Virginia Health Dept./IFB; 1948; 22min). Case history of a crippled child from the public health nurse's first visit to his home through diagnosis, treatment, and after-care. Points out the necessary consideration given to the child's emotional troubles.

Chapter 3. Techniques in Mental Hygiene: Leadership Personnel

Activity for Schizophrenia (USVA; 1950; 25min). Shows how physical therapists under the guidance of psychiatrists establish interpersonal relationships through intensified physical activities and motivate patients from lower levels of activity to more socialized levels.

Angry Boy (MHFB/IFB; 1950; 32min). Tells the story of emotional disturbances engendered by family tensions. Tommy, a preadolescent boy, is caught stealing. At a child guidance clinic, a psychiatric team traces his disturbances to its basic causes, and is able to help him.

Broken Appointment. See Chapter 2.

A Clinical Picture of Anxiety Hysteria (USVA; 1952; 26min). Illustrates psychotherapeutic interviewing principles and techniques through

an unrehearsed interview between a psychiatrist and a patient suffering from anxiety hysteria.

A Clinical Picture of Claustrophobia (USVA; 1952; 31min). Illustrates
psychotherapeutic interviewing principles and techniques through
an unrehearsed interview between a psychiatrist and a patient suffering from claustrophobia.

Face of Youth (Wisc U; 1952; 28min). Story of how parents, nurse, and
teacher work together to help two boys with their problems; and of
the experiences of the boys in a child guidance center where, with
the help of a therapist, they learn to adjust to their worlds.

A Friend at the Door (CNFB/Seminar; 1950; 28min). Illustrates the
help which can be given by rural social workers to an old age pen-
sioner, a child in juvenile court, an unmarried mother, and a family
distressed by the threat of illness and poverty.

The Lonely Night (MHFB; 1954; 62min). Story of a young woman's
journey out of the dark hours of emotional disturbance. Shows the
process of psychiatric treatment candidly and completely, and the
kind of family life that can help build emotional strength.

Out of True (BIS/IFB; 1951; 41min). Story of a typical case of mental
illness, followed through to its conclusion, centers upon Molly Slade
who lives with her husband, two children, and mother-in-law in a
crowded block of flats. Shows how Molly recovers through expert
psychiatric treatment and returns to her family.

Psychiatry in Action. See Chapter 1.

Psychotherapeutic Interviewing (USVA; 1950–1952). Series of 4 films
with the following titles and content:

> *Psychotherapeutic Interviewing: Introduction* (1950; 11min). Ex-
> plains basic principles of the doctor–patient relationship, and the
> structure and goals of the psychotherapeutic interview.

> *Psychotherapeutic Interviewing: Method of Procedure* (1950;
> 32min). Depicts an interview between a patient and a psychiatrist;
> analyzes the principles and methods employed in the interview;
> and emphasizes the importance of the doctor–patient relationship,
> planning in terms of goals, focusing upon relevant topics, and
> minimal activity on the part of the doctor.

> *An Approach to Understanding Dynamics* (1950; 34min). Depicts
> an interview between a patient and a psychiatrist; analyzes the
> dynamics of the interview; and explains the patient's reactions
> to certain experiences and the meaning of these reactions to the
> psychiatrist.

> *Non-verbal Communication* (1952; 27min). Discusses the recogni-

tion of the clues of nonverbal communication and the manner in which these clues can be used in an interview situation to obtain information and to further therapy. Illustrates the various points through pictures, with subtitles, of actual unrehearsed interview situations.

Chapter 4. Techniques in Mental Hygiene: Methods

Activity Group Therapy (Columbia; 1950; 50min). Film record of a group of emotionally disturbed and socially maladjusted boys undergoing activity group therapy. Shows the gradual improvement in personalities and the role of the therapist.

Emotional Health (McGraw; 1947; 20min). Explains that emotional upsets of college students are common, the instances in which professional counsel is needed, and some of the methods of psychiatric treatment.

The Fight for Better Schools (MOT/McGraw; 1950; 20min). Shows how interested citizens (of Arlington County, Virginia) are able by working together to effect legislation and revitalize the public schools.

Journey to Reality (USA; 1950; 30min). Portrays through dramatized sequences six patients with typical psychotic reactions entering a hospital; reviews the case histories and outlines appropriate occupational therapy for each patient. Emphasizes the medical officer's responsibility for prescribing and providing occupational therapy.

Judging Emotional Behavior (Churchill; 1953; 20min). A motion picture test designed to measure the sensitivity of individuals to the emotions of others. Ten sequences are shown in which two people react as if certain events described by a narrator were happening to them.

Role Playing in Human Relations Training (NEA; 1949; 25min). Portrays skills required in role-playing and the uses of role-playing in the study of human relationships.

Unconscious Motivation (Hartley/Assn; 1949; 38min). Shows how unconscious motives can influence and direct everyday thoughts, feelings, and actions; how psychological techniques are used to trace troublesome motives; and the benefits to health resulting from the discovery and release of such unconscious material.

When All the People Play (CNFB; 1949; 26min). Shows how a rural district "came alive" under the stimulus of a community recreation program.

MENTAL HOSPITALS

Breakdown (CNFB/McGraw; 1951; 40min). Case study of a young woman who has a schizophrenic breakdown. Follows the course of her treatment from a mental health clinic to a state hospital, and concludes with her discharge from this institution to complete her rehabilitation as a member of her family.

Care of the Sick (Ohio Dept. of Public Welfare/NAMH; 1950; 20min). Shows life in a mental hospital and tells the story of an attendant who learns how patients can be restored to useful living.

Hydrotherapy Procedures for Neuropsychiatric Patients (USVA; 1949; 22min). Describes hydrotherapy procedures for sedation and stimulation; and emphasizes the importance of care in handling patients with mental illness and of good relationships between the patient and the physical therapist.

Man to Man (MHFB/NAMH; 1954; 30min). Story of how Joe Fuller, a psychiatric aide who takes a temporary job in a state hospital, decides to stay permanently in this kind of work. Shows the nature of the hospital work and the satisfaction of bringing mentally ill patients back to health.

Mental Hospital (Oklahoma Dept. of Health/IFB; 1953; 20min). Day-to-day story of the treatment received by a mental patient from the time of his admission to the hospital until he is discharged.

Nurse's Day with the Mentally Ill (PCR; 1954; 22min color or b&w). Shows typical activities of a student nurse in a modern psychiatric hospital. Includes many spontaneous examples of the behavior of the mentally ill. Showings restricted to professional audiences.

A Positive Approach to the Psychiatric Patient (USVA; 1955; 30min color). Shows the treatment in Veterans Administration hospitals for psychiatric patients who have emerged from acute episodes of mental illness but who are not well enough to leave the hospital. Uses a hospital ward unit as the focal setting, and stresses the roles of the nurse, aide, and physician.

Rx Attitude (USVA; 1952; 18min). Stresses the importance of attitudes exhibited by hospital personnel toward mental patients, and portrays the effects of such attitudes upon patients in a Veterans Administration mental hospital.

Someone Who Cares (Ind U; 1955; 22min). Points out the too frequent overcrowding and monotony in mental hospitals, and gives examples of the contributions being made by citizen volunteers who bring to the mental patients program services such as games, music, and parties.

Working and Playing to Health (MHFB/IFB; 1954; 35min). Shows the programs of recreational, occupational, and industrial therapy for the patients of a state mental hospital. Explains how and why these techniques are used.

PART TWO. THE DEVELOPMENT OF THE INDIVIDUAL

Child Development (McGraw; 1950 and 1955). Series of 8 films correlated with Hurlock: *Child Growth and Development.*

> *Principles of Development* (1950; 17min). Outlines the fundamentals of child growth and development and considers the variables which make each child different from every other one.
>
> *Child Care and Development* (1950; 17min). Explains the habits of daily physical care that ensure a happy, healthy child. Covers good habits of eating, sleeping, bathing, the wearing of proper clothing, and outdoor exercise.
>
> *Heredity and Prenatal Development* (1950; 21min). Discusses cell growth and heredity, describes fertilization of ovum and traces development of fetus until delivery, considers development of physical functions of newborn, and stresses connection between physical and emotional sensitivity.
>
> *Children's Emotions* (1950; 22min). Discusses the major emotions of childhood—fear, anger, jealousy, curiosity, joy—and points out what the parent can do to lessen fears and promote the child's happiness and natural development.
>
> *Social Development* (1950; 16min). Offers an analysis of social behavior at different age levels and the reasons underlying the changes in behavior patterns as the child develops.
>
> *Play* (In preparation, 1955)
> *Brothers and Sisters* (In preparation, 1955)
> *Children and Fantasy* (In preparation, 1955)

He Acts His Age (CNFB/McGraw; 1949; 15min color or b&w). Survey of typical behavior patterns of children from ages one to fifteen, demonstrating that as children grow their interests, activities, and emotions change. Additional films, dealing with specific stages in development, are:

> *The Terrible Twos and Trusting Threes.* See Chapter 12.
> *The Frustrating Fours and Fascinating Fives.* See chapter 12.
> *From Sociable Six to Noisy Nine.* See Chapter 13.

Study in Human Development (PCR; 1946; four parts, each 17–19min silent). Film studies documenting developmental changes in manipulation, posture, locomotion, motor skills, social behavior from birth to five years of age. Titles are:

Six to Thirty Weeks
Forty-two Weeks to Fifteen Months
Nineteen Months to Two Years and Eight Months
Three Years to Five Years

Chapter 8. The Study of Personality Development

Personality Development (EBF; 1948). Series of 4 films with the following titles:

Answering the Child's Why (13min)
Baby Meets His Parents (11min)
Helping the Child to Accept the Do's (11min)
Helping the Child to Face the Dont's (11min)

Preface to a Life (USPHS; 1950; 29min). Parental influence on a child's developing personality, illustrated by a series of episodes showing the effects of an overly solicitous mother and an overly demanding father; and, in contrast, the healthy childhood resulting when both parents accept their child as an individual.

Symbols of Expression (PCR; 1952; 26min silent). Attempts to demonstrate that an individual's drawings, "doodlings," art productions, dance forms, signatures, or writings embody "key symbols" of his personality.

Unity of Personality (PCR; 1946; 18min silent). Demonstrates similarities of expressive behavior characteristics of five individuals with very different personalities. The behavior patterns shown include gestures, facial movements, handwriting, handling objects, athletic activities, and walking gaits.

Chapter 9. The Preindividual Factors: Eugenics

Genetics and Behavior (PCR; 1953; 16min silent color or b&w). Documents the thesis that the structure which limits behavior is inherited, but not behavior itself. Showings restricted to professional personnel.

Heredity (EBF; 1939; 11min). Explains with animated charts and animal picturization the Mendelian laws of inheritance.

Heredity and Family Environment (McGraw; 1954; 9min). Portrays by pictorial examples and explains through psychological interpretations the meanings of heredity and environment and their relationship.

In the Beginning (USDA; 1937; 17min). Shows by means of time-lapse cinematography the ovulation, fertilization, and early development of the mammalian (rabbit) egg.

Chapter 10. The Prenatal and Perinatal Period

All My Babies (Col U Press; 1953; 55min). Story of Mary Cooley, a midwife, from the time she takes a case until the baby is taken to its first well-baby clinic.

Before the Baby Comes (Knowledge Bldrs; 1940; 12min). Explains the value of prenatal examinations, and the clothes, diet, exercise, and other hints for expectant mothers.

Care of the Newborn Baby: The Nurse's Role in Instructing the Parents (USOE/UWF; 1945; 31min). Nurse's functions and duties in teaching parents to care for newborn babies; what the nurse can do in the home, clinic, and hospital; and how to hold, dress, bathe, and feed a baby.

Childbirth: Normal Delivery (Cited; 1950; 16min color). Gives a close-up of the actual birth of a baby. Photographed under medical supervision. Distribution restricted to medical schools, hospitals, nursing and educational institutions, and lectures on showings under medical supervision.

Labor and Childbirth (Med Film; 1950; 17min). Story of a young couple expecting their first child, beginning of labor, trip to the hospital, admission to maternity ward, delivery of the baby, and return to the hospital room with baby and husband.

Motherhood (NMP Co; 1943; 10min). Deals with prenatal care, including regular visits to the doctor, and the value of baths, rest, exercise, proper clothing, etc. for expectant mothers.

Postnatal Care (Med Film; 1952; 12min). Shows a mother in her hospital room, doing exercises, caring for her baby, nursing the baby, etc., and discusses the father's relationship to the new family situation.

Prenatal Care (Med Film; 1952; 23min). Portrays three women in normal pregnancy through the ninth-month period, and explains recommended exercise, clothing, and diet during this time.

Wise Parents, Healthy Babies (IIAA; 1947; 11min color). Explains how prenatal services safeguard the health of the prospective mother and child; shows the need for placing the baby under the care of a doctor, and the need for immunization of the baby against certain diseases.

Chapter 11. The Period of Infancy

Baby Meets His Parents (EBF; 1948; 11min). Points out how differences in personality can be accounted for not only by heredity but also by the human relationships and environmental factors experienced during the first years of life.

Baby's First Year (Knowledge Bldrs; 1940; 12min). Reviews in detail the baby's daily schedule, including feeding, bathing, sleep, and the value of proper care, food, and exercises.

Child Development (EBF; 1934; 11min each). Ten films, with the following self-descriptive titles, produced at the Yale University Clinic of Child Development with the collaboration of Dr. Arnold Gesell:

> *Thirty-six Weeks Behavior Day*
> *Baby's Day at Twelve Weeks*
> *Baby's Day at Forty-eight Weeks*
> *Behavior Patterns at One Year*
> *Early Social Behavior*
> *From Creeping to Walking*
> *Growth of Infant Behavior: Early Stages*
> *Growth of Infant Behavior: Later Stages*
> *Learning and Growth*
> *Posture and Locomotion*

Dr. Spock (MOT/McGraw; 1953; 27min). Presents the theories and practices of Dr. Spock and his suggestions to parents for dealing with children from infancy to age six.

Embryology of Human Behavior (AAMC/IFB; 1951; 28min color). Explains that a child grows in accordance with certain universal laws and at the same time develops as an individual. Traces the patterning processes of behavior.

Infant Care (IIAA; 1945; 9min color). Through animation shows the things a mother should do during the prenatal period and through infancy to have strong, sturdy children.

Infants Are Individuals (EBF; 1947; 15min). Demonstrates that individuality and personality are apparent in youngsters from their earliest day. Shows how certain behavior patterns disclosed in infancy persist into later life.

Judy's Diary (Wisc U; 1937). Pictures the development of a baby from birth to age two. Titles are:

> *By Experience I Learn* (25min silent)
> *Morning Until Night* (30min silent)
> *Now I Am Two* (30min silent)

Know Your Baby (CDHW/Sterling; 1947; 11min color or b&w). Illustrates methods of care of the new baby. Shows the consideration and understanding necessary until the family adjusts itself to the demands of the newcomer.

Life with Baby (MOT/McGraw; 1946; 18min). Shows how children grow mentally and physically. A popular version and condensation of the Gesell Child Development Series.

Life Begins (EBF; 1935; 60min). Pictures 24 years of clinical practice and research on problems of infancy at the Yale University Clinic of Child Development under the direction of Dr. Arnold L. Gesell.

Martha Belongs (Wisc U; 1949; 12min color). Emphasizes the early contacts of a baby with her own family and the need of an infant to have opportunities to develop at her own pace and to have freedom for exercise. Points up natural opportunities for sex education of older children in the family.

Mother and Her Child (CNFB; 1947; 55min color or b&w). Story of a couple, from the time they suspect they are going to have a baby until their son's first birthday. Pictures their monthly visits to the doctor; his advice on diet, exercise, and clothing; and instructions for care of the baby.

Nobody's Children (MOT/McGraw; 1947; 17min). Shows the dangers inherent in lax child adoption procedures and presents the more advanced methods of screening applicants and selecting the most suitable home for the child.

Some Basic Differences in New-born Infants During Lying-in Period (NYU; 1944; 23min silent). Actual records of children from the moment of birth.

Studies of the Psychoanalytic Research Project on Problems in Infancy (NYU; 1947–1953). Series of 11 films, all but one silent, documenting various aspects of infant behavior.

> *Anxiety: Its Phenomenology in the First Year of Life* (1953; 20min)
> *Birth and the First Fifteen Minutes of Life* (1947; 10min)
> *Genesis of Emotions* (1949; 30min)
> *Grasping* (1949; 20min)
> *Grief* (1947; 30min)
> *Motherlove* (1952; 20min)
> *Psychogenic Diseases in Infancy: An Attempt at Their Classification* (1952; 20min)
> *Shaping the Personality: The Role of Mother–Child Relations in Infancy* (1953; 30min)
> *The Smile of the Baby* (1948; 30min sound)
> *The Smiling Response* (1948; 20min)

Somatic Consequences of Emotional Starvation in Infants (1949; 30min)

Chapter 12. The Preschool Period

The Child at Play (TC; 1952; 18min). Shows the nature of children's spontaneous play as reviewed in a one-way vision room by depicting the unrestrained play activity of a three-year-old child and youngsters of various ages.

Child Grows Up (Knowledge Bldrs; 1940; 12min). Shows activities of the normal child from one to six, emphasizing habit training, proper play and equipment, nursery school experiences, food, and physical examinations.

A Child Went Forth (Brandon; 1942; 20min). Shows the experiences of children, ages two to seven, at a progressive summer camp and points out their creative power and initiative.

Fears of Children (MHFB/IFB; 1951; 30min). Parent–child situation in which the mother tends to coddle her five-year-old son and the father expects too much of him. Explains how the conflict magnifies the child's fears.

The Frustrating Fours and Fascinating Fives (CNFB/McGraw; 1953; 22min color or b&w). Portrays characteristic patterns of a four-year-old boy from imaginative craftsmanship to inconsistent destructiveness and the changes that occur as he grows into a five-year-old.

Large Muscle Motor Skills of Four Year Olds (Calif U; 1945; 10min silent color). Through individual sequences showing running, balancing, jumping, pedaling, pumping, kicking, throwing, catching and bouncing, hitting and punching, pushing and pulling, climbing, suspending own weight, tumbling, and guiding a wagon, indicates the types and levels of large muscle motor skills that are characteristic of children of this age.

Let Your Child Help You (NYU; 1947; 11min). Shows how very young children may help at home and thus achieve a sense of accomplishment and responsibility.

Mealtime Can Be a Happy Time (Wisc U; 1942; 22min). Designed to educate parents in the establishment of correct and pleasant eating habits for children.

Preschool Adventures (Iowa St U; 1941; 42min silent). Shows the preschool laboratories of the Iowa Child Welfare Research Station. Includes a wide variety of activities, and shows how major objectives in child development are reflected in various aspects of the preschool program.

Studies of Normal Personality Development (NYU, 1941–1953). Series of 10 films produced by the Department of Child Study at Vassar College.

> *Balloons: Aggression and Destructive Games* (1941; 20min)
> *Finger Painting* (1941; 22min color)
> *Frustration Play Techniques* (1942; 35min)
> *A Long Time to Grow. Part 1: Two- and Three-year-olds in Nursery School* (1951; 35min)
> *A Long Time to Grow. Part 2: Four- and Five-year-olds in School* (1953; 35min)
> *Meeting Emotional Needs in Childhood: The Groundwork of Democracy.* See Chapter 13.
> *Pay Attention* (1949; 30min)
> *Preschool Incidents. Part 1: When Should Grownups Help* (1951; 13min)
> *Preschool Incidents: Part 2: And Then Ice Cream* (1951; 10min)
> *Preschool Incidents. Part 3: When Should Grownups Stop Fights* (1952; 15min)

The Terrible Twos and Trusting Threes (CNFB/McGraw; 1950; 22min). A study of child behavior at two and three years, showing what to expect from youngsters of these ages, and suggesting how parents can deal constructively with their problems.

This Is Robert: A Study of Personality Growth in a Pre-school Child (NYU; 1942; 75min). Traces the development of an aggressive but appealing child from his early nursery school days to his first year in a public school.

Understanding Children's Drawings (NYU/Film Images; 1949; 10min). Follows the child's progress from primitive scribblings, through recognition of form and design, until finally there begins to emerge a composed storytelling picture.

Understanding Children's Play (NYU; 1948; 10min). How adults can understand and help children through observation of their use of toys and toy materials.

Walking Upstairs for the First Time: Creative Solution of a Conflict (Iowa St U; 1940; 5min silent). Title self-explanatory.

Why Won't Tommy Eat (CDHW/Sterling; 1948; 19min color). Uncovers both physical and mental causes of the problem of the child who refuses to eat.

Your Children and You (BIS; 1947; 31min). Concerns the care of young children from the first months to the age of four or five. Offers advice on physical and psychological training.

Your Children's Play (BIS/McGraw; 1952; 20min). Gives examples of play behavior of one- to eight-year-olds, and emphasizes the need for parents to understand the reasons for such behavior patterns.

Your Children's Sleep (BIS/EBF; 1950; 22min). Stresses the importance of sound, healthy sleep, and advises parents on ways in which they can help secure it for their children.

Chapter 13. The School Period

Answering the Child's Why (EBF; 1951; 13min). Dramatizes actual situations in which youngsters meet with positive or negative attitudes toward their questions, and suggests the resulting effects on their personalities.

Face of Youth. See Chapter 3.

Family Circles (CNFB/McGraw; 1949; 31min). Portrays, through three dramatized situations, the interplay between home and school influences, and how family attitudes affect children's success in school.

First Lessons (MHFB/IFB; 1952; 22min). Presents the many problems a teacher is faced with when an aggressive child becomes a member of the class, and shows how a teacher works to overcome these problems.

From Sociable Six to Noisy Nine (CNFB/McGraw; 1954; 22min color or b&w). Portrays characteristic patterns of behavior exhibition by children from six to nine, and constructive efforts of parents to understand and guide these children.

Guidance Problem for School and Home (TC; 1941; 18min). Depicts the problem of Danny, a second-grade child who has poor social adjustment and is not doing well in school. Shows how conferences between the teacher and his mother help solve the problem.

Individual Differences (McGraw; 1950; 23min). Case study of a shy, slow child who is different from his classmates and his older brother. Points out the need to recognize differences among individuals.

Human Growth (Brown Trust; 1948; 19min color). A mixed group of seventh-grade students view and discuss a film which traces human growth and development of the organism from mating through pregnancy and birth, then from infancy through childhood and adolescence to adulthood. Emphasizes male and female structural development.

Human Reproduction (McGraw; 1947; 20min). Explains the human reproductive systems and the process of conception, pregnancy, and childbirth. Describes the anatomy, physiology, and functions of the male and female reproductive organs and illustrates, by animated drawings, the body mechanisms of delivery.

Life with Junior (MOT/McGraw; 1948; 18min). Follows Junior through a typical day. Shows in some detail the work of the Child Study Association in America.

Meeting Emotional Needs in Childhood: The Groundwork of Democracy (NYU; 1947; 33min). Explains the basic emotional needs of children and how adjustments are made in play and at school.

New Tools for Learning (EBF; 1952; 19min). Shows how the film, along with a wide range of other materials, can bring richness and effectiveness to teaching, and demonstrates proper methods of using classroom films.

Problem Children (ODMH/PCR; 1946; 20min). Story of two junior high school boys and how their personalities are affected by their relationships in home and school. Illustrates how parents and teachers should work together to provide conditions favorable to the solution of these boys' problems.

The Problem of Pupil Adjustment. Part 1: The Drop-out (McGraw; 1950; 20min). Flash backs show how frustration of his interests caused a student to lose interest in high school.

The Problem of Pupil Adjustment. Part 2: The Stay-in (McGraw; 1950; 19min). Explains how a school adjusted its program to meet student needs and interests, and thus reduced its drop-out rate.

The Quiet One (Film Doc/Athena; 1948; 67min). Tells the story of Donald Peters, a mentally retarded Negro boy, who is an only child and the victim of a disrupted home in the Harlem district of New York City, and of his treatment at the Wiltwyck School at Esopus, N.Y.

School (OIAA/UWF; 1946; 21min). Shows one day's activities in an elementary school—the janitor opening the building, the children on their way to school, the first grade studying and playing, and a P.T.A. meeting in the evening.

The Story of Menstruation (Inter. Cel./Assn.; 1947; 10min). Diagrams and animated drawings illustrate the physiology of menstruation and relate it to homemaking and reproduction.

Who Will Teach Your Child (CNFB/McGraw; 1948; 24min). Raises three important questions of the teaching profession and through flash backs presents actual classroom situations in which the teachers cope with day-to-day problems of helping young minds in their development.

Why Can't Jimmy Read (Syracuse U; 1950; 15min). Portrays a typical case history from the files of the Syracuse University Reading Clinic.

Illustrates procedures used in diagnosis, and the valuable service
that can be performed by a reading clinic working with parents and
teachers.

Chapter 14. The Adolescent Period

Adolescent Development (McGraw; 1953). Series of 5 films correlated
with Hurlock: *Adolescent Development.*

> *The Meaning of Adolescence* (16min). Points to the unsure status
> of the adolescent, neither child nor adult, and provides an overview
> of the social, emotional, mental, and physical changes occurring
> in the years between childhood and adulthood. Emphasizes the
> need to help a teen-ager adjust to five aspects of adult life: physical
> maturity, social living, the opposite sex, religious beliefs, and a
> moral code.

> *Physical Aspects of Puberty* (19min). Describes, through anima-
> tion, the physiological aspects of puberty—primary and secondary
> sex characteristics, maturation in boys and in girls, variation
> among individuals, and the emotional and social effects of such
> variations.

> *Age of Turmoil* (20min). Portrays early adolescence, thirteen to
> fifteen years, and the behavior characteristics of giggling, noisi-
> ness, criticism of school, daydreaming, and seemingly useless activi-
> ties. Gives examples of different personality types and of various
> parent–child situations.

> *Social–Sex Attitudes in Adolescence* (22min). Portrays a boy and
> a girl taken through their entire adolescent experience, their early
> sex education, awareness of the opposite sex, dating, finding com-
> mon interests, falling in love, and marrying.

> *Meeting the Needs of Adolescents* (19min). Points out, through a
> study of a family with a seventeen-year-old girl and a fourteen-
> year-old boy, what parents can do to meet the needs of their
> adolescents.

Alice Adams—Money Sequence (TFC; 1935; 15min). An excerpt from
the feature film with the same title, showing family problems growing out of a father's lack of financial success.

Aptitudes and Occupations (Coronet; 1941; 16min). Discusses six of
the fundamental human abilities and indicates how a student may
with the aid of a school counselor determine how much of each of
these abilities he has.

A Chance to Live (MOT/McGraw; 1950; 19min). Story of an Italian boy who is given "a chance to live" by the American-supported Boys' Republic at Santa Marinella, near Rome; traces the boy's difficult adjustment, his struggle for friendship, and his eventual triumph.

Children of the City (BIS; 1944; 30min). Portrays the problem of juvenile delinquency and how it is handled in an urban area of Scotland; and describes in detail how three boys, from three different types of homes, are dealt with.

Counseling Adolescents (McGraw; 1954). Three motion pictures with follow-up filmstrips portraying the work of a student counselor and the psychology involved for counselor and student. Titles are:

A Counselor's Day (11min)
Using Analytical Tools (14min)
Diagnosis and Planning Adjustments in Counseling (18min)

Dating Do's and Dont's (Coronet; 1949; 14min). Shows the progress of the date, from choosing the right girl and asking her, through the last good night; raises some important questions and suggests partial answers.

Emotional Health. See Chapter 4.

Experimental Studies in Social Climates of Groups (Iowa St U; 1940; 30min). Shows behavior of groups of boys organized in clubs run on democratic principles, as an autocracy, and as a laissez-faire group. Shows responses when groups are changed from one type to another.

A Family Affair (MHFB/IFB; 1955; 35min). Story of a family whose relationships are strained to the breaking point when an adolescent son defies the authority of his parents. Consultation with a trained family caseworker helps the individuals to understand their own problems and to bring the family relationships into balance.

Farewell to Childhood (MHFB/IFB; 1952; 23min). Dramatized story of a teen-age girl, full of the swift emotions typical of adolescence, longing for and learning the privileges of adulthood. Portrays the adolescent moods of rebellion and trust, anger and irresolution, self-pity, and idealism—and her parents' bewilderment and confusion. Illustrates problem of relation of counselor to parents of child.

Going Steady (Coronet; 1951; 10min). Examines "going steady" by teen-agers as a normal step in the progress toward engagement and marriage, and brings out both advantages and disadvantages.

Head of the House (USIA/UWF; 1953; 40min). Depicts the emotional problems of a young boy, his rebellion against parental controls, particularly his father's repressive discipline, and his gradual development into a potential juvenile delinquent. Shows the assistance of a community social worker and a neighborhood welfare house in bringing about development of better understanding between father and son.

How Do You Know It's Love (Coronet; 1951; 13min). Discusses the need for mature conception of love and presents factors helpful in judging maturity of love, and typical stages in its development.

Learning to Understand Children. Part 1: A Diagnostic Approach (McGraw; 1947; 21min). Case study of Ada Adams, an emotionally and socially maladjusted girl of fifteen, and the efforts of her English teacher to study her case, and to understand her; shows some of the diagnostic techniques used.

Learning to Understand Children. Part 2: A Remedial Program (McGraw; 1947; 23min). A continuation of the case study of Ada Adams in which the teacher develops a plan for remedial action by making use of Ada's talent in art.

Problem Children. See Chapter 13.

Psychology for Living (McGraw; 1954). Series of 5 films correlated with Sorenson and Malm: *Psychology for Living.*

> *Facing Reality* (12min). Illustrates and explains some common defense mechanisms—rationalization, projection, negativism—and some typical escape mechanisms such as daydreaming, identification, suppression, and malingering.

> *Successful Scholarship* (11min). Presents a schedule of good study procedures and routines following a plan-place-method technique, and illustrates this method through a portrayal of an average college student.

> *Habit Patterns* (15min). Portrays by contrasting two adolescent girls the effects of disorderly habits on personality and social life.

> *Heredity and Family Environment.* See Chapter 9.

> *Toward Emotional Maturity* (11min). Portrays an eighteen-year-old girl faced with a conflict in feelings toward her parents and a boy that she likes very much, her review of previous incidents involving emotional turmoil, and her realization of the meaning of emotional maturity.

Shy Guy (Coronet; 1947; 13min color or b&w). Story of a shy adolescent boy, his problems, and the methods he can use to improve his social poise and relationships.

Who's Delinquent (RKO/McGraw; 1949; 16min). The newspaper of a typical American town investigates the causes of juvenile delinquency and shows a meeting of the townspeople in an effort to solve the problem.

You and Your Family (Assn; 1946; 8min). Presents three situations involving parents and adolescents. Gives no solutions but leaves the answers to the audience.

Chapter 15. The Young-adult Period

Assignment Home (USN; 1945; 26min). Stories of three Navy neuro-psychiatric discharge patients (one returning to a job, one going back to school and the other without plans), showing patients' problems of civilian life with suggestions for meeting different situations.

Broken Appointment. See Chapter 2.

Families First (NY St Dept Comm; 1948; 17min). Contrasts two middle-class families and shows the results of tensions and frustrations in one and of affection and harmonious relationships in the other.

Family Teamwork (Frith; 1947; 16min color). Shows how children and parents can help each other, how they may work together in the home and in their outside activities.

Marriage and Divorce (MOT/McGraw; 1949; 15min). Surveys the problems of broken homes and the increasing divorce rate by examining the effects of mechanization on present-day family relations.

Marriage for Moderns (McGraw; 1950 and 1954). Series of 8 films correlated with Bowman: *Marriage for Moderns.*

> *This Charming Couple* (1950; 19min). Portrays through dramatized situations a young married couple and the reasons for their failure to achieve marital happiness.

> *Marriage Today* (1950; 22min). As a follow-up film to *This Charming Couple,* answers some of the problems raised in the other film. Portrays two couples who have made their marriages work and how the individuals have made a success of their marriages.

> *Choosing for Happiness* (1950; 14min). Portrays through dramatized situations the reactions of a girl to various boy friends and her rejection of all of them, and they of her. Suggests that the girl should reevaluate herself and her demands on others.

> *It Takes All Kinds* (1950; 20min). Portrays through dramatized sequences a series of young couples reacting to tense situations; relates their reactions to their possibilities for marriage success or failure; and emphasizes the point that marriage partners should be carefully chosen.

> *Who's Boss* (1950; 16min). Portrays a young married couple, both of whom are individualists, their differences, and their decision to adjust their differences through cooperation.

Who's Right (1954; 18min). Dramatization of a quarrel between husband and wife, newly married, caused by her seeing his forcefulness as "bossism" and by his labeling her good taste as extravagance.

Jealousy (1954; 16min). Portrayal of a young wife, jealous of her husband, and her gradual realization that her behavior is an expression of her dissatisfaction with her role as homemaker.

In Time of Trouble (1954; 14min). Portrays the family minister counseling a young married couple and helping them understand the reasons for their disagreements and ways in which satisfactory adjustments can be made.

Marriage Is a Partnership (Coronet; 1951; 16min color or b&w). Answers some of the major questions that arise during the first married years—arguments, responsibilities, decisions, and loyalties.

Mental Mechanisms (CNFB/McGraw; 1947–1955). Series of 4 films portraying through dramatized case studies certain mental health problems of young adults and tracing their roots back through adolescence to childhood and infancy.

The Feeling of Rejection (1947; 23min). Documentary-dramatic study of a young woman whose feelings of rejection are manifested in maladjustment and physical illnesses. Traces, through flash backs, her feelings of rejection to childhood origins and, through psychiatric help, shows her beginning to understand her problem.

The Feeling of Hostility (1948; 27min). Documentary-dramatic study of Clare, a young woman apparently successful in her profession but a failure in personal relationships. Traces, through flash backs, her hostility to childhood experiences, and shows how psychiatric treatment helps her direct her hostility into constructive efforts.

Overdependency (1949; 32min). Dramatized story of a young married man whose inability to face the ordinary problems of life, including vague physical ailments and vocational maladjustment, stems from a childhood too dependent upon his mother and sister.

To Serve the Mind (1955; 25min). Case study of a doctor who suffers a schizophrenic breakdown, showing the various forms of treatment that gradually lead to his recovery and return to work.

Obligations (Simmel/Instr Films; 1950; 17min). Two families illustrate the correct and incorrect manner of taking care of their obligations to one another.

Palmour Street (HPI; 1950; 23min). Shows events in the daily life of Negro families living on Palmour Street in Gainesville, Ga.; illustrates certain basic concepts of mental health as they relate to family life, and some of the basic ways in which parents influence the mental and emotional development of their children.

A Planned Parenthood Story (Mayo; 1950; 18min). Story of a young couple who lost two babies, talk to their minister, learn of the services of "Planned Parenthood," and space the arrival of the next baby. Sponsored by the Planned Parenthood Federation of America.

Shyness (CNFB/McGraw; 1953; 23min). Portrays the lonely existence of a shy adult, and illustrates the causes of shyness through studies of three children. Explains the reasons for shyness and how this problem may be overcome.

Studies in Human Fertility: Methods for the Control of Conception (Ortho; 1941; 46min). Illustrates the normal anatomy and physiology of human reproduction, and methods for the control of conception.

The Supervisor as a Leader, Part 1 (USOE/UWF; 1944; 14min). Four dramatized episodes illustrating poor supervisory practices and the importance of the following rules: Always keep promises. Never take credit for someone else's work. Don't pass the buck. Don't play favorites.

The Supervisor as a Leader, Part 2 (USOE/UWF; 1944; 13min). Four more dramatized instances of poor supervision leading to the following generalizations: Be a leader/ not an authoritarian. Show appreciation for a job well done. Do not become angry. Protect the rights and feelings of workers.

Chapter 16. The Period of Middle Age

Date of Birth (CNFB/Seminar; 1950; 16min). Presents the actual record of employees in the over-forty-five age group, indicating that there is less absenteeism, lower turnover rate, and an equal standard of production among older workers.

The Menopause: Its Significance and Management (Schering; 1953; 23min color). Discusses symptomatology of the syndrome in terms of physiologic changes which occur, and describes treatment indicated in various clinical cases. Made by W. E. Brown, M.D., for professional audiences.

Chapter 17. The Period of Old Age

Adventure in Maturity (Oklahoma Dept. of Health/IFB; 1954; 20min color). Portrays a woman resigned to a rocking-chair existence who is taught by an older woman friend to learn about opportunities for older women in the community.

Grandma Moses (Film Images; 1950; 24min color). Scenes of the life and works of Grandma Moses, American primitive painter, who reached the age of ninety in 1950. Narration written and spoken by Archibald MacLeish.

Life with Grandpa (MOT/McGraw; 1949; 17min). Discusses the problems of old age and suggests various remedies for these problems including constructive efforts to lessen the feelings of loneliness and uselessness.

Make Way for Tomorrow (TFC; 1937; 18min). An excerpt from the feature film, with the same title, on indigent old age. Shows problems created when an elderly widow goes to live with her son's family.

Retire to Life (Oklahoma Dept. of Health/IFB; 1953; 23min). Story of a machinist who looked forward to a retirement of fishing and just plain loafing but soon feels useless and unwanted. A positive approach to retirement is emphasized.

The Steps of Age (MHFB/IFB; 1951; 25min). Presents the emotional problems and interpersonal relations within the family precipitated by the retirement of the father, a skilled mechanic. Emphasizes that one must begin early in life to adjust to the problems of old age.

Appendix. Review of Psychopathological States

The films in this section are all intended exclusively for showing to professional audiences and most of them are restricted to such showing.

Aphasia (USVA; 1950). Series of 3 films with the following individual titles and running times:

> *Introduction: Aphasia* (30min color)
> *Testing and Individual Therapy for the Aphasic Patient* (28min color)
> *Social Adjustment of the Aphasic Patient* (26min)

Athetoid Gestures in a Deteriorated Parergastic (Schizophrenic) Patient (PCR; 1938; 8min silent). Shows ritualistic, stereotypic gestures of a patient, age twenty-two.

Breakdown. See Chapter 4.

A Case of Aphasia (PCR; 1939; 15min). Psychiatric examination of a fifty-three-year-old male nurse who has suffered hemiplegia and aphasia. Film shows general narrowing of mental activity, specific difficulties in finding words, and moderate disturbances in comprehension.

Catatonic Behavior in a Deteriorated Parergastic (Schizophrenic) Patient (PCR; 1938; 8min silent). Shows posture, hypertrophied neck muscles, and ritualistic and stereotyped method of eating of a patient, age forty-five, who lay in bed for 18 months with head unsupported above the pillows during all waking hours.

A Character Neurosis with Depressive and Compulsive Trends in the Making: Life History of Mary from Birth to Fifteen Years (NYU; 1947; 6omin silent). Film record of a girl with superior biological capacity and an active congenital-activity type who develops, during her 15 years, a neurosis through interaction with those in her environment.

Combat Exhaustion (USA; 1945; 50min). Portrays a colonel in the U.S. Army Medical Corps addressing a group of doctors in the European theater of operations and explaining their responsibilities in treating psychiatric cases, particularly those resulting from combat exhaustion. Shows examples of different types of cases, the administration of drugs to produce a hypnotic state, and the treatment of psychotic patients in the hypnotic state.

Convulsive Shock Therapy in Affective Psychoses (PCR; 1943; 18min silent). Film shows cases in support of thesis that convulsive shock therapy is almost specific for terminating severe depressions and near-manic states.

Delusions and Hallucinations in a Senile Setting (PCR; 1939; 5min). A seventy-year-old man with advanced arteriosclerosis and auricular fibrilation begins to hear and respond to imaginary voices. Film shows him demonstrating his powers of communication.

Effect of Electroconvulsive Shock (E.C.S.) on "Conditioned Anxiety" (PCR; 1953; 14min silent color). Two demonstration experiments showing the effects of E.C.S. upon the behavior of white rats.

Experimental Neurosis in a Dog (PCR; 1939; 10min silent). Film record of a 7-year experiment of producing chronic disturbances in a dog by difficult differentiation of food signals.

The Feeble Minded (PCR; 1942; 41min). Lists 3 main groups of causes of feeblemindedness—defective embryonic development, brain injury, and interrupted development. Classifications of feeblemindedness are given in terms of psychological test results and basic psychology.

Functions of the Nervous System (PCR; 1949; 13min). Describes the central nervous system; cranial, cervical, thoracic, lumbar, and sacral connections; sympathetic ganglia; sense organs; and the mechanism of muscular coordination.

Huntington's Chorea (PCR; 1938; 11min silent). Shows characteristics of the disease including involuntary movements, standing posture, attempts at handwriting, ascent and descent on stairway, hand and finger tonicity, and uncontrollable expressions.

Introduction to Clinical Neurology (USPHS/PCR; 1938). Series of 4 films, all silent, with the following titles:

> *General Neurological Examination and Clinical Signs of Disorders of the Pyramidal System* (19min)
>
> *Disorders of the Extra-pyramidal System and the Posterior Columns* (20min)
>
> *Cerebellar Disorders, Disorders Involving the Lower Motor Neurones, and Convulsive States* (17min)
>
> *Functional Syndromes with Pronounced Physical Symptoms* (17min)

Introduction to Combat Fatigue: Doctor's Version (USN; 1944; 31min). Analyzes fear and relates the symptoms of combat fatigue (startle reaction, irritability, nightmares, tension, etc.) to their causes through flash backs of simulated action in a combat area.

Mental Symptoms (CNFB/McGraw; 1952). Series of 9 films illustrating major psychotic states.

> *Schizophrenia: Simple-type Deteriorated* (11min). Female patient, about forty, exhibits symptoms of simple schizophrenia of 10 years' standing.
>
> *Schizophrenia: Catatonic Type* (12min). Symptoms of stuporous catatonia in three male patients.
>
> *Schizophrenia: Hebephrenic Type* (13min). Interview between a psychiatrist and a male hebephrenic hospitalized for 13 years.
>
> *Paranoid Conditions* (13min). Symptoms exhibited by two patients, one an acute paranoid, the other a chronic paranoid.
>
> *Organic Reaction-type: Senile* (10min). Interview between a psychiatrist and a man and woman suffering from senile psychoses.
>
> *Depressive States, Part 1* (12min). Shows a middle-aged patient suffering from recurrent depressions.
>
> *Depressive States, Part 2* (11min). Manifestations of retarded depression and of severe depression with suicidal preoccupation.
>
> *Manic State* (15min). Elderly patient exhibits typical hypomanic symptoms during an interview.
>
> *Folie à Deux* (15min). Portrayal of psychotic symptoms in mother and daughter.

The N.P. Patient (USN; 1944; 28min). Illustrates how to care for and handle neuropsychiatric patients; typical cases and their treatment; and corpsmen's importance in patients' recovery.

Neuropsychiatric Disorders (NYU; 1944). Series of medical teaching films, made by S. P. Goodhart, M.D. and B. H. Harris, M.D. These films are approved by the American College of Surgeons. All of the films are silent:

> *Chorea* (16min)
> *Convulsive and Allied Conditions* (18min)
> *Dystonia Musculorum Deformans* (34min)
> *Encephalographic Studies in Extrapyramidal Diseases* (14min)
> *Epidemic Encephalitis* (31min)
> *Friedreich's Hereditary Ataxia and Little's Disease* (16min)
> *Neuro-ophthalmological Conditions: Pathological Ocular Manifestations of Clinical Interest* (18min)
> *Progressive Hepato-lenticular Degeneration* (14min)
> *Progressive Muscular Atrophies, Dystrophies, and Allied Conditions* (27min)
> *Psychoneuroses* (23min)
> *Somatic Endocrine Types* (26min)

Neuropsychiatry for the Medical Student: Clinical Types of Mental Deficiencies (Goldsborough; 1946; 60min color silent). Recommended "useful as a supplement in teaching psychiatry to advanced medical students" by the American College of Surgeons.

Paranoid State and Deterioration Following Head Injury (PCR; 1939; 11min). Film illustrates rambling flow of talk which conveys disjoined, inconsistent, but dominant notions of persecution.

Parergastic Reaction (Schizophrenia) in a Person of Low Intelligence (PCR; 1939; 15min). Shows stereotyped grimaces and speech, vagueness, concrete use of abstract expressions, and neologism in schizophrenic with suggested mental retardation and makes interesting comparative study of motility disorders.

Seizure: The Medical Treatment and Social Problems of Epilepsy (USVA; 1951; 48min). Explains the diagnostic and therapeutic treatment of epilepsy through a dramatized story of an epileptic veteran, the background of his condition, and his treatment in a Veterans Administration hospital. Describes the physiological basis of epilepsy, clinical manifestations of common types of seizures, and socio-economic problems facing an epileptic.

Symptoms of Schizophrenia (PCR; 1938; 18min silent). Demonstrates symptoms of schizophrenia, fairly typical of those found in psychopathic hospitals, such as social apathy, delusions, hallucinations, hebephrenic reactions, rigidity, etc.

LIST OF FILM SOURCES

AAMC—American Association of Medical Colleges, Chicago, Ill.

Assn—Association Films, Inc., 347 Madison Ave., New York 17, N.Y.

Athena—Athena Films, Inc., 165 W. 46th St., New York 19, N.Y.

BIS—British Information Services, 30 Rockefeller Plaza, New York 20, N.Y.

Brandon—Brandon Films, Inc., 200 W. 57th St., New York 19, N.Y.

Brown Trust—E. C. Brown Trust, 220 S.W. Alder St., Portland 4, Oregon.

Calif U—University of California, Educational Film Sales Dept., Los Angeles 24, Calif.

CDHW—Canadian Department of Health and Welfare, Ottawa, Canada

Churchill—Churchill-Wexler Film Productions, 801 N. Seward St., Los Angeles 38, Calif.

Cited—Cited Films, 30 Rockefeller Plaza, New York 20, N.Y.

CNFB—Canadian National Film Board, 1270 Avenue of the Americas, New York 20, N.Y.

Col U Press—Columbia University Press, Center for Mass Communication, 413 W. 117th St., New York 27, N.Y.

Coronet—Coronet Instructional Films, Coronet Bldg., Chicago 1, Ill.

EBF—Encyclopaedia Britannica Films, Inc., 1150 Wilmette Ave., Wilmette, Ill.

Film Images—Film Images, Inc., 18 E. 60th St., New York 22, N.Y.

Frith—Frith Films, 1816 N. Highland, Hollywood 28, Calif.

Goldsborough—John B. Goldsborough, M.D., 6727 N. Haight St., Portland, Oregon

HPI—Health Publications Institute, Inc., 216 N. Dawson St., Raleigh, N.C.

IFB—International Film Bureau, 57 E. Jackson Blvd., Chicago 4, Ill.

IIAA—Institute of Inter-American Affairs, Washington 25, D.C.

Ind U—Indiana University, Audio-Visual Center, Bloomington, Indiana

Instr Film—Instructional Films, Inc., 1150 Wilmette Ave., Wilmette, Ill.

Intern Cel—International Cellucotton Products Co., 919 N. Michigan Ave., Chicago 11, Ill.

Iowa St U—State University of Iowa, Bureau of Visual Instruction, Iowa City, Iowa

Knowledge Bldrs—Knowledge Builders, Floral Park, N.Y.

Mayo—Mayo-Video, 113 W. 57th St., New York 19, N.Y.

McGraw—McGraw-Hill Book Co., Text-Film Dept., 330 W. 42nd St.. New York 36, N.Y.

Med Film—Medical Films, Inc., 116 Natoma St., San Francisco 5, Calif.

MHFB—Mental Health Film Board, Inc., 116 E. 38th St., New York 16, N.Y.

NAMH—National Association of Mental Health, 13 E. 37th St., New York 16, N.Y.

NEA—National Education Assn., 1201 16th St., N.W., Washington 6, D.C.

NMP Co—National Motion Pictures Co., Mooresville, Ind.

NY St Dept Comm—New York State Department of Commerce, Film Library, 112 State St., Albany 7, N.Y.

NYU—New York University Film Library, 26 Washington Pl., New York 3, N.Y.

Oklahoma Dept. of Health—Oklahoma Department of Health, Oklahoma City, Okla.

OIMH—Ohio Division of Mental Hygiene, 1210 State Office Bldg., Columbus, Ohio

OIAA—Office of Inter-American Affairs, Washington 25, D.C.

Ortho—Ortho Products, Inc., Linden, N.J.

PCR—Psychological Cinema Register, Pennsylvania State University, State College, Pa.

Schering—Schering Corp., 2 Broad St., Bloomfield, N.J.

Seminar—Seminar Films, Inc., 347 Madison Ave., New York 17, N.Y.

Simmel—Simmel-Meservey, Inc., 854 S. Robertson Blvd., Los Angeles 35, Calif.

Sterling—Sterling Films, 205 E. 43rd St., New York 3, N.Y.

Syracuse U—Syracuse University, Audio-Visual Center, 121 College Pl., Syracuse 10, N.Y.

TC—Teachers College, Columbia University, 525 W. 120th St., New York 27, N.Y.

TFC—Teaching Film Custodians, Inc., 25 W. 43rd St., New York 36, N.Y.

USA—U.S. Department of the Army, Washington 25, D.C.

USDA—U.S. Department of Agriculture, Washington 25, D.C.

USIA—U.S. Information Agency, Washington 25, D.C.

USN—U.S. Department of the Navy, Washington 25, D.C.

USOE—U.S. Office of Education, Washington 25, D.C.

USPHS—U.S. Public Health Service, Washington 25, D.C.

USVA—U.S. Veterans Administration, Washington 25, D.C.

UWF—United World Films, Inc., 1445 Park Ave., New York 29, N.Y.

Wisc U—University of Wisconsin, Bureau of Visual Instruction, 1312
   W. Johnson St., Madison 6, Wisc.

Author Index

451

Subject Index

A

Abortion, after maternal rubella, 155
  as method of birth control, 149
  in pregnancy wastage, 400
Abstract thinking in intelligence tests, 254
Accidents in middle age, 347
Adaptation, definition of, 15
Adolescent period, 269–299
  allowances, 292
  association of sexes in, 272
  attitudes toward, 269–270
  "crushes," 295
  definition of, 269
  dependence-independence conflict, 291–293
  drive to earn money, 292
  emancipation from home, 292, 293, 302
  evaluation of physical prowess in, 296
  evaluation by social class, 280
  frequency of problems in, 270, 271
  group identification in, 291, 297
  idealism in organizations, 296
  in literature, 269–270
  male-female comparisons, 272–282
  male-female social patterns in, 295–296
  personality maturation, 290, 291, 302
  physical growth, 272–282
  relations with parents, 291–293, 302

Adolescent period, relations with parents, case illustration, 362–365
  relations with teachers, 293–295
  religious rites, 243
  reverie in, 297
  sex activity, 280–288
  "stages" in, 271–272
    case illustration, 362, 363
  tendency to make comparisons, 279
Adoption, as public health responsibility, 334
  in relation to sterility, 332
"Advice to the lovelorn," 59
Aesop, 56
Aged persons, attitudes toward aging, 379, 380
  clubs for, 382
  as economic threat, 369
  effect of stimulation on, 372
  family headship and, 375, 376
  forgetfulness in, 377
  increase in population of, 369
  irritability in, 371
  mental disease of, 371, 372, 401–403
  preoccupation with past, 377–378
  preservation of dignity of, 377
  productive power of, 370
  reaction to chronic disease in, 373, 374
  rehabilitation of, 371–372
  suicide in, 372
  suspiciousness in, 377–378
  (See also Old age; Senile psychosis)

457